GUIDE TO FOOD STORAGE

Follow this guide for food storage, and you can be sure that what's in your freezer, refrigerator, and pantry is fresh-tasting and ready to use in recipes.

In the Freezer (at -10° to 0° F)

Dairy and Eggs

Cheese, hard	6 months
Cheese, soft	6 months
Egg substitute, unopened	1 year
Egg whites	1 year
Egg yolks	1 year
Ice cream, sherbet	1 month

Fruits and Vegetables

Commercially frozen fruits	1 year
Commercially frozen vegetables	8 to 12 months

Meats, Poultry, and Seafood
Beef, Lamb, Pork, and Veal

Chops, uncooked	4 to 6 months
Ground and stew meat, uncooked	3 to 4 months
Ham, fully cooked, half	1 to 2 months
Roasts, uncooked	4 to 12 months
Steaks, uncooked	6 to 12 months

Poultry

All cuts, cooked	4 months
Boneless or bone-in pieces, uncooked	9 months

Seafood

Fish, fatty, uncooked	2 to 3 months
Fish, lean, uncooked	6 months

In the Refrigerator (at 34° to 40° F)

Dairy and Eggs

Butter	1 to 3 months
Buttermilk	1 to 2 weeks
Cheese, hard, wedge, opened	6 months
Cheese, semihard, block, opened	3 to 4 weeks
Cream cheese, fat-free, light, and 1/3-less-fat	2 weeks
Egg substitute, opened	3 days
Fresh eggs in shell	3 to 5 weeks

Meats, Poultry, and Seafood
Beef, Lamb, Pork, and Veal

Ground and stew meat, uncooked	1 to 2 days
Roasts, uncooked	3 to 5 days
Steaks and chops, uncooked	3 to 5 days

Chicken, Turkey, and Seafood

All cuts, uncooked	1 to 2 days

Fruits and Vegetables

Apples, beets, cabbage, carrots, celery, citrus fruits, eggplant, and parsnips	2 to 3 weeks
Apricots, asparagus, berries, cauliflower, cucumbers, mushrooms, okra, peaches, pears, peas, peppers, plums, salad greens, and summer squash	2 to 4 days
Corn, husked	1 day

In the Pantry (Keep these at room temperature for 6 to 12 months.)

Baking and Cooking Staples

Baking powder
Biscuit and baking mixes
Broth, canned
Cooking spray
Honey
Mayonnaise, fat-free, low-fat, and light (unopened)
Milk, canned evaporated fat-free
Milk, nonfat dry powder
Mustard, prepared (unopened)
Oils, olive and vegetable
Pasta, dried
Peanut butter
Rice, instant and regular
Salad dressings, bottled (unopened)
Seasoning sauces, bottled
Tuna, canned

Fruits, Legumes, and Vegetables

Fruits, canned
Legumes (beans, lentils, peas), dried or canned
Tomato products, canned
Vegetables, canned

WeightWatchers®
ANNUAL RECIPES *for* SUCCESS
2013

Oxmoor
House®

©2012 by Time Home Entertainment Inc.
135 West 50th Street, New York, NY 10020

ISBN-13: 978-0-8487-3639-2
ISBN-10: 0-8487-3639-7
ISSN: 1526-1565

Printed in the United States of America
First Printing 2012

Be sure to check with your health-care provider before making any changes to your diet. *Weight Watchers* and ***PointsPlus***® are the registered trademarks of Weight Watchers International, Inc., and are used under license by Oxmoor House, Inc.

OXMOOR HOUSE
Editorial Director: Leah McLaughlin
Creative Director: Felicity Keane
Brand Manager: Katie McHugh
Senior Editor: Heather Averett
Managing Editor: Rebecca Benton

WEIGHT WATCHERS® ANNUAL RECIPES FOR
    SUCCESS 2013
Editor: Rachel Quinlivan West, RD
Art Director: Claire Cormany
Project Editor: Emily Chappell
Director, Test Kitchen: Elizabeth Tyler Austin
Assistant Director, Test Kitchen: Julie Christopher,
    Julie Gunter
Recipe Editor: Alyson Moreland Haynes
Recipe Developers and Testers: Wendy Ball, RD;
    Victoria E. Cox; Stefanie Maloney; Callie Nash;
    Leah Van Deren
Photography Director: Jim Bathie
Senior Photo Stylist: Kay E. Clarke
Photo Stylist: Katherine Eckert Coyne
Assistant Photo Stylist: Mary Louise Menendez
Production Managers: Theresa Beste-Farley,
    Tamara Nall Wilder

CONTRIBUTORS
Project Editor: Lacie Pinyan
Designer: Teresa Cole
Copy Editors: Jacqueline Giovanelli, Carmine Loper
Indexer: Mary Ann Laurens
Menu Planner Editor: Carolyn Land Williams, MEd, RD
Nutritional Analysis: Keri Matherne, RD
Interns: Mackenzie Cogle; Jessica Cox, RD;
    Susan Kemp; Emily Robinson; Katie Strasser
Recipe Developers and Testers: Tamara Goldis,
    Erica Hopper, Tonya Johnson, Kyra Moncrief,
    Kathleen Royal Phillips
Photographers: John Autry, Beau Gustafson
Photo Stylists: Mindi Shapiro Levine, Anna Pollock
Food Stylist: Ana Price Kelly

TIME HOME ENTERTAINMENT INC.
Publisher: Jim Childs
VP, Strategy & Business Development: Steven Sandonato
Executive Director, Marketing Services: Carol Pittard
Executive Director, Retail & Special Sales: Tom Mifsud
Director, Bookazine Development & Marketing: Laura Adam
Executive Publishing Director: Joy Butts
Finance Director: Glenn Buonocore
Associate General Counsel: Helen Wan

Cover: Classic Lasagna, page 91

To order additional
publications, call
1-800-765-6400
or
1-800-491-0551

For more books to
enrich your life, visit
oxmoorhouse.com

To search, savor, and share
thousands of recipes, visit
myrecipes.com

WeightWatchers®
ANNUAL RECIPES *for* SUCCESS
2013

contents

Weight Watchers®

At Weight Watchers, weight management is a partnership that combines our knowledge with your efforts. We help you on your weight-loss journey to make positive behavioral changes in your life, inspiring you with our belief in your power to succeed and motivating you every step of the way.

WEIGHT WATCHERS INTERNATIONAL BACKGROUND

SINCE ITS FOUNDING IN 1963, Weight Watchers has helped millions achieve healthy, sustainable weight loss. Weight Watchers International, Inc., is the world's leading provider of weight-management services, operating globally through a network of company-owned and franchise operations. Weight Watchers holds more than 50,000 weekly meetings where members receive group support and learn about healthy eating patterns, behavior modification, and physical activity. **WeightWatchers.com** provides innovative subscription weight-management products over the Internet and is the leading Internet-based weight-management provider in the world. In addition, Weight Watchers offers a wide range of products, publications, and programs for those interested in weight loss and weight control.

For more information about the Weight Watchers program and a meeting near you, call 1-800-651-6000 or visit **weightwatchers.com**

THE WEIGHT WATCHERS COMMITMENT TO SCIENCE

Weight Watchers backs up its weight-management plans with a strong commitment to the science of weight loss. The research and conclusions of experts and health organizations worldwide, including the World Health Organization and the National Institutes of Health, are incorporated into the Weight Watchers offerings. Weight Watchers also conducts its own research on weight-loss methods. As scientific findings change, the Weight Watchers plans evolve.

Weight Watchers®
ANNUAL RECIPES FOR SUCCESS 2013

This new cookbook empowers you to make the right food choices every day. There's never been a better time to make a positive change in your health, and you can do it while still enjoying the foods you love. Here's how:

- Over 275 great-tasting recipes that bring pleasure back to mealtime
- A **PointsPlus**® value per serving for every recipe
- Nutritional analysis with every recipe (see "About Our Recipes" on page 16)
- More than 40 color photographs of delicious recipes
- Step-by-step recipe instructions, prep and cook times, and secrets from our Test Kitchen
- Five seasonal menus, each with a Game Plan to help make preparing the meal a cinch
- Four weeks of 7-Day Menu Planners that incorporate many recipes from the cookbook plus some new ones, too

OUR FAVORITE RECIPES

All of our recipes are rigorously tested to ensure ease of preparation and excellent taste. But some are a cut above the rest. Here are our favorites from this year. We hope you enjoy them just as much.

▶ SPICE-BAKED SWEET POTATO CHIPS WITH HONEY-LIME DIP

PointsPlus value per serving: 2

The cooking technique used in this recipe produced wonderfully crisp chips that tasted anything but light. (page 18)

▼ BRAZILIAN CHEESE PUFFS

PointsPlus value per serving: 1

These puffs are worth the effort—just 10 minutes of hands-on prep time. The payoff: A cheesy ball of good-ness that is slightly crisp on the outside and pleasantly stretchy and gooey on the inside. Enjoy them hot out of the oven. (page 34)

OUR FAVORITE RECIPES

▶ ALMOND SHORTBREAD
PointsPlus value per serving: 3
Shortbread is traditionally made with lots of butter, but our lightened version offers that same buttery crispness with significantly fewer calories. Our secret: A combination of butter and canola oil. You won't notice the difference—seriously! (page 44)

▶▶ BLUEBERRY PIE BARS
PointsPlus value per serving: 5
A sugar cookie base offers a crisp contrast to the sweetened crumbled topping—a delicious mix of fresh blueberries, oats, and sugar cookies. (page 45)

▶▶▶ CHOCOLATE–PEANUT BUTTER TRUFFLES
PointsPlus value per serving: 1
Don't let the size of these truffles fool you. Bursting with chocolate and peanut butter flavor, they're sure to satisfy your sweet tooth. (page 46)

▼ CURRIED GROUPER TACOS
PointsPlus value per serving: 10
Whole-wheat naan gives these tacos a different twist and marries well with the Indian-inspired flavors of curry and mango chutney. Thick Greek yogurt adds a rich, creamy finish to these hearty and filling tacos. (page 67)

OUR FAVORITE RECIPES

▶ ROASTED VEGETABLES OVER PARMESAN POLENTA

PointsPlus value per serving: 5

Roasting gives this vegetable medley tremendous depth of flavor. The creamy, cheesy polenta acts as a perfect base for the deliciously browned vegetables. (page 79)

▼ KUNG PAO PORK

PointsPlus value per serving: 7

There's no need to order takeout with this lightened twist on the classic dish that takes only 13 minutes! Put the rice on to cook when you start this recipe, and you'll have a one-dish dinner ready in no time. (page 93)

▲ SMOKED CHICKEN–PESTO PIZZA

PointsPlus value per serving: 7

Six flavor-packed ingredients elevate this pizza way above anything out of a box or from delivery. Getting a tasty meal on the table for family or friends is a cinch. (page 102)

◄ GREEK BRAISED CHICKEN THIGHS

PointsPlus value per serving: 9

Moist chicken paired with rich kalamata olives and sweet tomatoes stew to create a phenomenal one-dish meal. Serve with crusty bread, if you like. (page 105)

OUR FAVORITE RECIPES

▶ DOLMAS SALAD

PointsPlus value per serving: 5

Ready in 23 minutes, this salad is reminiscent of stuffed grape leaves—complete with salty grape leaves and tangy feta cheese—without the time and effort. (page 119)

▼ CATFISH PO'BOYS

PointsPlus value per serving: 7

Traditional po'boys can have a ***PointsPlus*** value per serving of 23 or more (and 2,000-plus milligrams of sodium). This sandwich clocks in well below that without sacrificing the crispy, crunchy coating, thanks to cornflake crumbs. (page 123)

▲ GRILLED ASPARAGUS WITH BLUE CHEESE–WALNUT TOPPING

PointsPlus value per serving: 1

The short ingredient list belies the big flavor this simple side dish offers. Don't skip toasting the walnuts—it enhances their nuttiness. (page 146)

FROZEN HONEYDEW LIMEADE

PointsPlus value per serving: 4

This refreshing frozen drink is perfect for summer. Mint and fresh lime juice give it a bright finish. (page 168)

ABOUT OUR RECIPES

Weight Watchers® Annual Recipes for Success 2013
gives you the nutrition facts you need to stay on track. Every recipe in this book includes a ***PointsPlus®*** value per serving. For more information on Weight Watchers, see page 7.

Each recipe has a list of nutrients—including fat, carbohydrates, fiber, and protein. You'll also find calories, saturated fat, monounsaturated fat, polyunsaturated fat, cholesterol, iron, sodium, and calcium as well as a serving size and the number of servings. Measurements are abbreviated g (grams) and mg (milligrams). Nutritional values used in our calculations either come from The Food Processor, Version 8.9 (ESHA Research), or are provided by food manufacturers.

NUTRITIONAL ANALYSIS IS BASED ON THESE ASSUMPTIONS:

- Unless otherwise indicated, meat, poultry, and fish always refer to skinned, boned, and cooked servings.

- When we give a range for an ingredient (3 to 3½ cups flour, for instance), we calculate using the lesser amount.

- Some alcohol calories evaporate during heating; the analysis reflects this.

- Only the amount of marinade absorbed by the food is used in calculations.

  Garnishes and optional ingredients are not included in an analysis.

Safety Note: Cooking spray should never be used near direct heat. Always remove a pan from heat before spraying it with cooking spray.

A NOTE ON USE FOR DIABETICS:

Almost all of our recipes can be incorporated into a diabetic diet by using the carbohydrate amount in the nutrient analysis and incorporating that into the carbohydrate amount recommended by your physician.

appetizers & beverages

Roasted Garlic–Cream Cheese Balls, *page 19*

CREAMY AVOCADO-EDAMAME DIP

PointsPlus value per serving: 3

HANDS-ON TIME: 10 min. ■ **TOTAL TIME:** 10 min.

Shelled edamame are, essentially, baby soybeans. These tender beans are very high in protein and pair perfectly with the creaminess of avocado.

- **3 ripe avocados**
- **½ cup frozen shelled edamame (green soybeans)**
- **4 ounces ⅓-less-fat cream cheese (about ½ cup)**
- **4 small green onions, coarsely chopped**
- **2 tablespoons fresh lemon juice**
- **½ teaspoon freshly ground black pepper**
- **½ teaspoon chili powder**
- **¼ teaspoon salt**
- **1 garlic clove, peeled**

1. Cut avocados in half; scoop out pulp. Discard shells. Place avocado, edamame, and remaining ingredients in a food processor or blender; process until smooth. Cover and chill, if desired. YIELD: 10 SERVINGS (SERVING SIZE: ¼ CUP).

PER SERVING: Calories 116; Fat 9.5g (sat 2.4g, mono 5.9g, poly 1.1g); Protein 3.4g; Carb 6.6g; Fiber 2g; Chol 8mg; Iron 0.9mg; Sodium 109mg; Calc 15mg

SPICE-BAKED SWEET POTATO CHIPS WITH HONEY-LIME DIP

PointsPlus value per serving: 2   *pictured on page 49*

HANDS-ON TIME: 12 min. ■ **TOTAL TIME:** 38 min.

The microwave is key in this recipe. It produces a deliciously crisp chip. Each microwave operates a little differently, so watch the potatoes while they cook and adjust the cook time as needed. Use a mandoline for evenly sliced potatoes.

- **¼ cup light sour cream**
- **¼ cup reduced-fat mayonnaise**
- **1 tablespoon honey**
- **1 teaspoon grated fresh lime rind**
- **¼ teaspoon salt**
- **¼ teaspoon ground ginger**
- **¼ teaspoon ground cinnamon**
- **⅛ teaspoon ground red pepper**
- **1 sweet potato**
- **Cooking spray**

1. Combine first 4 ingredients in a small bowl; cover and chill.

2. Combine salt and next 3 ingredients; set aside.
3. Cut sweet potato into ⅛-inch-thick slices. Place one-fourth of slices in a single layer on a microwave-safe plate; coat both sides of slices with cooking spray. Sprinkle evenly with one-fourth of spice mixture.
4. Microwave at HIGH 2 to 3 minutes; turn slices, and microwave 1½ to 3 minutes or until crisp but not browned. Place on a wire rack to cool completely. Repeat procedure with remaining potato slices, cooking spray, and spice mixture. Serve with dip. YIELD: 6 SERVINGS (SERVING SIZE: ABOUT 12 CHIPS AND 1½ TABLESPOONS DIP).

PER SERVING: Calories 75; Fat 2.2g (sat 0.9g, mono 0.4g, poly 0.6g); Protein 1g; Carb 13.6g; Fiber 1.2g; Chol 3mg; Iron 0.4mg; Sodium 206mg; Calc 13mg

ROASTED JALAPEÑO–BLACK BEAN HUMMUS

PointsPlus value per serving: 1

HANDS-ON TIME: 4 min. ■ **TOTAL TIME:** 26 min.

Serve this dip with cool fresh veggies like carrots, celery sticks, jicama strips, or bell pepper wedges. Or, spread it on a burger or sandwich for a creamy kick.

- **4 jalapeño peppers**
- **1 (15-ounce) can black beans, rinsed and drained**
- **½ cup cilantro sprigs**
- **2 tablespoons fresh lime juice**
- **2 tablespoons water**
- **½ teaspoon roasted ground cumin**
- **4 garlic cloves, peeled**

1. Preheat broiler.
2. Place jalapeño peppers on a foil-lined baking sheet; broil 7 minutes or until blackened, turning occasionally. Place in a paper bag; fold to close tightly. Let stand 15 minutes. Peel and cut in half lengthwise. Discard seeds and membranes.
3. Place peppers, beans, and remaining ingredients in a food processor or blender; process until smooth. YIELD: 6 SERVINGS (SERVING SIZE: ¼ CUP).

PER SERVING: Calories 44; Fat 0.3g (sat 0g, mono 0g, poly 0.1g); Protein 2.9g; Carb 9g; Fiber 2.9g; Chol 0mg; Iron 0.8mg; Sodium 101mg; Calc 21mg

ROASTED GROUND CUMIN

This spice adds robust flavor without the work of roasting and grinding cumin yourself. You can also use it to enhance chili, fajitas, or tacos. It's available in most large supermarkets.

ROASTED GARLIC–CREAM CHEESE BALLS

PointsPlus value per serving: 1   *pictured on page 51*

HANDS-ON TIME: 15 min. ■ **TOTAL TIME:** 15 min.

Spread this garlicky goodness on flatbread crackers, toasted baguette slices, or apple slices.

> 1 (8-ounce) block ⅓-less-fat cream cheese, softened
> 2 teaspoons bottled minced roasted garlic
> ¼ teaspoon ground cumin
> ⅛ teaspoon crushed red pepper
> ⅛ teaspoon freshly ground black pepper
> 6 tablespoons chopped fresh cilantro

1. Combine first 5 ingredients in a small bowl, stirring until well blended.
2. Shape mixture into 24 (½-inch) balls. Place cilantro in a shallow dish. Roll each ball in cilantro. Chill until ready to serve. YIELD: 24 SERVINGS (SERVING SIZE: 1 BALL).

PER SERVING: Calories 25; Fat 2.1g (sat 1.4g, mono 0.5g, poly 0.1g); Protein 0.7g; Carb 0.8g; Fiber 0g; Chol 7mg; Iron 0mg; Sodium 37mg; Calc 7mg

EGGPLANT ROULADE WITH BASIL AND SUN-DRIED TOMATOES

PointsPlus value per serving: 1

HANDS-ON TIME: 45 min. ■ **TOTAL TIME:** 1 hr., 5 min.

> 4 (6-ounce) Japanese eggplants
> Cooking spray
> ¾ cup julienne-cut sun-dried tomatoes, packed without oil
> 4 ounces shredded fontina cheese
> ⅓ cup basil leaves, cut into thin strips
> ½ teaspoon freshly ground black pepper
> ¼ teaspoon kosher salt

1. Preheat oven to 375°.
2. Cut each eggplant lengthwise into 7 (⅛-inch-thick) slices. Cut slices to measure 6 inches in length. Heat a large nonstick skillet over medium heat. Coat pan with cooking spray. Coat eggplant slices on both sides with cooking spray. Place 5 to 6 eggplant slices in pan; cook 2 to 3 minutes on each side or until lightly browned. Place slices on paper towels, and cool. Repeat procedure with remaining eggplant slices.
3. Place 1 rounded teaspoon sun-dried tomato, 1 rounded teaspoon cheese, and about ½ teaspoon basil at one end of each eggplant slice, leaving about ½-inch border at end. Roll up eggplant slices, jelly-roll fashion, starting at the end with the filling.

4. Place rolls, seam sides down, in an 8-inch square glass or ceramic baking dish coated with cooking spray. (Rolls will be tightly packed together.) Sprinkle with pepper and salt. Bake at 375° for 15 minutes or until golden brown and cheese is melted. YIELD: 14 SERVINGS (SERVING SIZE: 2 PIECES).

PER SERVING: Calories 50; Fat 2.7g (sat 1.6g, mono 0.7g, poly 0.2g); Protein 3g; Carb 4.2g; Fiber 1.3g; Chol 9mg; Iron 0.3mg; Sodium 160mg; Calc 50mg

JAPANESE EGGPLANT

Japanese eggplant is the skinny cousin of the more familiar Italian version commonly seen in supermarkets. It features a thinner skin and sweeter, more delicate flavor.

HAM-AND-SWISS QUICHE CUPS

PointsPlus value per serving: 2

HANDS-ON TIME: 10 min. ■ **TOTAL TIME:** 28 min.

Use two muffin tins when preparing this recipe, placing a wonton in every other cup. The extra space keeps them from sticking together.

> Cooking spray
> 12 wonton wrappers
> 2 large eggs
> 1 tablespoon light sour cream
> 2 ounces shredded Swiss cheese (about ½ cup)
> ⅓ cup finely chopped ham

1. Preheat oven to 350°.
2. Coat 2 (12-cup) muffin pans with cooking spray. Working with 1 wonton wrapper at a time (cover remaining wrappers with a damp towel to keep from drying), press wrappers into bottoms of every other muffin cup.
3. Combine eggs and sour cream, stirring with a whisk. Stir in cheese and ham. Spoon about 1 tablespoon egg mixture into each wonton cup. Bake at 350° for 16 to 18 minutes or until golden brown. Cool in pans 2 minutes; serve warm. YIELD: 12 SERVINGS (SERVING SIZE: 1 QUICHE CUP).

PER SERVING: Calories 59; Fat 2.6g (sat 1.3g, mono 0.7g, poly 0.2g); Protein 3.7g; Carb 5.1g; Fiber 0.2g; Chol 43mg; Iron 0.5mg; Sodium 93mg; Calc 48mg

MINI TWICE-BAKED POTATOES

PointsPlus value per serving: 3

HANDS-ON TIME: 15 min. ■ **TOTAL TIME:** 1 hr., 25 min.

7 small red potatoes
2 ounces reduced-fat shredded cheddar cheese (about ½ cup)
½ cup reduced-fat sour cream
1 tablespoon chopped fresh chives
½ teaspoon freshly ground black pepper
½ teaspoon smoked paprika
¼ teaspoon salt
4 center-cut bacon slices, cooked and crumbled

1. Preheat oven to 400°.
2. Place potatoes on a foil-lined baking sheet. Bake at 400° for 45 minutes or until tender; cool slightly. Cut each potato in half lengthwise; carefully scoop out pulp into a small bowl, leaving shells intact.
3. Add cheese and next 5 ingredients to pulp; stir well. Spoon 1 heaping tablespoon potato mixture into each potato shell, and place stuffed potatoes on foil-lined baking sheet. Sprinkle stuffed potatoes evenly with crumbled bacon. Bake at 400° for 15 minutes or until cheese mixture is melted and lightly browned. Serve immediately. YIELD: 14 SERVINGS (SERVING SIZE: ½ POTATO).

PER SERVING: Calories 117; Fat 1.7g (sat 0.6g, mono 0.4g, poly 0.4g); Protein 4.4g; Carb 21.2g; Fiber 0.9g; Chol 2mg; Iron 1mg; Sodium 234mg; Calc 80mg

CENTER-CUT BACON

Center-cut bacon still has the same satisfying flavor, but because it's cut closer to the bone, it contains about 20% less saturated fat than regular bacon. A two-slice serving has a *PointsPlus* value of 1.

CHICKEN FAJITA WONTONS

PointsPlus value per serving: 1

HANDS-ON TIME: 20 min. ■ **TOTAL TIME:** 41 min.

Pick up prechopped bell pepper and onion along with a rotisserie chicken and a package of wonton wrappers at the grocery store, and you've got the makings of a quick-and-easy appetizer.

Cooking spray
¾ cup refrigerated prechopped tricolor bell pepper
½ cup finely chopped onion
½ cup finely chopped cooked chicken
2 teaspoons lower-sodium soy sauce
¼ teaspoon freshly ground black pepper
24 wonton wrappers
Refrigerated fresh salsa (optional)

1. Preheat oven to 450°.
2. Heat a medium nonstick skillet over medium-high heat. Coat pan with cooking spray. Add bell pepper and onion; sauté 5 minutes or until tender. Add chicken, soy sauce, and black pepper, stirring to combine. Remove from heat; cool 15 minutes.
3. Working with 1 wonton wrapper at a time (cover remaining wrappers with a damp towel to keep them from drying), spoon about 1 teaspoon chicken mixture into center of each wrapper. Moisten edges of wrapper with water; bring 2 opposite corners together. Pinch edges together to seal, forming a triangle. Coat triangles with cooking spray; place on a large baking sheet.
4. Bake at 450° for 14 to 16 minutes or until golden. Serve warm with fresh salsa, if desired. YIELD: 24 SERVINGS (SERVING SIZE: 1 WONTON).

PER SERVING: Calories 32; Fat 0.3g (sat 0.1g, mono 0.1g, poly 0.1g); Protein 1.8g; Carb 5.3g; Fiber 0.3g; Chol 3mg; Iron 0.3mg; Sodium 59mg; Calc 5mg

FIG–GOAT CHEESE PHYLLO BITES

PointsPlus value per serving: 2

HANDS-ON TIME: 9 min. ■ **TOTAL TIME:** 27 min.

The tang of goat cheese laced with the sweetness of figs is topped off with the crunch of toasty walnuts and creates a delightful bite.

1 (1.9-ounce) package mini phyllo shells
2 ounces crumbled goat cheese (about ½ cup)
2 ounces ⅓-less-fat cream cheese (about ¼ cup), softened
¼ cup fig preserves, finely chopped
¼ cup chopped dried Calimyrna figs
¼ cup chopped walnuts, toasted

1. Preheat oven to 350°.
2. Place phyllo shells on a baking sheet; bake at 350° for 3 minutes. Cool completely.
3. While shells cool, combine goat cheese and cream cheese in a small bowl; stir well. Combine fig preserves and dried figs in a small bowl; stir well.
4. Spoon about 2 teaspoons cheese mixture into each phyllo cup; top each with 1½ teaspoons fig mixture. Sprinkle each cup with ¾ teaspoon walnuts. YIELD: 15 SERVINGS (SERVING SIZE: 1 PHYLLO BITE).

PER SERVING: Calories 70; Fat 4.1g (sat 1.4g, mono 0.9g, poly 1.1g); Protein 1.5g; Carb 7g; Fiber 0.4g; Chol 6mg; Iron 0.3mg; Sodium 46mg; Calc 20mg

CALIMYRNA FIGS

The dense texture and subtle, sweet flavor of fresh figs is hard to beat. There are literally hundreds of varieties. Calimyrna figs are known for their nutlike flavor and tender, golden skin. Figs are extremely perishable; use them soon after purchasing, or store them in the refrigerator in a single layer for no more than two or three days.

CHICKEN CAESAR SALAD BITES

PointsPlus value per serving: 1

HANDS-ON TIME: 20 min. ■ **TOTAL TIME:** 20 min.

Classic Caesar salad flavors top garlicky pita chips in this easy appetizer. Purchase a rotisserie chicken from the grocery store to keep prep time to a minimum.

2 cups finely chopped cooked chicken breast
½ cup chopped arugula
¼ cup fat-free Caesar dressing
2 tablespoons fresh lemon juice
⅛ teaspoon freshly ground black pepper
24 Parmesan garlic-herb pita chips

1. Combine first 5 ingredients in a medium bowl. Spoon about 1 tablespoon chicken mixture onto each pita chip. YIELD: 24 SERVINGS (SERVING SIZE: 1 BITE).

PER SERVING: Calories 38; Fat 1g (sat 0.2g, mono 0.1g, poly 0.1g); Protein 4g; Carb 3g; Fiber 0.2g; Chol 10mg; Iron 0.3mg; Sodium 79mg; Calc 3mg

PIMIENTO CHEESE PINWHEELS

PointsPlus value per serving: 1

HANDS-ON TIME: 15 min. ■ **TOTAL TIME:** 3 hr., 15 min.

Pimiento cheese is a Southern staple traditionally served as a sandwich or cracker spread or stuffed in crisp celery sticks. Here it makes a cool and creamy filling rolled up in a tortilla.

2 ounces ⅓-less-fat cream cheese (about ¼ cup)
2 tablespoons light mayonnaise
3 ounces reduced-fat sharp cheddar cheese, shredded
2 ounces reduced-fat jalapeño cheddar cheese, shredded
2 tablespoons diced pimiento
1½ teaspoons grated onion
¼ teaspoon freshly ground black pepper
¼ teaspoon finely chopped garlic
3 (6½-inch) flour tortillas

1. Place cream cheese and mayonnaise in a small bowl; beat with a mixer at medium speed until well blended. Add cheddar cheese and next 5 ingredients; beat just until blended. Cover and chill at least 3 hours.
2. Spread cheese mixture evenly over tortillas; roll up. Cut each rolled tortilla into 8 slices. Serve immediately. YIELD: 24 SERVINGS (SERVING SIZE: 1 PINWHEEL).

PER SERVING: Calories 43; Fat 2.4g (sat 1.1g, mono 0g, poly 0g); Protein 2.3g; Carb 3.1g; Fiber 0.4g; Chol 6mg; Iron 0.1mg; Sodium 99mg; Calc 115mg

MINI CAPRESE PITAS

PointsPlus value per serving: 1

HANDS-ON TIME: 5 min. ■ **TOTAL TIME:** 5 min.

Traditional Caprese salad features slices of tomato, fresh basil, and mozzarella. Sun-dried tomato pesto stands in for fresh tomatoes in this crispy cracker appetizer.

> **12 pita crackers**
> **¼ cup sun-dried tomato pesto**
> **12 medium basil leaves**
> **3 ounces fresh mozzarella cheese**
> **2 tablespoons balsamic glaze**

1. Spread pita crackers evenly with pesto; top each with a basil leaf.
2. Cut mozzarella into 6 thin slices; cut each slice in half. Place 1 cheese slice on top of each basil leaf; drizzle evenly with balsamic glaze. Serve immediately. YIELD: 12 SERVINGS (SERVING SIZE: 1 MINI PITA).

PER SERVING: Calories 44; Fat 2.5g (sat 1.1g, mono 0.2g, poly 0.1g); Protein 1.9g; Carb 3.5g; Fiber 0.2g; Chol 6mg; Iron 0.3mg; Sodium 81mg; Calc 3mg

SPINACH, ARTICHOKE, AND BACON CROSTINI

PointsPlus value per serving: 2

HANDS-ON TIME: 15 min. ■ **TOTAL TIME:** 24 min.

Crostini is Italian for "little toasts." Crown them with a bacon-laced spinach and artichoke topping. You'll need to buy a 12-ounce baguette to get 28 slices.

> **3 center-cut bacon slices**
> **1 (9-ounce) package frozen artichoke hearts, thawed, drained, and chopped**
> **2 cups chopped fresh baby spinach**
> **¼ teaspoon freshly ground black pepper**
> **3 ounces finely shredded pecorino Romano cheese (about ¾ cup), divided**
> **28 (⅜-inch-thick) slices diagonally cut French bread baguette, toasted**

1. Preheat oven to 400°.
2. Cook bacon in a large nonstick skillet over medium heat 4 minutes or until crisp. Remove bacon, reserving 1 teaspoon drippings in pan. Crumble bacon; set aside.

3. Add artichoke hearts, spinach, and pepper to drippings in pan; sauté 2 minutes or until spinach wilts. Remove from heat. Stir in 2 ounces cheese and crumbled bacon.
4. Arrange baguette slices in a single layer on a baking sheet. Spoon about 1 tablespoon artichoke mixture onto each baguette slice; sprinkle slices evenly with remaining 1 ounce cheese. Bake at 400° for 5 minutes or until cheese melts. YIELD: 28 SERVINGS (SERVING SIZE: 1 CROSTINO).

PER SERVING: Calories 69; Fat 1.1g (sat 0.5g, mono 0.3g, poly 0g); Protein 2.7g; Carb 12.8g; Fiber 1.3g; Chol 3mg; Iron 0.8mg; Sodium 179mg; Calc 24mg

DATE AND WALNUT CROSTINI

PointsPlus value per serving: 2

HANDS-ON TIME: 15 min. ■ **TOTAL TIME:** 28 min.

Enjoy a glass of the port used in this recipe with these crusty, sweet slices.

> **1 cup whole pitted dates**
> **½ cup walnuts**
> **¼ cup port or other sweet red wine**
> **⅛ teaspoon salt**
> **24 (¼-inch-thick) slices diagonally cut French baguette**
> **1 ounce shaved fresh Parmesan cheese**

1. Preheat oven to 375°.
2. Combine first 4 ingredients in a medium saucepan; bring to a boil over medium heat. Reduce heat, and simmer 10 minutes or until slightly syrupy; cool slightly.
3. While date mixture cooks, place baguette slices on a baking sheet; bake at 375° for 10 to 12 minutes or until lightly browned and crisp.
4. Place date mixture in a food processor; process 1 minute or until smooth. Spread each baguette slice with about 1½ teaspoons date mixture and 1 slice shaved Parmesan. YIELD: 24 SERVINGS (SERVING SIZE: 1 CROSTINO).

PER SERVING: Calories 69; Fat 1.7g (sat 0.3g, mono 0.3g, poly 1g); Protein 1.9g; Carb 12.1g; Fiber 0.8g; Chol 1mg; Iron 0.5mg; Sodium 99mg; Calc 19mg

ASIAN LETTUCE WRAPS

PointsPlus value per serving: 1

HANDS-ON TIME: 24 min. ■ **TOTAL TIME:** 24 min.

Boston and iceberg lettuces are ideal choices for these wraps. If you'd like a sturdier wrap, use napa cabbage or green cabbage leaves.

> ¼ cup lower-sodium soy sauce
> 1 tablespoon hot chile sauce with garlic
> 2 teaspoons dark sesame oil
> Cooking spray
> 1 pound ground chicken
> 1 tablespoon refrigerated pureed fresh ginger, divided
> 1 (8-ounce) can sliced water chestnuts, drained and chopped
> ½ cup sliced green onions
> ¼ cup chopped fresh cilantro
> 16 large Boston or iceberg lettuce leaves

1. Combine first 3 ingredients in a small bowl; set aside.
2. Heat a large nonstick skillet over medium-high heat. Coat pan with cooking spray. Add chicken and ginger; cook 5 minutes or until browned, stirring to crumble. Stir in water chestnuts and green onions; cook 1 minute, stirring occasionally. Stir in soy sauce mixture. Remove from heat; stir in cilantro.
3. Place about ¼ cup chicken mixture in center of each lettuce leaf. Fold in edges of leaves; roll up. Serve immediately. YIELD: 16 SERVINGS (SERVING SIZE: 1 WRAP).

PER SERVING: Calories 57; Fat 3g (sat 0.7g, mono 0.2g, poly 0.3g); Protein 5.2g; Carb 2.8g; Fiber 1g; Chol 19mg; Iron 0.3mg; Sodium 181mg; Calc 12mg

MARINATED CHEESE

PointsPlus value per serving: 1

HANDS-ON TIME: 8 min. ■ **TOTAL TIME:** 9 hr., 8 min.

Creamy cubes of mozzarella take a long soak in a fragrant, Italian-flavored marinade. Skewer the cubes onto wooden picks to serve, if desired.

> 2 (8-ounce) packages part-skim mozzarella cheese
> ⅓ cup chopped sun-dried tomato halves, packed without oil (8 halves)
> ⅓ cup olive oil
> 2 tablespoons chopped fresh parsley
> ½ teaspoon garlic powder
> ¼ teaspoon dried Italian seasoning
> ¼ teaspoon freshly ground black pepper

1. Cut cheese into 36 (1-inch) cubes; place cheese cubes and tomato in a large zip-top plastic bag.
2. Combine oil and remaining ingredients in a small bowl, stirring well with a whisk. Pour over cheese and tomato; seal bag. Chill at least 8 hours. Let stand at room temperature 1 hour before serving. YIELD: 36 SERVINGS (SERVING SIZE: 1 CHEESE CUBE).

PER SERVING: Calories 52; Fat 4g (sat 1.6g, mono 2g, poly 0.3g); Protein 3.2g; Carb 0.7g; Fiber 0.1g; Chol 8mg; Iron 0.1mg; Sodium 79mg; Calc 100mg

MARINATED SHRIMP COCKTAIL

PointsPlus value per serving: 2

HANDS-ON TIME: 8 min. ■ **TOTAL TIME:** 2 hr., 8 min.

Prepare this dish in a nonmetal bowl. The acid from the citrus can react with metal, causing off flavors. Serve with baked tortilla chips to scoop up bites of this chopped shrimp cocktail.

> ¼ cup finely chopped red onion
> ¼ cup prepared cocktail sauce
> 3 tablespoons finely chopped and seeded jalapeño pepper
> 2 tablespoons fresh lime juice
> 2 tablespoons fresh orange juice
> 1 tablespoon fresh lemon juice
> 4 teaspoons chopped fresh cilantro
> 1 pound coarsely chopped cooked peeled shrimp

1. Combine first 7 ingredients in a glass bowl. Add shrimp; toss to combine. Cover and chill 2 to 3 hours before serving. YIELD: 6 SERVINGS (SERVING SIZE: ½ CUP).

PER SERVING: Calories 93; Fat 0.9g (sat 0.2g, mono 0.2g, poly 0.4g); Protein 16.2g; Carb 4.1g; Fiber 0.4g; Chol 147mg; Iron 2.5mg; Sodium 303mg; Calc 33mg

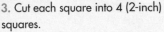

HOW TO PREPARE MINTED WATERMELON-FETA SANDWICHES

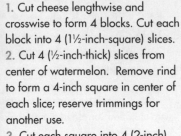

1. Cut cheese lengthwise and crosswise to form 4 blocks. Cut each block into 4 (1½-inch-square) slices.
2. Cut 4 (½-inch-thick) slices from center of watermelon. Remove rind to form a 4-inch square in center of each slice; reserve trimmings for another use.
3. Cut each square into 4 (2-inch) squares.
4. Cut each 2-inch square in half horizontally. Assemble sandwiches.

MINTED WATERMELON-FETA SANDWICHES

PointsPlus value per serving: 2

HANDS-ON TIME: 17 min. ■ **TOTAL TIME:** 1 hr., 17 min.

The sweet crispness of the watermelon contrasts with the salty creaminess of the feta cheese in these petite sandwiches.

½ cup sugar
½ cup water
20 small mint leaves, divided
1 (8-ounce) package feta cheese
1 (6- to 7-pound) seedless watermelon

1. Combine sugar, ½ cup water, and 4 mint leaves in a small saucepan. Bring to a boil; cook 2 minutes or until sugar dissolves. Cool sugar syrup completely. Discard mint leaves.
2. Cut cheese lengthwise and crosswise to form 4 blocks. Cut each block into 4 (1½-inch–square) slices.
3. Cut 4 (½-inch-thick) slices from center of watermelon. Remove rind to form a 4-inch square in center

of each slice; reserve trimmings for another use. Cut each square into 4 (2-inch) squares. Cut each square in half horizontally. Place 1 slice of feta between two watermelon squares. Brush tops of sandwiches with sugar syrup. Top each sandwich with a mint leaf. YIELD: 16 SERVINGS (SERVING SIZE: 1 SANDWICH).

PER SERVING: Calories 54; Fat 2.1g (sat 1.4g, mono 0.5g, poly 0.1g); Protein 1.6g; Carb 7.9g; Fiber 0.2g; Chol 8mg; Iron 0.2mg; Sodium 106mg; Calc 50mg

FROZEN LATTE

PointsPlus value per serving: 2

HANDS-ON TIME: 5 min. ■ **TOTAL TIME:** 5 min.

Make your own gourmet coffee-shop beverage at home with this pick-me-up recipe.

2 cups 1% low-fat milk
⅓ cup "measures-like-sugar" calorie-free sweetener
2 tablespoons instant espresso granules
2 cups ice cubes

1. Place all ingredients in a blender; process until smooth. YIELD: 4 SERVINGS (SERVING SIZE: ABOUT 1½ CUPS).

PER SERVING: Calories 63; Fat 1.2g (sat 0.8g, mono 0.3g, poly 0.1g); Protein 4.3g; Carb 8.7g; Fiber 0g; Chol 6mg; Iron 0.1mg; Sodium 54mg; Calc 147mg

SPARKLING DARK CHERRY LIMEADE

PointsPlus value per serving: 2

HANDS-ON TIME: 8 min. ■ **TOTAL TIME:** 8 min.

Cherry-flavored sparkling water adds fizzy sweetness to this refreshing cooler.

1 (12-ounce) package frozen pitted dark sweet cherries, thawed
½ cup water
4 cups cherry sparkling water
1¼ cups refrigerated limeade
¼ cup fresh lime juice (about 2 limes)

1. Place cherries and ½ cup water in a blender; process until smooth. Press mixture through a sieve over a bowl, reserving liquid; discard solids. Combine cherry liquid, sparkling water, limeade, and lime juice in a pitcher. Chill until ready to serve. YIELD: 7 SERVINGS (SERVING SIZE: 1 CUP).

PER SERVING: Calories 70; Fat 0.1g (sat 0g, mono 0g, poly 0g); Protein 0.7g; Carb 14.9g; Fiber 2.5g; Chol 0mg; Iron 0.6mg; Sodium 1mg; Calc 15mg

SPARKLING WHITE SANGRIA

PointsPlus value per serving: 5   *pictured on page 50*

HANDS-ON TIME: 5 min. ■ **TOTAL TIME:** 12 hr., 36 min.

Add the strawberries right before serving to keep this summery white wine punch bright and colorful.

1 cup water
¼ cup sugar
1 (750-milliliter) bottle pinot grigio
¾ cup orange-flavored liqueur
1 cup sliced peeled peaches
1 large navel orange, sliced
1 lemon, sliced
2 cups chilled club soda
2 cups sliced fresh strawberries

1. Combine 1 cup water and sugar in a small saucepan. Bring to a boil over high heat, stirring until sugar dissolves. Remove from heat; cool 30 minutes.
2. Combine sugar mixture, wine, and next 4 ingredients in a large pitcher; cover and chill at least 12 hours and up to 24 hours. Add club soda and strawberries; stir gently. Serve immediately. YIELD: 11 SERVINGS (SERVING SIZE: 1 CUP).

PER SERVING: Calories 154; Fat 0.1g (sat 0g, mono 0g, poly 0.1g); Protein 0.5g; Carb 16.7g; Fiber 1.1g; Chol 0mg; Iron 0.2mg; Sodium 10mg; Calc 14mg

BLACKBERRY-BASIL SMASH

PointsPlus value per serving: 3

HANDS-ON TIME: 10 min. ■ **TOTAL TIME:** 10 min.

2 cups fresh blackberries
12 basil leaves, divided
Ice cubes
2 cups diet lemon-lime soda
½ cup vodka

1. Divide blackberries evenly among 4 (6-ounce) glasses; place 2 basil leaves in each glass. Mash fruit and basil together with the back of a spoon. Fill glasses with ice. Pour ½ cup soda and 2 tablespoons vodka into each glass; stir. Top each serving with 1 basil leaf. YIELD: 4 SERVINGS (SERVING SIZE: ABOUT ¾ CUP).

PER SERVING: Calories 96; Fat 0.4g (sat 0g, mono 0.1g, poly 0.2g); Protein 1.1g; Carb 7g; Fiber 3.6g; Chol 0mg; Iron 0.5mg; Sodium 14mg; Calc 24mg

RASPBERRY-LEMON CHILLER

PointsPlus value per serving: 4

HANDS-ON TIME: 6 min. ■ **TOTAL TIME:** 6 min.

Thread raspberries, lemon, and mint onto a wooden stick for a pretty garnish.

1 cup fresh raspberries, divided
2 cups reduced-sugar refrigerated lemonade
½ cup citrus vodka
Ice cubes
4 thin lemon slices
Fresh mint leaves

1. Place ¾ cup raspberries, lemonade, and vodka in a blender; process until smooth. Press mixture through a sieve over a bowl or pitcher, reserving liquid; discard solids. Serve over ice. Garnish with remaining ¼ cup raspberries, lemon slices, and mint. YIELD: 4 SERVINGS (SERVING SIZE: ¾ CUP).

PER SERVING: Calories 107; Fat 0.2g (sat 0g, mono 0g, poly 0.1g); Protein 0.4g; Carb 9.3g; Fiber 0.3g; Chol 0mg; Iron 0.2mg; Sodium 1mg; Calc 10mg

BUYING RASPBERRIES

These intensely flavored, antioxidant-packed berries are usually available from May through November. Choose brightly colored, plump berries without hulls. Like blackberries, if the hulls are still attached, the berries are not mature and will be tart.

FROZEN STRAWBERRY MOJITO

PointsPlus value per serving: 3

HANDS-ON TIME: 4 min. ■ **TOTAL TIME:** 4 min.

1 (10-ounce) package frozen strawberry halves in light syrup
1 cup white rum
⅓ cup mint leaves
1 teaspoon grated fresh lime rind
⅓ cup fresh lime juice (about 3 limes)
4 teaspoons measures-like-sugar sweetener
2 cups ice
Fresh mint leaves (optional)

1. Place first 7 ingredients in a blender; process until smooth. Garnish with mint leaves, if desired. Serve immediately. YIELD: 8 SERVINGS (SERVING SIZE: ½ CUP).

PER SERVING: Calories 96; Fat 0.1g (sat 0g, mono 0g, poly 0g); Protein 0.3g; Carb 8.7g; Fiber 0.8g; Chol 0mg; Iron 0.3mg; Sodium 1mg; Calc 8mg

GIN AND GINGER FIZZ

PointsPlus value per serving: 4

HANDS-ON TIME: 6 min. ■ **TOTAL TIME:** 6 min.

1 cup gin
3 tablespoons agave nectar
¼ cup fresh lemon juice (about 2 small lemons)
¼ cup fresh lime juice (about 2 limes)
2 teaspoons grated peeled fresh ginger
14 to 16 ice cubes
1 cup club soda
1 cup diet ginger ale
Lime wedges (optional)

1. Combine first 6 ingredients in a cocktail shaker; strain gin mixture into 6 highball or other similar-sized glasses. Add club soda and ginger ale evenly to glasses. Garnish each with a lime wedge, if desired. YIELD: 6 SERVINGS (SERVING SIZE: ¾ CUP).

PER SERVING: Calories 121; Fat 0g (sat 0g, mono 0g, poly 0g); Protein 0.1g; Carb 9.8g; Fiber 0.1g; Chol 0mg; Iron 0mg; Sodium 18mg; Calc 2mg

BOURBON-PEACH ICED TEA

PointsPlus value per serving: 4

HANDS-ON TIME: 15 min. ■ **TOTAL TIME:** 1 hr., 45 min.

Peach nectar and honey sweeten the tea and bourbon in this cocktail's nod to two Southern classics.

2 cups water
2 regular-sized tea bags
¼ cup honey
1 cup peach nectar
½ cup bourbon
Ice cubes
Fresh mint sprigs (optional)

1. Bring 2 cups water to a boil in a medium saucepan; remove from heat. Add tea bags; cover and steep 10 minutes.

2. Discard tea bags. Add honey to tea, stirring until dissolved. Stir in peach nectar; refrigerate 1½ hours or until thoroughly chilled. Stir in bourbon. Serve over ice, and garnish with mint, if desired. YIELD: 5 SERVINGS (SERVING SIZE: ABOUT ¾ CUP).

PER SERVING: Calories 129; Fat 0g (sat 0g, mono 0g, poly 0g); Protein 0.2g; Carb 20.8g; Fiber 0.3g; Chol 0mg; Iron 0.2mg; Sodium 4mg; Calc 4mg

RASPBERRY DARK HOT CHOCOLATE

PointsPlus value per serving: 3

HANDS-ON TIME: 6 min. ■ **TOTAL TIME:** 11 min.

Dark chocolate and raspberry liqueur complement each other in this decadent after-dinner drink.

1¾ cups fat-free milk
1 cup water
2 tablespoons brown sugar
1 tablespoon unsweetened cocoa
Dash of salt
2 ounces chopped bittersweet chocolate
¼ cup Chambord (raspberry-flavored liqueur)

1. Combine first 5 ingredients in a small, heavy saucepan over medium-high heat; cook until sugar dissolves and tiny bubbles form around edge of pan, stirring frequently (do not boil). Remove from heat.
2. Add chopped chocolate, stirring until chocolate melts. Stir in liqueur. YIELD: 6 SERVINGS (SERVING SIZE: ½ CUP).

PER SERVING: Calories 127; Fat 4.2g (sat 2.1g, mono 1.5g, poly 0.1g); Protein 3.3g; Carb 17g; Fiber 0.8g; Chol 1mg; Iron 0.4mg; Sodium 56mg; Calc 93mg

CHAMBORD

Chambord, a liqueur made from raspberries, has a luscious ruby-red hue and rich, sweet flavor. It's delicious drizzled over ice cream. A 2-tablespoon serving has a ***PointsPlus*** value of 2.

breads

Honey Whole-Wheat Biscuits, *page 28*

Rerolling the dough maximizes the number of biscuits you get, but reroll only once. Working the dough too much yields tough biscuits. After cutting the dough with a biscuit cutter, gather the remaining dough, and pat or roll to the same thickness as the initial roll. Cut the rerolled dough with the biscuit cutter, and discard the remaining dough.

HONEY WHOLE-WHEAT BISCUITS

PointsPlus value per serving: 3   *pictured on page 52*

HANDS-ON TIME: 7 min. ■ **TOTAL TIME:** 20 min.

A hint of sweet honey complements the nutty whole-wheat flavor of these biscuits. For added sweetness, drizzle the warm biscuits with more honey or serve with jam.

  Cooking spray
  4.75 ounces whole-wheat flour (about 1 cup)
  4.5 ounces all-purpose flour (about 1 cup)
  2½ teaspoons baking powder
  ½ teaspoon salt
  5 tablespoons chilled butter, cut into small pieces
  ¾ cup nonfat buttermilk
  ¼ cup honey

1. Preheat oven to 425°. Place rack in upper third of oven.
2. Cover a baking sheet with parchment paper; coat paper with cooking spray. Set aside.
3. Weigh or lightly spoon flours into dry measuring cups; level with a knife. Combine flours, baking powder, and salt in a bowl; cut in chilled butter with a pastry blender or 2 knives until mixture resembles coarse meal.
4. Combine buttermilk and honey, stirring with a whisk. Add buttermilk mixture to flour mixture, stirring just until moist.
5. Turn dough out onto a lightly floured surface; knead lightly 4 times. Gently roll or pat dough to a ¾-inch thickness; cut with a 2-inch biscuit cutter into 11 biscuits. Gather remaining dough. Roll to a ¾-inch thickness, and cut into 3 biscuits. Place biscuits 1 inch

apart on prepared baking sheet. Bake at 425° for 13 minutes or until golden. Serve warm. YIELD: 14 SERVINGS (SERVING SIZE: 1 BISCUIT).

PER SERVING: Calories 122; Fat 4.4g (sat 2.7g, mono 1.1g, poly 0.3g); Protein 2.6g; Carb 18.7g; Fiber 1.3g; Chol 11mg; Iron 0.8mg; Sodium 197mg; Calc 65mg

PARMESAN-CHIVE DROP BISCUITS

PointsPlus value per serving: 4

HANDS-ON TIME: 6 min. ■ **TOTAL TIME:** 18 min.

Serve these fragrant, cheesy biscuits alongside scrambled eggs to shake up your breakfast routine.

  10.8 ounces low-fat baking mix (about 2¾ cups)
  ¼ teaspoon freshly ground black pepper
  ¼ cup chilled unsalted butter, cut into small pieces
  ⅔ cup grated fresh Parmesan cheese
  3 tablespoons chopped fresh chives
  1 cup evaporated low-fat milk
  Cooking spray

1. Preheat oven to 425°.
2. Weigh or lightly spoon baking mix into dry measuring cups; level with a knife. Combine baking mix and pepper in a bowl; cut in chilled butter with a pastry blender or 2 knives until mixture resembles coarse meal. Stir in cheese and chives. Add milk; stir just until moist.
3. Drop dough by level ¼ cupfuls 2 inches apart onto a large baking sheet lined with parchment paper; coat tops of mounds heavily with cooking spray. Bake at 425° for 12 minutes or until golden. Serve warm. YIELD: 14 SERVINGS (SERVING SIZE: 1 BISCUIT).

PER SERVING: Calories 144; Fat 6.2g (sat 3g, mono 2.1g, poly 0.5g); Protein 4.5g; Carb 18g; Fiber 0.3g; Chol 15mg; Iron 0.9mg; Sodium 335mg; Calc 179mg

MAPLE-BACON CORNMEAL BISCUITS

PointsPlus value per serving: 3

HANDS-ON TIME: 7 min. ■ **TOTAL TIME:** 17 min.

2.9 ounces low-fat baking mix (about ¾ cup)
¼ cup stone-ground yellow cornmeal
3 center-cut bacon slices, cooked and crumbled
⅓ cup nonfat buttermilk
2 tablespoons maple syrup
2 tablespoons unsalted butter, melted
Cooking spray

1. Preheat oven to 425°.
2. Weigh or lightly spoon baking mix into dry measuring cups; level with a knife. Combine baking mix, cornmeal, and crumbled bacon in a medium bowl. Combine buttermilk, maple syrup, and butter in another bowl, stirring with a whisk. Add buttermilk mixture to baking mix mixture, stirring just until moist.
3. Drop dough by heaping tablespoonfuls 2 inches apart onto a large ungreased baking sheet to form 8 mounds; coat tops of mounds with cooking spray. Bake at 425° for 10 minutes or until golden. YIELD: 8 SERVINGS (SERVING SIZE: 1 BISCUIT).

PER SERVING: Calories 109; Fat 4.2g (sat 2g, mono 1.2g, poly 0.3g); Protein 2.3g; Carb 15.6g; Fiber 0.4g; Chol 10mg; Iron 0.6mg; Sodium 166mg; Calc 74mg

DROP BISCUITS

Drop biscuits have a higher proportion of liquid to dry ingredients than rolled biscuits, so you'll have a thick batter rather than a soft dough.

WHOLE-WHEAT CHOCOLATE CHIP LOAF

PointsPlus value per serving: 5

HANDS-ON TIME: 5 min. ■ **TOTAL TIME:** 1 hr., 5 min.

A perfect after-school snack or quick breakfast bread, this slightly sweet loaf is chock-full of whole grains.

Cooking spray
3.6 ounces whole-wheat flour (about ¾ cup)
3.4 ounces all-purpose flour (about ¾ cup)
¾ cup packed brown sugar
⅔ cup quick-cooking oats
1 teaspoon baking soda
¼ teaspoon salt
1 cup plain fat-free yogurt
¼ cup canola oil
1 large egg
½ cup semisweet chocolate minichips

1. Preheat oven to 350°.
2. Coat an 8 x 4–inch loaf pan with cooking spray; dust with flour.
3. Weigh or lightly spoon flours into dry measuring cups; level with a knife. Combine flours, brown sugar, and next 3 ingredients in a large bowl, stirring with a whisk. Make a well in center of mixture. Combine yogurt, oil, and egg in a small bowl; add to flour mixture, stirring until just moist. Fold in chocolate chips. Spoon batter into prepared pan.
4. Bake at 350° for 45 minutes or until a wooden pick inserted in center comes out clean. Cool 15 minutes in pan on a wire rack; remove from pan. Cool completely on wire rack. YIELD: 14 SERVINGS (SERVING SIZE: 1 SLICE).

PER SERVING: Calories 185; Fat 6.7g (sat 1.5g, mono 3.3g, poly 1.3g); Protein 3.6g; Carb 29.4g; Fiber 1.8g; Chol 15mg; Iron 1.2mg; Sodium 151mg; Calc 41mg

WALNUT-RAISIN BEER BREAD

PointsPlus value per serving: 4

HANDS-ON TIME: 7 min. ■ **TOTAL TIME:** 1 hr., 55 min.

No kneading needed for this bread...just spoon the soft, batterlike dough into a loaf pan, and bake.

- **13.5 ounces self-rising flour (about 3 cups)**
- **½ cup chopped walnuts**
- **½ cup raisins**
- **3 tablespoons sugar**
- **⅛ teaspoon salt**
- **1 (12-ounce) bottle light beer**
- **2 tablespoons unsalted butter, melted**
- **Cooking spray**

1. Preheat oven to 375°.
2. Weigh or lightly spoon flour into dry measuring cups; level with a knife. Combine flour and next 4 ingredients in a large bowl; make a well in center of mixture. Add beer and butter to flour mixture. Stir just until moist.
3. Spoon batter into a 9 x 5–inch loaf pan coated with cooking spray. Bake at 375° for 40 to 45 minutes or until a wooden pick inserted in center comes out clean. Cool 5 minutes in pan on a wire rack; remove from pan. Cool at least 1 hour on wire rack before slicing.
YIELD: 15 SERVINGS (SERVING SIZE: 1 SLICE).

PER SERVING: Calories 158; Fat 4.4g (sat 1.3g, mono 0.8g, poly 2g); Protein 3.3g; Carb 26.2g; Fiber 1.1g; Chol 4mg; Iron 1.4mg; Sodium 338mg; Calc 92mg

SQUASH-CORN MUFFINS

PointsPlus value per serving: 3

HANDS-ON TIME: 6 min. ■ **TOTAL TIME:** 24 min.

Use the abundance of yellow squash in your garden to make these moist muffins, a perfect accompaniment to a summer vegetable supper.

- **2 cups self-rising cornmeal mix**
- **¼ teaspoon freshly ground black pepper**
- **1 large egg**
- **1 cup 1% low-fat milk**
- **1 cup shredded yellow squash (about 1 medium)**
- **⅓ cup finely chopped onion**
- **¼ cup canola oil**
- **Cooking spray**

1. Preheat oven to 400°.
2. Lightly spoon cornmeal mix into dry measuring cups; level with a knife. Combine cornmeal and pepper in a medium bowl; make a well in center of mixture. Combine egg and next 4 ingredients in a bowl; add to cornmeal mixture. Stir just until moist.
3. Spoon batter evenly into 16 muffin cups coated with cooking spray. Bake at 400° for 18 to 20 minutes or until muffins spring back when touched lightly in center. Remove muffins from pans immediately; cool on a wire rack. **YIELD: 16 SERVINGS (SERVING SIZE: 1 MUFFIN).**

PER SERVING: Calories 95; Fat 4.5g (sat 0.5g, mono 2.4g, poly 1g); Protein 2g; Carb 12.5g; Fiber 1.2g; Chol 14mg; Iron 0.7mg; Sodium 227mg; Calc 42mg

OVERMIXING

As in all light baking, precise measurements are key, but you'll also need to pay attention to how you mix the ingredients. Creating a well in the center of the dry ingredients is the best way to incorporate the wet ingredients without overmixing, stirring just until the dry ingredients have been incorporated. (A few lumps are OK.) If you overmix the batter, the bread will be dense and chewy; if you undermix, patches of flour will speckle the bread.

STRAWBERRY-ALMOND MUFFINS

PointsPlus value per serving: 5   *pictured on page 51*

HANDS-ON TIME: 12 min. ■ **TOTAL TIME:** 29 min.

Dried strawberries add chewy sweetness to this breakfast treat. Substitute dried cranberries for the strawberries, if you like.

7.9 ounces all-purpose flour (about 1¾ cups)
1 cup chopped dried strawberries
½ cup packed brown sugar
1 teaspoon baking powder
1 teaspoon baking soda
¼ teaspoon salt
1 cup nonfat buttermilk
¼ cup almond butter
2 tablespoons butter, melted
½ teaspoon almond extract
1 large egg, lightly beaten
Cooking spray
¼ cup chopped slivered almonds

1. Preheat oven to 400°.
2. Weigh or lightly spoon flour into dry measuring cups; level with a knife. Combine flour and next 5 ingredients in large bowl; make a well in center of mixture. Combine buttermilk and next 4 ingredients in a small bowl; add to flour mixture, stirring just until moist. Spoon batter evenly into 12 muffin cups coated with cooking spray. Sprinkle evenly with almonds.
3. Bake at 400° for 17 minutes or until muffins spring back when touched lightly in center. Remove muffins from pan immediately; serve warm. YIELD: 12 SERVINGS (SERVING SIZE: 1 MUFFIN).

PER SERVING: Calories 202; Fat 6.6g (sat 1.7g, mono 3.3g, poly 1.1g); Protein 4.6g; Carb 31.4g; Fiber 1.4g; Chol 23mg; Iron 1.3mg; Sodium 254mg; Calc 81mg

SPICED PANCAKES

PointsPlus value per serving: 5

HANDS-ON TIME: 7 min. ■ **TOTAL TIME:** 32 min.

9 ounces all-purpose flour (about 2 cups)
2 tablespoons brown sugar
2 teaspoons baking soda
2 teaspoons apple pie spice
⅛ teaspoon salt
2 cups low-fat buttermilk (1%)
⅓ cup egg substitute
2 tablespoons butter, melted
Butter-flavored cooking spray
Powdered sugar (optional)

1. Weigh or lightly spoon flour into dry measuring cups; level with a knife. Combine flour and next 4 ingredients in a large bowl; stir well with a whisk. Combine buttermilk, egg substitute, and butter in a bowl. Add buttermilk mixture to flour mixture, stirring until smooth.
2. Heat a large nonstick skillet or griddle over medium heat. Coat pan with cooking spray. Pour about ¼ cup batter per pancake onto pan, gently spreading batter with back of a spoon. Cook 3 minutes or until tops are covered with bubbles and edges look cooked. Carefully turn pancakes over; cook 2 minutes or until lightly browned. Sprinkle with powdered sugar, if desired. YIELD: 8 SERVINGS (SERVING SIZE: 2 PANCAKES).

PER SERVING: Calories 187; Fat 4.3g (sat 2.4g, mono 1g, poly 0.4g); Protein 6.7g; Carb 30g; Fiber 1.1g; Chol 10mg; Iron 1.8mg; Sodium 456mg; Calc 88mg

BANANA BREAD PANCAKES

PointsPlus value per serving: 6

HANDS-ON TIME: 27 min. ■ **TOTAL TIME:** 27 min.

For the best flavor, choose overripe bananas with skin that is speckled with brown spots—they'll impart a natural sweetness to the pancakes. Add ½ teaspoon cinnamon to the batter, if desired.

1 cup fat-free half-and-half
1 cup mashed ripe banana (about 2 large)
1½ cups vanilla fat-free yogurt, divided
1 teaspoon vanilla extract
1 large egg
7.8 ounces low-fat baking mix (about 2 cups)
Cooking spray
24 banana slices (about 1 large)
½ cup low-fat granola without raisins

1. Combine half-and-half, banana, ½ cup yogurt, vanilla, and egg in a bowl, stirring well with a whisk. Weigh or lightly spoon baking mix into dry measuring cups; level with a knife. Place baking mix in a medium bowl. Add mashed banana mixture, stirring until smooth.
2. Heat a large nonstick skillet or griddle over medium heat. Coat pan with cooking spray. Pour about ¼ cup batter per pancake onto pan, gently spreading batter with back of a spoon. Cook 2 minutes or until tops are covered with bubbles and edges look cooked. Carefully turn pancakes over; cook 2 minutes or until bottoms are lightly browned. Repeat procedure with remaining batter. Top servings evenly with remaining 1 cup yogurt and banana slices; sprinkle evenly with granola. YIELD: 8 SERVINGS (SERVING SIZE: 2 PANCAKES, 2 TABLESPOONS YOGURT, 3 BANANA SLICES, AND 1 TABLESPOON GRANOLA).

PER SERVING: Calories 229; Fat 2.9g (sat 0.3g, mono 1.4g, poly 0.5g); Protein 6.1g; Carb 43.4g; Fiber 1.9g; Chol 27mg; Iron 1.5mg; Sodium 413mg; Calc 262mg

SILVER DOLLAR PANCAKES

These small pancakes are 2 to 3 inches in diameter, requiring a tablespoon measure to pour the batter. You can adjust the measurements slightly up or down depending on the size you'd like to make them.

SILVER DOLLAR PANCAKES WITH CHERRY-ORANGE SYRUP

PointsPlus value per serving: 6

HANDS-ON TIME: 20 min. ■ **TOTAL TIME:** 25 min.

2 cups pitted dark sweet cherries, halved
1 teaspoon grated fresh orange rind
⅓ cup fresh orange juice
¼ cup sugar
1.7 ounces all-purpose flour (about 6 tablespoons)
0.6 ounces whole-wheat pastry flour (about 2 tablespoons)
1 tablespoon sugar
½ teaspoon baking powder
¼ teaspoon baking soda
⅛ teaspoon salt
½ cup low-fat buttermilk (1%)
½ teaspoon canola oil
1 large egg
Cooking spray

1. Combine first 4 ingredients in a medium saucepan. Bring to a boil over medium-high heat; reduce heat, and simmer 17 minutes or until sauce thickens. Keep warm.
2. While syrup simmers, weigh or lightly spoon flours into dry measuring cups; level with a knife. Combine flour and next 4 ingredients in a medium bowl, stirring with a whisk; make a well in center of mixture. Combine buttermilk, oil, and egg in a bowl, stirring well with a whisk; add to flour mixture, stirring with a whisk until smooth.
3. Heat a large nonstick skillet or griddle over medium heat. Coat pan with cooking spray. Spoon about 1 tablespoon batter per pancake onto pan. Cook 1 to 2 minutes or until tops are covered with bubbles and edges look cooked. Carefully turn pancakes over; cook 1 minute or until bottoms are lightly browned. Repeat procedure with remaining batter. Serve with syrup. YIELD: 4 SERVINGS (SERVING SIZE: 4 PANCAKES AND 2 TABLESPOONS SYRUP).

PER SERVING: Calories 223; Fat 2.5g (sat 0.6g, mono 0.8g, poly 0.5g); Protein 5.3g; Carb 46.7g; Fiber 1.4g; Chol 54mg; Iron 1.2mg; Sodium 330mg; Calc 90mg

CHOCOLATE-BANANA WAFFLES

PointsPlus value per serving: 5

HANDS-ON TIME: 7 min. ■ **TOTAL TIME:** 12 min.

You won't have to call the family to breakfast—just the smell of chocolate and banana wafting from these warm waffles will rally the troops.

> 4.5 ounces all-purpose flour (about 1 cup)
> 2 teaspoons baking powder
> ⅛ teaspoon salt
> ⅔ cup 1% chocolate low-fat milk
> ⅓ cup chopped banana
> 1 large egg yolk
> ⅓ cup semisweet chocolate minichips
> 2 large egg whites
> Cooking spray
> 1 tablespoon powdered sugar

1. Weigh or lightly spoon flour into a dry measuring cup; level with a knife. Combine flour, baking powder, and salt in a large bowl, stirring with a whisk. Combine milk, banana, and egg yolk in a small bowl. Add milk mixture to flour mixture, stirring just until moist. Stir in chocolate chips.
2. Beat egg whites with a mixer at high speed until stiff peaks form (do not overbeat). Fold egg whites into batter.
3. Preheat a Belgian waffle iron. Coat waffle iron with cooking spray. Spoon ⅓ cup batter per 4-inch waffle onto hot waffle iron, spreading batter to edges. Cook 2 to 3 minutes or until steaming stops. Repeat procedure with remaining batter. Sprinkle with powdered sugar before serving. YIELD: 6 SERVINGS (SERVING SIZE: 1 WAFFLE AND ½ TEASPOON POWDERED SUGAR).

PER SERVING: Calories 171; Fat 4.3g (sat 2.2g, mono 1.4g, poly 0.3g); Protein 5.2g; Carb 29.2g; Fiber 1.5g; Chol 36mg; Iron 1.4mg; Sodium 228mg; Calc 124mg

KEEP IT WARM

Since waffles and pancakes are made one or a few at a time, you'll want to keep the cooked ones warm while you finish preparing the rest. Preheat the oven to 200°, and place the prepared food on a baking sheet or oven-safe platter.

BLUEBERRY-LIME COFFEE CAKE

PointsPlus value per serving: 5

HANDS-ON TIME: 5 min. ■ **TOTAL TIME:** 40 min.

This coffee cake showcases antioxidant-rich fresh blueberries. Tossing the blueberries with some of the baking mix helps prevent them from sinking to the bottom of the cake.

> 8.8 ounces low-fat baking mix (about 2¼ cups), divided
> ⅔ cup sugar
> 1 tablespoon grated fresh lime rind
> 1 large egg
> ⅔ cup 2% reduced-fat milk
> 1½ cups fresh blueberries
> Cooking spray

1. Preheat oven to 400°.
2. Weigh or lightly spoon baking mix into dry measuring cups; level with a knife. Combine 7.8 ounces baking mix (about 2 cups), sugar, and rind in a medium bowl; make a well in center of mixture. Combine egg and milk in a small bowl, stirring with a whisk. Add to flour mixture, stirring until just moist. Combine blueberries and remaining 1 ounce baking mix (about ¼ cup) in a small bowl; gently fold into batter.
3. Spread batter into a 9-inch round cake pan coated with cooking spray. Bake at 400° for 22 to 25 minutes or until a wooden pick inserted in center comes out clean. Cool 10 minutes in pan on a wire rack; remove from pan. Cool completely on wire rack. Cut into 10 wedges. YIELD: 10 SERVINGS (SERVING SIZE: 1 WEDGE).

PER SERVING: Calories 168; Fat 2.5g (sat 0.4g, mono 1.2g, poly 0.4g); Protein 3.2g; Carb 34.4g; Fiber 0.9g; Chol 22mg; Iron 1.1mg; Sodium 282mg; Calc 118mg

BRAZILIAN CHEESE PUFFS

PointsPlus value per serving: 1   *pictured on page 53*

HANDS-ON TIME: 10 min. ■ **TOTAL TIME:** 28 min.

These are a popular Brazilian treat, sold at snack bars and kiosks. Look for tapioca flour in large supermarkets or health food markets. This flour yields a cheesy ball of goodness that is slightly crisp on the outside and pleasantly stretchy and gooey on the inside. Enjoy these cheesy puffs hot out of the oven while they're full of steam—delicious! Be sure to place the first 5 ingredients in the blender in the order listed. If queso fresco is not available, substitute feta cheese.

½ cup 1% low-fat milk
¼ cup olive oil
½ teaspoon kosher salt
1 large egg
1 garlic clove, peeled
4.2 ounces tapioca flour (about 1 cup)
¾ cup (3 ounces) crumbled queso fresco
Cooking spray

1. Preheat oven to 400°.
2. Place first 5 ingredients in a blender. Weigh or lightly spoon flour into a dry measuring cup; level with a knife. Add flour to blender; process until smooth. Add cheese; process 2 seconds. Immediately pour batter into 24 miniature muffin cups coated with cooking spray, filling two-thirds full.
3. Bake at 400° for 15 to 18 minutes or until puffed and golden. Cool 3 minutes in pans on a wire rack; remove from pans. Serve warm. YIELD: 24 SERVINGS (SERVING SIZE: 1 PUFF).

PER SERVING: Calories 47; Fat 2.8g (sat 0.6g, mono 1.8g, poly 0.3g); Protein 0.9g; Carb 4.8g; Fiber 0g; Chol 10mg; Iron 0.1mg; Sodium 50mg; Calc 18mg

JALAPEÑO CORN BREAD

PointsPlus value per serving: 3

HANDS-ON TIME: 10 min. ■ **TOTAL TIME:** 25 min.

Pair this kicked-up corn bread with a bowl of warm vegetable soup for supper on a cold winter's night.

3 tablespoons canola oil, divided
2 cups self-rising cornmeal mix
1 teaspoon chili powder
1 large egg
1¾ cups nonfat buttermilk
⅓ cup chopped seeded jalapeño pepper (2 peppers)

1. Preheat oven to 400°.
2. Coat a 10-inch cast-iron skillet with 2 tablespoons oil. Heat skillet in oven at 400° for 10 minutes.
3. Combine cornmeal mix and chili powder in a medium bowl, stirring with a whisk. Combine remaining 1 tablespoon oil, egg, buttermilk, and jalapeño, stirring with a whisk until blended; add to cornmeal mixture, stirring just until moist. Pour batter into preheated skillet.
4. Bake at 400° for 15 minutes or until a wooden pick inserted into center comes out clean. Cut into 12 wedges. Serve warm. YIELD: 12 SERVINGS (SERVING SIZE: 1 WEDGE).

PER SERVING: Calories 117; Fat 4.6g (sat 0.4g, mono 2.4g, poly 1.1g); Protein 3.2g; Carb 16.9g; Fiber 1.4g; Chol 18mg; Iron 0.8mg; Sodium 334mg; Calc 73mg

desserts

Oatmeal-Pear Crisp, *page 40*

PUMPKIN CAKE WITH CINNAMON-BUTTERMILK GLAZE

PointsPlus value per serving: 3

HANDS-ON TIME: 5 min. ■ **TOTAL TIME:** 1 hr., 33 min.

Add just a pinch of nutmeg to the batter, if you'd like, to complement the cinnamon flavor of the cake.

1 (16.25-ounce) box white cake mix
¾ teaspoon ground cinnamon, divided
⅛ teaspoon ground nutmeg (optional)
1 cup nonfat buttermilk, divided
1 (15-ounce) can unsweetened pumpkin
Cooking spray
1 cup powdered sugar

1. Preheat oven to 350°.
2. Combine cake mix, ½ teaspoon cinnamon, and, if desired, nutmeg. Add ¾ cup buttermilk and pumpkin; beat with a mixer at medium speed 1 minute. Pour batter into a 13 x 9–inch metal baking pan coated with cooking spray.
3. Bake at 350° for 28 to 30 minutes or until a wooden pick inserted in center comes out clean. Cool completely on a wire rack.
4. Combine remaining ¼ teaspoon cinnamon, remaining ¼ cup buttermilk, and powdered sugar in a small saucepan. Bring to a boil, stirring constantly; pour over cooled cake. YIELD: 24 SERVINGS (SERVING SIZE: 1 PIECE).

PER SERVING: Calories 112; Fat 2.2g (sat 0.4g, mono 0.9g, poly 0.8g); Protein 1.4g; Carb 22g; Fiber 0.7g; Chol 0mg; Iron 0.5mg; Sodium 138mg; Calc 55mg

BANANA-COCONUT UPSIDE-DOWN CAKE

PointsPlus value per serving: 6   *pictured on page 54*

HANDS-ON TIME: 10 min. ■ **TOTAL TIME:** 42 min.

Caramel-drenched bananas and sweet, flaky coconut add a taste of the tropics to this easy dessert.

Cooking spray
2 bananas, cut into ¼-inch-thick slices
⅓ cup fat-free caramel sundae syrup
⅓ cup flaked sweetened coconut
5 tablespoons butter
⅔ cup sugar
½ cup low-fat buttermilk (1%)
1 teaspoon vanilla extract
2 large eggs
5.6 ounces all-purpose flour (about 1¼ cups)
1 teaspoon baking powder
¼ teaspoon baking soda
¼ teaspoon salt

1. Preheat oven to 350°.
2. Coat a 9–inch square metal baking pan heavily with cooking spray. Arrange banana slices in bottom of pan. Drizzle caramel topping over bananas; sprinkle with coconut.
3. Place butter in a large microwave-safe bowl; cover and microwave at HIGH 1 minute or until butter melts. Add sugar, buttermilk, and vanilla, stirring with a whisk until blended. Stir in eggs.
4. Weigh or lightly spoon flour into dry measuring cups; level with a knife. Combine flour and remaining ingredients in a small bowl. Add flour mixture to butter mixture, stirring just until blended. Pour batter into prepared pan.
5. Bake at 350° for 30 minutes or until a wooden pick inserted in center comes out clean. Cool 1 minute in pan on a wire rack. Invert cake onto a platter; cut into 12 pieces. Serve warm or at room temperature. YIELD: 12 SERVINGS (SERVING SIZE: 1 PIECE).

PER SERVING: Calories 209; Fat 6.6g (sat 4g, mono 1.6g, poly 0.4g); Protein 3g; Carb 34.9g; Fiber 1.1g; Chol 48mg; Iron 0.9mg; Sodium 196mg; Calc 40mg

BROWN SUGAR BUNDT CAKE

PointsPlus value per serving: 6

HANDS-ON TIME: 10 min. ■ **TOTAL TIME:** 2 hr., 22 min.

Brown sugar is made with molasses, which gives it color and rich flavor. Dark brown sugar simply contains more molasses than light brown, which adds more depth of flavor to this cake.

1¾ cups packed dark brown sugar
¾ cup butter, softened
3 large egg whites
2 tablespoons vanilla extract
13.5 ounces all-purpose flour (about 3 cups)
1 teaspoon baking powder
½ teaspoon salt
1 cup fat-free milk
Cooking spray

1. Preheat oven to 350°.
2. Place sugar and butter in a large bowl; beat with a mixer at medium speed until well blended. Add egg whites, 1 at a time, beating well after each addition. Beat in vanilla.
3. Weigh or lightly spoon flour into dry measuring cups; level with a knife. Combine flour, baking powder, and salt, stirring well with a whisk. Add flour mixture and milk alternately to sugar mixture, beginning and ending with flour mixture.
4. Pour batter into a 12-cup Bundt pan coated with cooking spray. Bake at 350° for 50 to 55 minutes or until a wooden pick inserted in center comes out clean. Cool 10 minutes in pan on a wire rack; remove from pan. Cool completely on wire rack. **YIELD: 18 SERVINGS (SERVING SIZE: 1 SLICE).**

PER SERVING: Calories 238; Fat 8g (sat 4.9g, mono 2g, poly 0.4g); Protein 3.3g; Carb 38g; Fiber 0.6g; Chol 21mg; Iron 1.1mg; Sodium 172mg; Calc 46mg

MAKING BREAD PUDDING

Bread puddings are among the most flexible of recipes. Assemble and bake them immediately, or cover and refrigerate them overnight before baking. For the best texture, use day-old, very dry bread. Very fresh bread will yield a slightly spongy texture. Leave the crusts on the bread for more texture. Whole-grain breads give these puddings a nutty taste and a slightly drier texture, and they can be strong in flavor, which might overpower the delicate taste of other ingredients.

PINEAPPLE BREAD PUDDING

PointsPlus value per serving: 4

HANDS-ON TIME: 10 min. ■ **TOTAL TIME:** 1 hr., 30 min.

3 large eggs
1 (13.5-ounce) can light coconut milk
½ cup packed brown sugar
⅛ teaspoon salt
6 cups (½-inch) day-old cubed French bread
1 (8-ounce) can crushed pineapple in juice, drained
Cooking spray

1. Combine first 4 ingredients in a large bowl, stirring with a whisk. Add bread and pineapple, tossing gently to coat. Spoon mixture into an 8-inch square glass or ceramic baking dish coated with cooking spray. Cover and chill 30 minutes.
2. Preheat oven to 350°.
3. Bake, uncovered, at 350° for 50 minutes or until golden and set. Serve warm. **YIELD: 9 SERVINGS (SERVING SIZE: ⅑ OF PUDDING).**

PER SERVING: Calories 163; Fat 2.7g (sat 1.1g, mono 0.7g, poly 0.4g); Protein 5.3g; Carb 30.1g; Fiber 0.8g; Chol 71mg; Iron 1.4mg; Sodium 225mg; Calc 33mg

If you're out, try this simple substitution to avoid a trip to the supermarket: Combine 1 cup of milk and 1 tablespoon of lemon juice in a small bowl. Let the mixture stand for five minutes. Your homemade buttermilk is now ready for use in your recipe as directed. This also works with low-fat and fat-free milks and distilled vinegar in place of lemon juice.

FRESH FRUIT SHORTCAKES

PointsPlus value per serving: 7

HANDS-ON TIME: 11 min. ■ **TOTAL TIME:** 23 min.

Scooping frozen yogurt onto the warm, sugary biscuits slightly melts it, creating creamy goodness to mix with the syrupy fruit. We gave this summer classic one of our highest ratings.

- 1½ cups quartered fresh strawberries
- 1½ cups fresh blackberries
- 1 cup sliced peeled peaches
- 1 tablespoon granulated sugar
- 4.5 ounces all-purpose flour (about 1 cup)
- 1¼ teaspoons baking powder
- ¼ teaspoon salt
- 3 tablespoons chilled butter
- 6 tablespoons low-fat buttermilk (1%)
- Cooking spray
- 1 tablespoon turbinado sugar or granulated sugar
- 1¼ cups vanilla fat-free frozen yogurt

1. Preheat oven to 425°.
2. Combine first 3 ingredients in a medium bowl; toss gently with 1 tablespoon granulated sugar. Cover and chill until ready to serve.
3. Weigh or lightly spoon flour into a dry measuring cup; level with a knife. Combine flour, baking powder, and salt in a bowl; cut in butter with a pastry blender or 2 knives until mixture resembles coarse meal. Add buttermilk; stir just until moist.
4. Turn dough out onto a lightly floured surface; knead lightly 5 times. Roll dough to a ¾-inch thickness; cut into 5 biscuits with a 2-inch biscuit cutter. Place biscuits on a baking sheet coated with cooking spray. Coat tops of biscuits with cooking spray; sprinkle evenly with turbinado sugar. Bake at 425° for 12 minutes or until golden.
5. Cut biscuits in half horizontally. Place two biscuit halves on each of 5 plates. Top each serving with ¼ cup frozen yogurt and ⅔ cup fruit mixture. Serve immediately. YIELD: 5 SERVINGS.

PER SERVING: Calories 278; Fat 8g (sat 4.6g, mono 1.9g, poly 0.6g); Protein 6.5g; Carb 45.5g; Fiber 4.3g; Chol 24mg; Iron 1.7mg; Sodium 319mg; Calc 157mg

LEMON–POPPY SEED CUPCAKES

PointsPlus value per serving: 3

HANDS-ON TIME: 5 min. ■ **TOTAL TIME:** 54 min.

The springtime combination of lemon and poppy seeds in these delicious cupcakes earned one of our highest ratings. You'll need one large lemon to prepare this recipe.

- 1 (9-ounce) package golden yellow cake mix
- 1 large egg
- ½ cup low-fat buttermilk (1%)
- 1 tablespoon poppy seeds
- 2 tablespoons fresh lemon juice, divided
- 1½ teaspoons grated fresh lemon rind, divided
- ½ cup powdered sugar

1. Preheat oven to 400°.
2. Place 12 paper muffin cup liners in muffin cups. Set aside.
3. Place cake mix, egg, buttermilk, poppy seeds, 1 tablespoon lemon juice, and 1 teaspoon lemon rind in a bowl; stir well with a whisk. Pour batter evenly into prepared muffin cups. Bake at 400° for 12 minutes or until cupcakes spring back when touched lightly in center. Cool cupcakes 2 minutes in pan on a wire rack. Remove from pan; cool completely on wire rack.
4. While cupcakes cool, combine powdered sugar, remaining 1 tablespoon lemon juice, and remaining ½ teaspoon lemon rind in a small bowl, stirring with a whisk. Spoon icing into a small zip-top plastic bag. Snip a tiny hole in 1 corner of bag; drizzle icing over cooled cupcakes. YIELD: 12 SERVINGS (SERVING SIZE: 1 CUPCAKE).

PER SERVING: Calories 122; Fat 2.7g (sat 0.6g, mono 1.1g, poly 0.8g); Protein 1.9g; Carb 23g; Fiber 0.2g; Chol 18mg; Iron 0.6mg; Sodium 159mg; Calc 23mg

These baked cakes get their light texture and puffed appearance from the beaten egg whites that are folded in. Egg whites incorporate more air when they're not completely cold: Separate the eggs first, and then leave the whites out on the counter for about 20 minutes before whipping—just long enough to take the chill off. Be careful not to get any egg yolk in the whites. Even a small amount of yolk can inhibit the whites from reaching full volume.

CHOCOLATE-RASPBERRY SOUFFLÉS

PointsPlus value per serving: 5

HANDS-ON TIME: 13 min. ■ **TOTAL TIME:** 26 min.

Tart raspberries pair beautifully with rich dark chocolate in this elegant dessert.

> Cooking spray
> ¾ cup sugar, divided
> ¼ cup unsweetened cocoa
> 4 teaspoons cornstarch
> ⅛ teaspoon salt
> ½ cup 1% low-fat milk
> 1 large egg yolk, lightly beaten
> 4 ounces dark chocolate, finely chopped
> ¼ cup Chambord (or other raspberry-flavored liqueur)
> 5 large egg whites
> ¼ teaspoon cream of tartar
> 1 cup fresh raspberries

1. Preheat oven to 375°.
2. Coat 10 (4-ounce) ramekins or custard cups with cooking spray; sprinkle insides of cups evenly with ¼ cup sugar, shaking off excess. Place prepared ramekins on a baking sheet.
3. Combine ¼ cup sugar, cocoa, cornstarch, and salt in a small saucepan; gradually add milk, stirring with a whisk until blended. Bring to a boil over medium heat; cook 1 minute or until thick, stirring constantly with a whisk. Remove from heat. Gradually add a small amount of hot milk mixture to egg yolk, stirring constantly with a whisk. Return milk mixture to pan. Add chocolate and liqueur, stirring until chocolate melts. Set aside.

4. Place egg whites and cream of tartar in a large bowl; beat with a mixer at high speed until foamy. Add remaining ¼ cup sugar, 1 tablespoon at a time, beating until stiff peaks form. Gently stir one-fourth of egg white mixture into chocolate mixture; gently fold in remaining egg white mixture. Spoon evenly into prepared ramekins.
5. Bake at 375° for 13 minutes or until puffy and set. Top with fresh raspberries. Serve immediately. YIELD: 10 SERVINGS (SERVING SIZE: 1 SOUFFLÉ).

PER SERVING: Calories 171; Fat 4.8g (sat 2.6g, mono 1.7g, poly 0.3g); Protein 3.6g; Carb 28.9g; Fiber 2.1g; Chol 23mg; Iron 0.9mg; Sodium 63mg; Calc 24mg

CINNAMON APPLE TART

PointsPlus value per serving: 4

HANDS-ON TIME: 12 min. ■ **TOTAL TIME:** 33 min.

If your puff pastry dough starts to get soft, pop it in the freezer for a few minutes. Keeping the dough cold is key to this beautiful five-ingredient tart.

> 3 Granny Smith apples, peeled and cut into ¼-inch-thick slices (about 1½ pounds)
> 3 tablespoons sugar
> 1 teaspoon ground cinnamon
> ½ (17.3-ounce) package frozen puff pastry dough, thawed
> Cooking spray
> 2 tablespoons apple jelly

1. Preheat oven to 425°.
2. Combine first 3 ingredients, tossing well to coat. Set aside.
3. Roll dough into a 10 x 14–inch rectangle on a lightly floured surface; transfer to a large baking sheet coated with cooking spray. Score a ½-inch border around edge of pastry (do not cut through dough). Arrange apple mixture evenly over pastry within border.
4. Bake at 425° for 20 to 23 minutes or until golden brown. Remove from oven. Microwave jelly at HIGH 30 seconds or until melted; brush evenly over apple mixture. Cut into 10 pieces. Serve warm. YIELD: 10 SERVINGS (SERVING SIZE: 1 PIECE).

PER SERVING: Calories 164; Fat 6.7g (sat 1.8g, mono 3.7g, poly 0.8g); Protein 2.1g; Carb 24.4g; Fiber 1.9g; Chol 0mg; Iron 0.8mg; Sodium 120mg; Calc 7mg

CARADAMOM-ROASTED STONE FRUITS WITH TOASTED POUND CAKE

PointsPlus value per serving: 4

HANDS-ON TIME: 5 min. ■ **TOTAL TIME:** 17 min.

1 cup pitted sweet cherries
2 tablespoons honey
¼ teaspoon ground cardamom
3 ripe plums, cut into wedges
2 ripe peaches, cut into wedges
Butter-flavored cooking spray
2 tablespoons Riesling or other slightly sweet white wine
6 (½-inch-thick) slices frozen reduced-fat pound cake
¼ cup plus 2 tablespoons frozen fat-free whipped topping, thawed

1. Preheat oven to 450°.
2. Combine first 5 ingredients on a large rimmed baking sheet coated with cooking spray. Bake at 450° for 12 minutes or until tender, stirring once. Drizzle with wine; toss gently.
3. While fruit roasts, toast pound cake. Place pound cake slices on 6 dessert plates. Spoon roasted fruit evenly over pound cake, and top with whipped topping. YIELD: 6 SERVINGS (SERVING SIZE: 1 SLICE POUND CAKE, ½ CUP FRUIT, AND 1 TABLESPOON WHIPPED TOPPING).

PER SERVING: Calories 135; Fat 1.3g (sat 0.3g, mono 0.1g, poly 0.1g); Protein 1.7g; Carb 29.9g; Fiber 1.5g; Chol 0mg; Iron 1.2mg; Sodium 76mg; Calc 14mg

OATMEAL-PEAR CRISP

PointsPlus value per serving: 6   *pictured on page 56*

HANDS-ON TIME: 20 min. ■ **TOTAL TIME:** 1 hr., 5 min.

This comfort-food favorite made it to the top of the list, receiving our highest rating. Be sure to choose firm ripe pears so the fruit holds its shape.

12 peeled firm ripe Bartlett pears, cored and sliced (8 cups)
½ cup packed brown sugar
3 tablespoons all-purpose flour
Cooking spray
½ (17.5-ounce) package oatmeal cookie mix
¼ cup water
¼ cup chilled butter, cut into pieces

1. Preheat oven to 375°.
2. Combine pear slices, brown sugar, and flour in a medium bowl; pour pear mixture into a 13 x 9–inch glass or ceramic baking dish coated with cooking spray.
3. Combine cookie mix and ¼ cup water in a bowl; cut in butter with a pastry blender or 2 knives until mixture is crumbly. Sprinkle topping evenly over pear mixture.
4. Bake at 375° for 45 minutes or until pear is tender and topping is golden. YIELD: 12 SERVINGS (SERVING SIZE: ¹⁄₁₂ OF CRISP).

PER SERVING: Calories 234; Fat 8g (sat 3.4g, mono 3.2g, poly 0.8g); Protein 2g; Carb 41g; Fiber 3.4g; Chol 10mg; Iron 0.8mg; Sodium 129mg; Calc 24mg

PICKING PEARS

Test for ripeness by applying light thumb pressure near the pear's stem. If it is ripe, there will be a slight give. If pears aren't quite ripe, place them on your kitchen counter in a brown paper bag, and check them daily. It may take three to five days for them to fully ripen. Once ripe, store them in the refrigerator for three to five days.

When preparing Chocolate-Banana Cream Pie, use bananas that have some black spots on their skin. They may look past their prime to some, but that speckled skin means the starch in the banana has been converted into sugar, leaving you with a sweeter banana and a sweeter pie.

CHOCOLATE-BANANA CREAM PIE

PointsPlus value per serving: 5

HANDS-ON TIME: 13 min. ■ **TOTAL TIME:** 3 hr., 13 min.

You won't feel one pang of guilt enjoying this dreamy chocolate dessert.

1 (1.4-ounce) package sugar-free chocolate instant
    pudding mix
1½ cups fat-free milk
3 medium bananas, sliced
1 (6-ounce) reduced-fat graham cracker crust
1 cup frozen reduced-calorie whipped topping, thawed

1. Combine pudding mix and milk, stirring with a whisk 2 minutes.
2. Place half of banana slices in a single layer in bottom of crust; top with half of pudding. Top with remaining half of banana slices and remaining half of pudding. Spread evenly with whipped topping. Chill at least 3 hours before serving. YIELD: 8 SERVINGS (SERVING SIZE: 1 SLICE).

PER SERVING: Calories 184; Fat 4.8g (sat 1.6g, mono 2.1g, poly 0.2g); Protein 3.7g; Carb 33.4g; Fiber 1.1g; Chol 1mg; Iron 0.8mg; Sodium 251mg; Calc 64mg

BABY STRAWBERRY CREAM PIES

PointsPlus value per serving: 4

HANDS-ON TIME: 10 min. ■ **TOTAL TIME:** 2 hr., 10 min.

These tasty little pies are a great way to use summer's freshest strawberries.

2 cups chopped fresh strawberries
1 teaspoon sugar
1 cup water
1 tablespoon cornstarch
2 teaspoons fresh lemon juice
1 (0.3-ounce) package sugar-free strawberry-flavored
    gelatin
1 (4-ounce) package mini graham cracker pie crusts
¼ cup strawberry fruit spread
½ cup frozen fat-free whipped topping, thawed

1. Combine strawberries and sugar in a medium bowl. Set aside.
2. Combine 1 cup water, cornstarch, and lemon juice in a small saucepan, stirring until well blended. Bring to a boil, and cook 1 minute or until thick, stirring constantly. Add gelatin, stirring until gelatin dissolves. Pour over strawberries, stirring to coat.
3. Spoon about ¼ cup gelatin mixture into each crust. Cover and chill 2 hours or until firm.
4. Place spread in a small microwave-safe bowl; microwave at HIGH 30 seconds or just until spread melts. Drizzle melted spread evenly over pies; top evenly with whipped topping. YIELD: 6 SERVINGS (SERVING SIZE: 1 PIE AND 4 TEASPOONS WHIPPED TOPPING).

PER SERVING: Calories 159; Fat 5.1g (sat 0.8g, mono 2g, poly 1.3g); Protein 2.2g; Carb 26.5g; Fiber 2g; Chol 0mg; Iron 0.5mg; Sodium 124mg; Calc 9mg

DULCE DE LECHE CHEESECAKE

PointsPlus value per serving: 7

HANDS-ON TIME: 8 min.   ■   **TOTAL TIME:** 8 hr., 38 min.

Dulce de leche literally means "candy of milk," a caramel-like delight originating in Latin America. It's what gives this highly rated cheesecake its characteristic flavor.

> ¾ cup dulce de leche
> 1½ (8-ounce) blocks ⅓-less-fat cream cheese, softened
> 2 large eggs
> 1 (6-ounce) reduced-fat graham cracker crust
> 10 tablespoons frozen reduced-calorie whipped topping, thawed

1. Preheat oven to 325°.
2. Place dulce de leche in a microwave-safe bowl. Microwave at HIGH 45 seconds, stirring until smooth.
3. Place cream cheese in a bowl; beat with a mixer at medium speed until light and fluffy. Beat in eggs and dulce de leche until smooth. Pour filling into crust. Bake at 325° for 30 minutes or until edge is set and center is still slightly soft. Cool completely in pan on a wire rack. Cover and chill at least 8 hours. Serve with whipped topping. YIELD: 10 SERVINGS (SERVING SIZE: 1 SLICE AND 1 TABLESPOON WHIPPED TOPPING).

PER SERVING: Calories 249; Fat 12.6g (sat 6.7g, mono 4g, poly 0.6g); Protein 5.8g; Carb 28.8g; Fiber 0g; Chol 73mg; Iron 0.5mg; Sodium 247mg; Calc 93mg

BUTTERSCOTCH DROP COOKIES

PointsPlus value per serving: 3

HANDS-ON TIME: 12 min.   ■   **TOTAL TIME:** 1 hr., 11 min.

We liked the chewiness of these cookies. For a crisper cookie, add a minute or two to the baking time.

> 1½ cups packed brown sugar
> ½ cup unsalted butter, softened
> 2 large egg whites
> 9 ounces self-rising flour (about 2 cups)
> 1 cup butterscotch chips
> Cooking spray

1. Preheat oven to 350°.
2. Combine sugar and butter in a large bowl; beat with a mixer at medium speed until light and fluffy. Add egg whites; beat well. Weigh or lightly spoon flour into dry measuring cups; level with a knife. Add flour to sugar mixture; beat at low speed until well blended. Stir in chips.
3. Drop dough by level tablespoons 2 inches apart onto baking sheets coated with cooking spray. Bake, 1 batch at a time, at 350° for 8 to 10 minutes or until lightly browned. Cool 3 minutes on pans or until firm. Remove cookies from pans; cool on wire racks. YIELD: 43 COOKIES (SERVING SIZE: 1 COOKIE).

PER SERVING: Calories 99; Fat 3.7g (sat 2.7g, mono 0.6g, poly 0.1g); Protein 0.8g; Carb 15.2g; Fiber 0.2g; Chol 6mg; Iron 0.3mg; Sodium 84mg; Calc 27mg

BROWN BUTTER–CHOCOLATE CHIP COOKIES

PointsPlus value per serving: 3

HANDS-ON TIME: 17 min. ■ **TOTAL TIME:** 58 min.

Cooking butter over low heat until it turns light golden brown lends a complex, nutty flavor to these not-so-ordinary chocolate chip cookies. But watch closely—the butter can quickly go from browned to burned if left unattended. If you don't have egg substitute, simply use two lightly beaten egg whites.

½ cup butter
9 ounces all-purpose flour (about 2 cups)
1 teaspoon baking soda
¼ teaspoon salt
¾ cup granulated sugar
¾ cup packed brown sugar
1 teaspoon vanilla extract
¼ cup egg substitute
1 cup semisweet chocolate chips

1. Preheat oven to 350°.
2. Melt butter in a small saucepan over medium-low heat. Cook 5 minutes or until foaming subsides and milk solids turn golden brown, stirring occasionally. Remove from heat; cool completely.
3. Weigh or lightly spoon flour into dry measuring cups; level with a knife. Combine flour, baking soda, and salt, stirring with a whisk.
4. Combine brown butter and sugars in a large bowl. Add vanilla and egg substitute; stir well. Stir in flour mixture and chips.
5. Lightly press dough into level tablespoon measures; drop dough 2 inches apart onto baking sheets lined with parchment paper. Bake at 350° for 10 minutes or until lightly browned. Cool 1 minute on pans; cool completely on wire racks. YIELD: 36 SERVINGS (SERVING SIZE: 1 COOKIE).

PER SERVING: Calories 105; Fat 4g (sat 2.5g, mono 1.1g, poly 0.2g); Protein 1.1g; Carb 17g; Fiber 0.5g; Chol 7mg; Iron 0.5mg; Sodium 75mg; Calc 8mg

SOFTENED BUTTER

When softening butter, don't be tempted to take the shortcut approach and microwave it. It can backfire when the butter softens too much (or melts). If it's too soft, your cookie batter will spread too much. It's best to let butter stand at room temperature for 30 to 45 minutes to get the right consistency. You can speed the process by cutting the butter into tablespoon-sized portions before letting it stand. Softened butter should yield slightly to gentle pressure, but you don't want to be able to sink your finger way down into it.

CHOCOLATE-DIPPED VANILLA SHORTBREAD

PointsPlus value per serving: 4

HANDS-ON TIME: 16 min. ■ **TOTAL TIME:** 1 hr., 15 min.

6 tablespoons unsalted butter, softened
4.5 ounces all-purpose flour (about 1 cup)
½ cup powdered sugar
1 tablespoon ice water
½ teaspoon vanilla extract
Cooking spray
2 ounces dark chocolate, melted

1. Preheat oven to 350°.
2. Place butter in a medium bowl; beat with a mixer at medium speed until light and fluffy.
3. Weigh or lightly spoon flour into a dry measuring cup; level with a knife. Combine flour and powdered sugar, stirring well with a whisk. Gradually add flour mixture to butter, beating until well blended. Add 1 tablespoon ice water and vanilla, stirring just until combined.
4. Press dough into bottom of an 8-inch round cake pan coated with cooking spray. Bake at 350° for 18 minutes or until golden brown. Score shortbread to form 10 wedges; remove round of shortbread from pan. Cool completely on a wire rack.
5. Gently separate shortbread round into individual wedges. Dip points of each wedge in melted chocolate up to 2 inches. Let stand 5 minutes on wire rack or until chocolate is firm. YIELD: 10 SERVINGS (SERVING SIZE: 1 WEDGE).

PER SERVING: Calories 160; Fat 9g (sat 5.5g, mono 2.5g, poly 0.4g); Protein 1.6g; Carb 19.1g; Fiber 0.6g; Chol 19mg; Iron 0.8mg; Sodium 1mg; Calc 4mg

ALMOND SHORTBREAD

PointsPlus value per serving: 3   *pictured on page 53*

HANDS-ON TIME: 5 min. ▪ **TOTAL TIME:** 33 min.

Shortbread is a classic Scottish dessert consisting of three basic ingredients: flour, sugar, and butter. The version featured here received our Test Kitchen's highest rating.

 6 tablespoons sugar, divided
 ¼ cup unsalted butter, softened
 ¼ cup canola oil
 ¼ teaspoon almond extract
 4.5 ounces all-purpose flour (about 1 cup)
 Cooking spray
 ¾ cup honey-roasted almonds, chopped

1. Preheat oven to 375°.
2. Combine 5 tablespoons sugar, butter, oil, and almond extract in a medium bowl, stirring until smooth. Weigh or lightly spoon flour into a dry measuring cup; level with a knife. Add flour to sugar mixture; stir until a soft dough forms.
3. Press dough into bottom of an 8-inch square metal baking pan coated with cooking spray. Sprinkle dough with almonds, pressing lightly to adhere. Sprinkle remaining 1 tablespoon sugar over almonds.
4. Bake at 375° for 18 minutes or until golden brown. Cut into 18 squares. Cool 10 minutes in pan on a wire rack. **YIELD: 18 SERVINGS (SERVING SIZE: 1 SQUARE).**

PER SERVING: Calories 119; Fat 8.1g (sat 1.9g, mono 2.6g, poly 1g); Protein 1.4g; Carb 10.2g; Fiber 0.2g; Chol 7mg; Iron 0.3mg; Sodium 54mg; Calc 2mg

BROWN SUGAR FUDGE BROWNIES

PointsPlus value per serving: 3

HANDS-ON TIME: 9 min. ▪ **TOTAL TIME:** 33 min.

Sweetened with brown sugar and laced with just enough cocoa to please the chocolate lover, these dense, chewy brownies have something for everyone. You can use either dark or light brown sugar in this recipe. Since it has more molasses, dark brown sugar will lend a richer flavor.

 3 ounces all-purpose flour (about ⅔ cup)
 ¼ cup unsweetened cocoa
 2 large eggs
 1 cup packed brown sugar
 5 tablespoons butter, melted
 Cooking spray

1. Preheat oven to 350°.
2. Weigh or lightly spoon flour into a dry measuring cup; level with a knife. Combine flour and cocoa in a small bowl. Combine eggs, sugar, and butter in a large bowl, stirring until blended. Add flour mixture to egg mixture, stirring just until combined.
3. Spread batter into an 8-inch square metal baking pan coated with cooking spray. Bake at 350° for 24 minutes or until a wooden pick inserted in center comes out with a few moist crumbs attached. Cool in pan on a wire rack. **YIELD: 16 SERVINGS (SERVING SIZE: 1 BROWNIE).**

PER SERVING: Calories 115; Fat 4.5g (sat 2.6g, mono 1.2g, poly 0.3g); Protein 1.6g; Carb 18.2g; Fiber 0.6g; Chol 36mg; Iron 0.6mg; Sodium 105mg; Calc 35mg

BLUEBERRY PIE BARS

PointsPlus value per serving: 5   *pictured on page 55*

HANDS-ON TIME: 10 min. ■ **TOTAL TIME:** 2 hr.

Juicy summer blueberries and a crisp shortbread-like crust partner perfectly in these cookie bars. Old-fashioned rolled oats are the best oat option here because they give these bars a delicious chewiness. The smaller, flatter flakes of instant oats won't lend the same texture.

> **Cooking spray**
> **1 (16.5-ounce) package refrigerated sugar cookie dough, divided**
> **½ cup old-fashioned rolled oats**
> **½ cup sugar**
> **2 tablespoons cornstarch**
> **4 cups fresh blueberries**

1. Preheat oven to 375°.
2. Coat a 9-inch square metal baking pan with cooking spray. With moist hands, press three-fourths of cookie dough evenly into bottom of pan. Bake at 375° for 15 minutes or until golden brown.
3. Combine remaining one-fourth of cookie dough with oats in a small bowl, crumbling with fingers. Combine sugar and cornstarch in a medium bowl; add blueberries, tossing to coat. Sprinkle blueberry mixture evenly over crust; crumble oat mixture evenly over blueberry mixture.
4. Bake at 375° for 35 minutes or until oat mixture is golden brown and filling is bubbly. Cool at least 1 hour before serving. YIELD: 16 SERVINGS (SERVING SIZE: 1 SQUARE).

PER SERVING: Calories 190; Fat 6.4g (sat 1.6g, mono 0.1g, poly 0.1g); Protein 1.6g; Carb 32.4g; Fiber 1.2g; Chol 10mg; Iron 0.6mg; Sodium 81mg; Calc 2mg

BLACKBERRY PANNA COTTA

PointsPlus value per serving: 4

HANDS-ON TIME: 12 min. ■ **TOTAL TIME:** 8 hr., 42 min.

Panna cotta is a classic Italian gelatin dessert. Serve it chilled or at room temperature. This is also delicious paired with blueberries or strawberries.

> **1 tablespoon unflavored gelatin**
> **3½ cups 2% reduced-fat milk, divided**
> **¾ cup sugar, divided**
> **1 teaspoon grated fresh lemon rind**
> **Cooking spray**
> **2 cups fresh blackberries**
> **2 teaspoons fresh lemon juice**

1. Sprinkle gelatin over 1 cup milk in a medium saucepan; let stand 1 minute. Cook over medium-low heat, stirring with a whisk until gelatin dissolves. Add ½ cup sugar; cook over medium heat, stirring until sugar dissolves. Remove from heat.
2. Add remaining 2½ cups milk and lemon rind to gelatin mixture. Pour mixture evenly into 8 (6-ounce) custard cups coated with cooking spray. Cover and chill 8 to 12 hours.
3. Remove panna cotta from refrigerator; let stand 30 minutes.
4. While panna cotta stands, combine blackberries with remaining ¼ cup sugar and lemon juice; coarsely mash with a fork. Let stand 30 minutes.
5. Loosen edges of panna cotta with a knife or rubber spatula. Place a plate, upside down, on top of each cup; invert onto plates. Serve with blackberry mixture.
YIELD: 8 SERVINGS (SERVING SIZE: 1 PANNA COTTA AND 3 TABLESPOONS BLACKBERRY MIXTURE).

PER SERVING: Calories 146; Fat 2.4g (sat 1.4g, mono 0.6g, poly 0.2g); Protein 4.8g; Carb 27.5g; Fiber 1.8g; Chol 9mg; Iron 0.3mg; Sodium 46mg; Calc 136mg

CHOCOLATE–PEANUT BUTTER TRUFFLES

PointsPlus value per serving: 1   *pictured on page 56*

HANDS-ON TIME: 25 min. ■ **TOTAL TIME:** 1 hr., 25 min.

These rich bites are ideal make-ahead treats. Freeze them in a single layer in an airtight container up to one month, and then simply thaw at room temperature an hour before serving. Make sure the cream cheese is softened before you begin mixing. It will blend together with the other ingredients more easily and thoroughly, ensuring you get chocolate–peanut butter goodness in every bite.

⅓ cup peanut butter chips
4 ounces ⅓-less-fat cream cheese (about ½ cup), softened
1 (16-ounce) package powdered sugar
¼ cup unsweetened cocoa

1. Place chips in a medium microwave-safe glass bowl; microwave at HIGH 30 to 45 seconds or until almost melted, stirring until smooth. Add cream cheese; beat with a mixer at medium speed until blended. Add powdered sugar, one-fourth of package at a time, beating well after each addition. (Mixture will be very stiff and dry.)
2. Press mixture into a 6-inch square on plastic wrap; wrap in plastic wrap. Chill at least 1 hour.
3. Remove top sheet of plastic wrap; cut mixture into 48 portions, shaping each into a ball. Roll balls in cocoa. YIELD: 48 SERVINGS (SERVING SIZE: 1 TRUFFLE).

PER SERVING: Calories 53; Fat 1g (sat 0.8g, mono 0.1g, poly 0.1g); Protein 0.6g; Carb 10.6g; Fiber 0.2g; Chol 2mg; Iron 0.1mg; Sodium 13mg; Calc 2mg

HORCHATA SHAKE

PointsPlus value per serving: 3

HANDS-ON TIME: 3 min. ■ **TOTAL TIME:** 3 min.

Horchata is a cinnamon-laced drink based on traditional agua frescas of Mexico and Guatemala. A frozen banana whirred up with the vanilla-flavored milk base creates a refreshing shake.

1½ cups unsweetened vanilla-flavored almond milk
1½ cups rice milk
1 ripe banana, peeled and frozen
¼ cup sugar
½ teaspoon ground cinnamon
Ice cubes

1. Place first 5 ingredients in a blender; fill remainder of blender with ice. Process until smooth. YIELD: 5 SERVINGS (SERVING SIZE: 1 CUP).

PER SERVING: Calories 110; Fat 1.5g (sat 0g, mono 1g, poly 0.4g); Protein 0.8g; Carb 24.4g; Fiber 1g; Chol 0mg; Iron 0.2mg; Sodium 81mg; Calc 153mg

DATE MILK SHAKES

PointsPlus value per serving: 6

HANDS-ON TIME: 7 min. ■ **TOTAL TIME:** 7 min.

Date milk shakes are a popular cool treat in sunny Southern California where extremely large Medjool dates grow abundantly.

½ cup fat-free milk
⅓ cup chopped Medjool dates (about 3)
2 cups vanilla fat-free ice cream
1 tablespoon flaxseed meal
⅛ teaspoon ground cinnamon

1. Place milk and dates in a blender; process until smooth. Add ice cream, flaxseed meal, and cinnamon; process until blended. Serve immediately. YIELD: 3 SERVINGS (SERVING SIZE: ABOUT ⅔ CUP).

PER SERVING: Calories 221; Fat 1.1g (sat 0g, mono 0.2g, poly 0.8g); Protein 6.3g; Carb 49.7g; Fiber 2g; Chol 1mg; Iron 0.2mg; Sodium 77mg; Calc 172mg

ABOUT DATES

Dates have the lowest moisture content of any whole fruit, giving them a long shelf life. They can be stored at room temperature in an airtight container for several months. Packed with antioxidants, dates are also a good source of fiber and provide a healthy dose of potassium.

FRESH CHERRY–CHOCOLATE ICE CREAM

PointsPlus value per serving: 4

HANDS-ON TIME: 8 min. ■ **TOTAL TIME:** 8 min.

Make your own gourmet ice cream store creation at home with this simple mixing method.

2 cups vanilla light ice cream
¾ cup fresh or frozen pitted and quartered Bing cherries
¼ cup thinly sliced dark chocolate candy bar
Chocolate syrup (optional)

1. Place ice cream in a bowl or on a work surface. Using two large metal spoons, mash ice cream to soften slightly; sprinkle with cherries and chocolate candy.
2. Working quickly, continue mashing ice cream with two spoons until blended but not too soft. Spoon into serving dishes. Drizzle with chocolate syrup, if desired, and serve immediately. YIELD: 4 SERVINGS (SERVING SIZE: ABOUT ½ CUP).

PER SERVING: Calories 157; Fat 5.9g (sat 3.5g, mono 1g, poly 0.2g); Protein 3.6g; Carb 23.8g; Fiber 1.3g; Chol 21mg; Iron 0.3mg; Sodium 45mg; Calc 64mg

STRAWBERRY-LEMONADE POPS

PointsPlus value per serving: 1

HANDS-ON TIME: 12 min. ■ **TOTAL TIME:** 4 hr., 12 min.

The lemonade base for these icy pops is made using a sweetener with half the calories of sugar: That's one sweet treat. You'll need about 9 small lemons to yield ¾ cup juice. If you don't have popsicle molds, use paper cups and insert sticks into the center of each cup after freezing the mixture about 30 minutes.

1 cup measures-like-sugar sweetener
1 cup water
¾ cup fresh lemon juice
2 cups frozen whole strawberries

1. Combine first 3 ingredients in a medium saucepan. Cook over low heat, stirring until sweetener dissolves. Pour mixture into a blender. Add strawberries; process until smooth.
2. Pour mixture into 10 (3½–ounce) ice-pop molds. Top with lid; insert craft sticks. Freeze 4 hours or until thoroughly frozen. YIELD: 10 SERVINGS (SERVING SIZE: 1 POP).

PER SERVING: Calories 20; Fat 0g (sat 0g, mono 0g, poly 0g); Protein 0.1g; Carb 5.2g; Fiber 0.4g; Chol 0mg; Iron 0.2mg; Sodium 2mg; Calc 7mg

POPSICLES

To release the popsicles from the mold, submerge the mold about halfway in warm water for 20 to 30 seconds or until the pops begin to release. Or to remove just one or two pops, wrap a towel dampened in warm water around individual molds for the same amount of time.

POMEGRANATE-ORANGE GRANITA

PointsPlus value per serving: 1

HANDS-ON TIME: 15 min. ■ **TOTAL TIME:** 4 hr., 15 min.

Pomegranate juice packs a healthy punch of flavor in this sweet Italian ice.

1 cup fresh orange juice
1 tablespoon sugar
3 cups pomegranate juice
½ teaspoon grated fresh orange rind

1. Combine orange juice and sugar in a small saucepan; bring to a boil, stirring until sugar dissolves.
2. Pour orange juice mixture into a 13 x 9–inch glass or ceramic baking dish. Stir in pomegranate juice and rind; place in freezer 1 hour.
3. Remove dish from freezer, and scrape mixture with a fork. Return dish to freezer. Repeat stirring procedure every 20 minutes or until mixture is completely frozen (about 4 hours). **YIELD: 14 SERVINGS (SERVING SIZE:** ½ CUP).

PER SERVING: Calories 42; Fat 0g (sat 0g, mono 0g, poly 0g); Protein 0.3g; Carb 10.3g; Fiber 0g; Chol 0mg; Iron 0.1mg; Sodium 7mg; Calc 11mg

HOW TO MAKE GRANITA

1. Freeze the sweetened syrup until the edges begin to ice (about 45 minutes to 1 hour). Scrape with a fork to make small ice crystals.
2. Keep fluffing the mixture every 45 minutes until the mixture is completely frozen. You can make granita up to 2 days ahead; fluff with a fork just before serving.

LEMON-LIME SHERBET

PointsPlus value per serving: 3   *pictured on page 57*

HANDS-ON TIME: 12 min. ■ **TOTAL TIME:** 3 hr., 2 min.

Two lemons plus two limes equals a refreshing treat that garnered our Test Kitchen's highest rating. Freshly grated lemon zest makes a pretty garnish.

1 cup sugar
½ cup water
2 lemons
2 limes
3 cups 1% low-fat milk

1. Combine sugar and ½ cup water in a small saucepan; bring to a boil, stirring until sugar dissolves. Cool 5 minutes; refrigerate 45 minutes or until chilled.
2. Grate rind and squeeze juice from lemons to measure 2 teaspoons and ¼ cup respectively. Repeat procedure with limes to measure 2 teaspoons and ¼ cup respectively. Combine rinds, juices, chilled sugar mixture, and milk.
3. Pour mixture into the freezer can of a 4-quart ice-cream freezer; freeze according to manufacturer's instructions. Spoon sherbet into a freezer-safe container; cover and freeze 2 hours or until firm. **YIELD: 10 SERVINGS (SERVING SIZE:** ½ CUP).

PER SERVING: Calories 112; Fat 0.7g (sat 0.5g, mono 0.2g, poly 0g); Protein 2.5g; Carb 25g; Fiber 0.1g; Chol 4mg; Iron 0mg; Sodium 32mg; Calc 89mg

Spice-Baked Sweet Potato Chips with Honey-Lime Dip, *page 18*

49

Sparkling White Sangria, *page 25*

Roasted Garlic–Cream Cheese Balls, *page 19*

Strawberry-Almond Muffins, *page 31*

Honey Whole-Wheat
Biscuits, *page 28*

Brazilian Cheese Puffs, *page 34*

Almond Shortbread, *page 44*

Banana-Coconut Upside-Down Cake, *page 36*

Blueberry Pie Bars, *page 45*

Chocolate–Peanut Butter
Truffles, *page 46*

Oatmeal-Pear Crisp,
page 40

Lemon-Lime Sherbet,
page 48

Mediterranean-Style
Grouper, *page 66*

58

Salmon with Cucumber-Orange Salsa, *page 68*

Curried Grouper Tacos, *page 67*

Seared Tuna Steaks with
Wasabi Aioli, *page 71*

Veggie Omelet with
Goat Cheese, *page 78*

Sun-Dried Tomato Strata, *page 79*

Roasted Vegetables over
Parmesan Polenta, *page 79*

Buckwheat Noodle Stir-Fry
Salad, *page 120*

fish & shellfish

Salmon with Cucumber-Orange Salsa, page 68

MEDITERRANEAN-STYLE GROUPER

PointsPlus value per serving: 6   *pictured on page 58*

HANDS-ON TIME: 12 min. ▪ **TOTAL TIME:** 26 min.

Serve this Greek-inspired dish with crusty bread to soak up all the saucy goodness.

> **Cooking spray**
> **1 tablespoon olive oil**
> **1 cup thinly sliced onion**
> **2 large garlic cloves, sliced**
> **2 cups grape tomatoes**
> **¼ cup sliced pitted kalamata olives**
> **½ cup dry white wine**
> **4 (6-ounce) grouper fillets or halibut steaks**
>   **(about 1¼ inches thick)**
> **¼ teaspoon coarse sea salt**
> **¼ teaspoon freshly ground black pepper**
> **2 tablespoons chopped fresh parsley**

1. Heat a large nonstick skillet over medium heat. Coat pan with cooking spray. Add oil to pan; swirl to coat. Add onion and garlic; sauté 3 minutes or until tender. Add tomatoes and olives; sauté 1 minute. Add wine; cook 1 minute.

2. Nestle fillets into sauce; sprinkle with salt and pepper. Cover and simmer 8 minutes or until fish flakes easily when tested with a fork. Remove from heat; sprinkle with parsley. YIELD: 4 SERVINGS (SERVING SIZE: 1 FILLET AND ABOUT ½ CUP TOMATO MIXTURE).

PER SERVING: Calories 255; Fat 7.7g (sat 1.2g, mono 4.6g, poly 1.2g); Protein 34.2g; Carb 8.5g; Fiber 1.9g; Chol 63mg; Iron 1.8mg; Sodium 384mg; Calc 76mg

FISH CAKES WITH LEMON-DILL TARTAR SAUCE

PointsPlus value per serving: 5

HANDS-ON TIME: 12 min. ▪ **TOTAL TIME:** 22 min.

We've turned up the volume on standard tartar sauce with the addition of fresh lemon and dill, also classic fish accompaniments.

> **2 lemons, divided**
> **¼ cup tartar sauce**
> **5 teaspoons chopped fresh dill, divided**
> **1¼ pounds grouper or other firm white fish fillets, cut into**
>   **2-inch pieces**
> **½ cup finely chopped celery**
> **½ cup finely chopped green onions**
> **⅓ cup dry breadcrumbs**
> **⅜ teaspoon salt**
> **¼ teaspoon freshly ground black pepper**
> **1 large egg**
> **Cooking spray**

1. Grate rind and squeeze juice from 1 lemon to measure 1 teaspoon and 1 tablespoon respectively. Combine rind, juice, tartar sauce, and 1 tablespoon dill in a small bowl. Cut remaining lemon into 4 wedges.

2. Place fish in a food processor; pulse 10 times or until finely chopped. Combine fish, remaining 2 teaspoons dill, celery, and next 5 ingredients in a medium bowl. Divide mixture into 4 equal portions, shaping each into a ½-inch-thick patty.

3. Heat a large nonstick skillet over medium heat. Coat fish cakes with cooking spray; add to pan. Cook 5 minutes on each side or until golden brown. Serve fish cakes with tartar sauce and lemon wedges. YIELD: 4 SERVINGS (SERVING SIZE: 1 FISH CAKE, 1 TABLESPOON TARTAR SAUCE, AND 1 LEMON WEDGE).

PER SERVING: Calories 228; Fat 6.2g (sat 1.3g, mono 1.4g, poly 2.2g); Protein 30.4g; Carb 10.5g; Fiber 1.2g; Chol 108mg; Iron 2.2mg; Sodium 510mg; Calc 78mg

CURRIED GROUPER TACOS

PointsPlus value per serving: 10   *pictured on page 60*

HANDS-ON TIME: 8 min. ■ **TOTAL TIME:** 16 min.

Similar in appearance to a pita, naan is available in the bakery section of most supermarkets.

- **1 pound grouper or other firm white fish fillets, cut into 4 pieces**
- **1 teaspoon olive oil**
- **1 tablespoon curry powder**
- **⅛ teaspoon salt**
- **Cooking spray**
- **1 cup plain 2% reduced-fat Greek yogurt**
- **2 tablespoons mango chutney**
- **4 pieces whole-wheat naan bread**
- **¼ cup cilantro leaves**

1. Preheat grill to medium–high heat.
2. Rub fish with oil; sprinkle both sides with curry powder and salt. Place fish on grill rack coated with cooking spray; grill 4 to 5 minutes on each side or until fish flakes easily when tested with a fork.
3. While fish cooks, combine yogurt and chutney; spread ¼ cup yogurt mixture in each naan. Place 1 fish portion in each naan; sprinkle evenly with cilantro. YIELD: 4 SERVINGS (SERVING SIZE: 1 NAAN, 3 OUNCES FISH, AND ¼ CUP YOGURT MIXTURE).

PER SERVING: Calories 429; Fat 6.8g (sat 1.2g, mono 1.4g, poly 0.6g); Protein 36.9g; Carb 54.1g; Fiber 8.5g; Chol 46mg; Iron 4.2mg; Sodium 548mg; Calc 99mg

GREEK YOGURT

The thick consistency of this yogurt adds richness and delicious mouthfeel to a dish—even in the nonfat variety. Watch the fat content when purchasing though as some full-fat varieties can be high in saturated fat. It's also higher in protein than regular yogurt because its made by draining off more of the whey. Use it as a substitute for sour cream.

PAN-SEARED GROUPER WITH BASIL-LIME PESTO

PointsPlus value per serving: 9

HANDS-ON TIME: 7 min. ■ **TOTAL TIME:** 20 min.

Walnuts add rich texture and healthy omega-3 fats to this citrusy basil pesto. You can also use the pesto on homemade pizzas or as a spread on sandwiches. One tablespoon has a *PointsPlus* value per serving of 2.

- **4 (6-ounce) grouper or other firm white fish fillets**
- **½ teaspoon salt, divided**
- **¼ teaspoon freshly ground black pepper**
- **¼ cup olive oil, divided**
- **2 garlic cloves, peeled**
- **1 cup packed basil leaves**
- **¼ cup walnut halves**
- **2 tablespoons grated fresh Parmesan cheese**
- **1 teaspoon grated fresh lime rind**
- **1 tablespoon fresh lime juice**

1. Sprinkle fillets evenly with ¼ teaspoon salt and pepper. Heat a large nonstick skillet over medium heat. Add 1 tablespoon oil; swirl to coat. Add fillets; cook 6 minutes on each side or until fish flakes easily when tested with a fork.
2. With a food processor on, drop garlic through food chute; process until minced. Add remaining ¼ teaspoon salt, remaining 3 tablespoons oil, basil, and remaining ingredients; process until smooth, scraping sides of bowl once. Serve pesto over fish. YIELD: 4 SERVINGS (SERVING SIZE: 1 FILLET AND 2 TABLESPOONS PESTO).

PER SERVING: Calories 334; Fat 20.1g (sat 3.1g, mono 11g, poly 5g); Protein 35.3g; Carb 2.1g; Fiber 0.7g; Chol 65mg; Iron 2.2mg; Sodium 425mg; Calc 102mg

SALMON WITH CUCUMBER-ORANGE SALSA

PointsPlus value per serving: 6   *pictured on page 59*

HANDS-ON TIME: 7 min. ■ **TOTAL TIME:** 14 min.

You can take this recipe outside to the grill. Prepare the recipe just like it is here, brushing the fillets with the olive oil. Grill over high heat for the same amount of time as the fillets cook in the skillet. Pair with whole-wheat couscous.

> 2 tablespoons orange marmalade
> 4 teaspoons fresh lime juice
> ⅜ teaspoon salt, divided
> 1 small cucumber
> ½ cup coarsely chopped fresh orange sections
> 3 tablespoons chopped fresh cilantro
> 2 tablespoons finely chopped red onion
> 1½ tablespoons minced seeded jalapeño pepper
> 4 (6-ounce) skinless salmon fillets (about 1 inch thick)
> ¼ teaspoon freshly ground black pepper
> 1 teaspoon olive oil
> Lime wedges (optional)

1. Combine marmalade, lime juice, and ⅛ teaspoon salt in a medium bowl, stirring with a whisk.
2. Peel cucumber; cut in half lengthwise, and remove seeds. Slice cucumber crosswise to measure 1 cup. Add cucumber slices, orange sections, and next 3 ingredients to marmalade mixture; toss gently to coat.
3. Sprinkle fillets with remaining ¼ teaspoon salt and pepper. Heat a large nonstick skillet over medium-high heat. Add oil; swirl to coat. Add fillets; cook 2 to 3 minutes on each side or until fish flakes easily when tested with a fork or until desired degree of doneness. Serve with salsa and, if desired, lime wedges. YIELD: 4 SERVINGS (SERVING SIZE: 1 FILLET AND ⅓ CUP SALSA).

PER SERVING: Calories 254; Fat 7.5g (sat 1.7g, mono 3.1g, poly 2g); Protein 34.5g; Carb 11.1g; Fiber 1g; Chol 80mg; Iron 1mg; Sodium 312mg; Calc 85mg

SALMON CAKES WITH LEMON-CHIVE YOGURT

PointsPlus value per serving: 6

HANDS-ON TIME: 10 min. ■ **TOTAL TIME:** 16 min.

The classic spring flavors of salmon, lemon, and chives partner perfectly in this warm-weather entrée.

> 1½ (1-ounce) slices firm whole-wheat bread
> 1 (1-pound) skinless salmon fillet, cut into 1-inch pieces
> 1 lemon
> 1 large egg
> ¼ cup light mayonnaise
> 2 tablespoons chopped fresh chives, divided
> ¼ teaspoon salt
> ¼ teaspoon ground red pepper
> Cooking spray
> ½ cup plain fat-free yogurt

1. Tear bread into small pieces, and place in a food processor; pulse until mixture resembles fine crumbs. Remove breadcrumbs, and set aside. Place salmon in food processor; pulse until chopped. Set aside.
2. Grate rind and squeeze juice from lemon to measure 1 teaspoon and 2 teaspoons respectively.
3. Combine ½ teaspoon lemon rind, egg, mayonnaise, 1 tablespoon chives, salt, and pepper in a large bowl; stir in breadcrumbs and salmon. Divide mixture into 4 equal portions, shaping each into a ½-inch-thick patty.
4. Heat a large nonstick skillet over medium-high heat. Coat pan with cooking spray. Add salmon cakes; cook 3 minutes on each side or until golden brown.
5. Combine remaining ½ teaspoon lemon rind, lemon juice, remaining 1 tablespoon chives, and yogurt. Serve yogurt mixture with salmon cakes. YIELD: 4 SERVINGS (SERVING SIZE: 1 CAKE AND 2 TABLESPOONS YOGURT MIXTURE).

PER SERVING: Calories 242; Fat 10.7g (sat 1.9g, mono 3.2g, poly 5.3g); Protein 27g; Carb 8.6g; Fiber 0.9g; Chol 117mg; Iron 1.4mg; Sodium 428mg; Calc 74mg

BARBECUE-GLAZED SALMON

PointsPlus value per serving: 6

HANDS-ON TIME: 3 min. ■ **TOTAL TIME:** 26 min.

Sweet barbecue sauce, tangy mustard, and tart lemon hit just about every flavor note in this speedy recipe.

Cooking spray
4 (6-ounce) salmon fillets
½ cup barbecue sauce
1 tablespoon stone-ground mustard
1 tablespoon fresh lemon juice
½ teaspoon freshly ground black pepper

1. Line a baking sheet with foil; coat with cooking spray.
2. Place salmon on baking sheet. Combine barbecue sauce and next 3 ingredients; brush half of mixture evenly over salmon. Let stand 15 minutes.
3. Preheat broiler.
4. Broil 8 minutes or until sauce begins to lightly brown and fish flakes easily when tested with a fork or until desired degree of doneness. Pour remaining barbecue sauce mixture into a small saucepan. Cook over medium heat 2 minutes or until warmed through. Serve with salmon. YIELD: 4 SERVINGS (SERVING SIZE: 1 FILLET AND 1 TABLESPOON PLUS 1 TEASPOON BARBECUE SAUCE MIXTURE).

PER SERVING: Calories 252; Fat 6.1g (sat 1g, mono 1.6g, poly 2.4g); Protein 34g; Carb 13.2g; Fiber 0.3g; Chol 88mg; Iron 1.4mg; Sodium 554mg; Calc 28mg

BROILING

The broiler is a great cooking tool capable of quickly browning casseroles and gratins; searing and cooking steaks, pork chops, and fish fillets; and toasting breads. It delivers crusty exteriors while keeping food moist within. Proximity to the heat source is absolutely key.

You want food near enough to the heat element for good browning but not so close that the exterior burns before the interior is done. Use the top two rack positions (3 to 5 inches from the heating element) to brown gratins and cook thin cuts of meat. If you choose to use the top rack, keep an eagle eye on the food—it can go from browned to scorched in seconds. Middle rack positions are for items like bone-in chicken or thick steaks to ensure they don't burn before they're done cooking.

ALMOND-CRUSTED SALMON

PointsPlus value per serving: 9

HANDS-ON TIME: 8 min. ■ **TOTAL TIME:** 2 hr., 20 min.

Smoky-flavored almonds add not only crunch to this salmon, but also a depth of flavor and aroma you just can't achieve with the plain variety.

3 tablespoons lower-sodium soy sauce
3 tablespoons maple syrup
4 (6-ounce) skinless salmon fillets
½ cup smoked whole almonds
⅓ cup panko (Japanese breadcrumbs)
Cooking spray
¼ teaspoon freshly ground black pepper

1. Combine soy sauce and syrup in a large zip-top plastic bag. Add salmon to bag; seal. Marinate in refrigerator 2 hours, turning occasionally.
2. Preheat oven to 400°.
3. Place almonds in a food processor; pulse until coarsely ground. Combine almonds and panko in a shallow bowl. Line a shallow baking pan with foil. Coat foil with cooking spray.
4. Remove salmon from marinade, reserving marinade. Sprinkle salmon with pepper; dredge in almond mixture, pressing to adhere. Place on prepared pan. Bake at 400° for 12 to 15 minutes or until fish flakes easily when tested with a fork or until desired degree of doneness.
5. Bring reserved marinade to a boil in a small saucepan; boil 2 minutes or until slightly thickened. Serve sauce with salmon. YIELD: 4 SERVINGS (SERVING SIZE: 1 FILLET AND 2 TEASPOONS SAUCE).

PER SERVING: Calories 369; Fat 15.1g (sat 1.6g, mono 7.1g, poly 4.5g); Protein 39g; Carb 18.5g; Fiber 2.2g; Chol 88mg; Iron 2.4mg; Sodium 427mg; Calc 82mg

CRISPY OVEN-BAKED SNAPPER WITH CORN RELISH

PointsPlus value per serving: 8

HANDS-ON TIME: 6 min. ■ **TOTAL TIME:** 20 min.

Supper's on the table in a flash with this zesty entrée. Cook some rice for a side dish while the fish bakes.

4 (6-ounce) red snapper or other firm white fish fillets
2 tablespoons creamy mustard blend
1 cup French fried onions, crushed
Cooking spray
1 teaspoon olive oil
1 cup frozen whole-kernel corn
½ cup chopped red bell pepper
½ cup chopped sweet onion
4 teaspoons fresh lime juice
¼ teaspoon salt
¼ teaspoon freshly ground black pepper
4 lime wedges

1. Preheat oven to 450°.
2. Brush fillets evenly with mustard blend; sprinkle evenly with fried onions, pressing to adhere. Place fillets on the rack of a broiler pan coated with cooking spray. Bake at 450° for 14 minutes or until fish flakes easily when tested with a fork.
3. While fish bakes, heat a large nonstick skillet over medium-high heat. Add oil; swirl to coat. Add corn, bell pepper, and onion to pan; sauté 8 minutes or until browned and tender. Stir in lime juice, salt, and black pepper. Serve relish over fish with lime wedges. YIELD: 4 SERVINGS (SERVING SIZE: 1 FILLET, 5 TABLESPOONS RELISH, AND 1 LIME WEDGE).

PER SERVING: Calories 321; Fat 10.5g (sat 2.4g, mono 3.9g, poly 2.3g); Protein 37.5g; Carb 18.4g; Fiber 2.2g; Chol 63mg; Iron 0.8mg; Sodium 382mg; Calc 71mg

TILAPIA PICCATA

PointsPlus value per serving: 6

HANDS-ON TIME: 5 min. ■ **TOTAL TIME:** 11 min.

Piccata is an Italian method of preparation where a thin slice of meat (or in this case, fish) is sautéed and served with a buttery lemon sauce. We just call it quick, easy, and delicious!

3 tablespoons all-purpose flour
4 (6-ounce) tilapia fillets
¼ teaspoon salt
¼ teaspoon freshly ground black pepper
2 tablespoons butter, divided
Cooking spray
¼ cup dry white wine
3 tablespoons fresh lemon juice
4 teaspoons capers
¼ teaspoon sugar
2 tablespoons chopped fresh parsley
4 lemon wedges

1. Place flour in a shallow bowl. Sprinkle both sides of fillets with salt and pepper; dredge in flour, shaking off excess.
2. Melt 1 tablespoon butter in a large nonstick skillet coated with cooking spray over medium-high heat. Add fillets to pan, and cook 2 minutes on each side or until fish flakes easily when tested with a fork. Remove fish from pan; keep warm.
3. Add wine, lemon juice, capers, and sugar to pan; cook 1 minute. Remove from heat; add remaining 1 tablespoon butter, stirring until melted. Stir in parsley. Serve sauce over fish with lemon wedges. YIELD: 4 SERVINGS (SERVING SIZE: 1 FILLET, 1 TABLESPOON SAUCE, AND 1 LEMON WEDGE).

PER SERVING: Calories 259; Fat 9g (sat 4.8g, mono 2.5g, poly 1g); Protein 35g; Carb 7.7g; Fiber 0.9g; Chol 100mg; Iron 1.4mg; Sodium 364mg; Calc 31mg

PECAN AND CORNMEAL–CRUSTED TROUT

PointsPlus value per serving: 10

HANDS-ON TIME: 5 min. ▪ **TOTAL TIME:** 13 min.

The crunchy pecans take on a real depth of flavor as they toast in the minimal amount of oil used to brown the fish.

½ cup yellow cornmeal
½ cup ground pecans
4 (6-ounce) skin-on trout fillets
½ teaspoon freshly ground black pepper
¼ teaspoon salt
4 teaspoons olive oil, divided
Lemon wedges (optional)

1. Combine cornmeal and pecans in a shallow dish. Pat fillets dry; sprinkle flesh sides with pepper and salt. Dredge fillets in cornmeal mixture.
2. Heat a large nonstick skillet over medium-high heat. Add 2 teaspoons oil; swirl to coat. Add 2 fillets; cook 2 minutes on each side or until fish flakes easily when tested with a fork. Remove from pan, and keep warm. Repeat procedure with remaining oil and fillets. Serve with lemon wedges, if desired. YIELD: 4 SERVINGS (SERVING SIZE: 1 FILLET).

PER SERVING: Calories 407; Fat 22.1g (sat 3.6g, mono 11.4g, poly 5.8g); Protein 32.6g; Carb 18.1g; Fiber 1.9g; Chol 90mg; Iron 1.3mg; Sodium 221mg; Calc 123mg

TROUT

Trout is a fatty, flaky fish high in heart-healthy omega-3 fatty acids. It has a delicate flavor and firm texture. If you can't find trout, salmon is a good substitute.

WASABI POWDER

This dried Japanese horseradish is pale green with a bright heat and zesty flavor. Look for it in the Asian section of supermarkets.

SEARED TUNA STEAKS WITH WASABI AIOLI

PointsPlus value per serving: 7   *pictured on page 61*

HANDS-ON TIME: 7 min. ▪ **TOTAL TIME:** 17 min.

Pair these tuna steaks with an Asian-flavored slaw or sautéed fresh snow peas.

2 (6-ounce) yellowfin tuna steaks (about ¾ inch thick)
2 tablespoons lower-sodium soy sauce
2 teaspoons wasabi powder (dried Japanese horseradish)
2 teaspoons water
¼ cup low-fat mayonnaise
½ teaspoon minced garlic
2 teaspoons sesame oil
¼ teaspoon freshly ground black pepper
2 tablespoons sliced green onions (optional)

1. Combine steaks and soy sauce in a large zip-top plastic bag; seal. Marinate 10 minutes, turning occasionally.
2. While steaks marinate, combine wasabi powder and 2 teaspoons water in a small bowl, stirring with a whisk. Stir in mayonnaise and garlic. Set aside.
3. Heat a medium nonstick skillet over medium-high heat. Add oil; swirl to coat. Remove steaks from soy sauce; discard marinade. Sprinkle steaks with pepper. Add steaks to pan; cook 2 minutes on each side or until desired degree of doneness. Serve steaks with wasabi mixture; sprinkle with green onions, if desired. YIELD: 2 SERVINGS (SERVING SIZE: 1 TUNA STEAK AND 2 TABLESPOONS WASABI AIOLI).

PER SERVING: Calories 282; Fat 8.4g (sat 1.4g, mono 2.5g, poly 3.5g); Protein 40.2g; Carb 8.8g; Fiber 0.1g; Chol 77mg; Iron 1.3mg; Sodium 529mg; Calc 29mg

TUSCAN MARINATED GRILLED TUNA

PointsPlus value per serving: 6

HANDS-ON TIME: 10 min. ■ **TOTAL TIME:** 46 min.

This dish brings you the flavors of Tuscany with the classic seasonings of that region—rosemary, lemon, fennel, and capers.

2 tablespoons chopped fresh rosemary
2 tablespoons olive oil, divided
1 teaspoon grated fresh lemon rind
1 tablespoon fresh lemon juice
½ teaspoon freshly ground black pepper
¼ teaspoon salt
4 (6-ounce) tuna steaks
1 small fennel bulb, cut into 8 wedges
1 tablespoon water
Cooking spray
2 tablespoons capers

1. Combine rosemary, 1½ tablespoons oil, lemon rind, and next 3 ingredients in a large zip-top plastic bag. Add steaks; seal and marinate in refrigerator 30 minutes, turning occasionally.
2. Preheat grill to medium-high heat.
3. Place fennel in a single layer in a microwave-safe dish; add 1 tablespoon water. Cover with plastic wrap; vent. Microwave at HIGH 6 minutes or until tender. Brush wedges with remaining 1½ teaspoons oil.
4. Remove steaks from marinade, discarding marinade. Place steaks and fennel wedges on grill rack coated with cooking spray; grill steaks and fennel 2 minutes on each side until fish is medium-rare or desired degree of doneness and fennel is charred. Serve tuna and fennel with capers. YIELD: 4 SERVINGS (SERVING SIZE: 1 TUNA STEAK, 2 FENNEL WEDGES, AND 1½ TEASPOONS CAPERS).

PER SERVING: Calories 267; Fat 8.7g (sat 1.4g, mono 5.2g, poly 1.2g); Protein 40.7g; Carb 5.3g; Fiber 2.2g; Chol 77mg; Iron 1.9mg; Sodium 369mg; Calc 63mg

SEARED TUNA WITH EDAMAME SALAD

PointsPlus value per serving: 8

HANDS-ON TIME: 14 min. ■ **TOTAL TIME:** 14 min.

2 tablespoons lower-sodium soy sauce
2 tablespoons seasoned rice wine vinegar
2 teaspoons dark sesame oil
1 teaspoon wasabi paste
4 (6-ounce) yellowfin tuna steaks (about 1½ inches thick)
½ teaspoon freshly ground black pepper
Cooking spray
1 (10-ounce) package fresh shelled edamame (green soybeans; about 1⅓ cups)
1 small cucumber, peeled, halved lengthwise, seeded, and thinly sliced (about 1⅓ cups)
½ cup (¼-inch) diagonally sliced green onions
2 tablespoons chopped fresh cilantro

1. Combine first 4 ingredients in a small bowl, stirring well with a whisk. Set aside.
2. Heat a large cast-iron skillet over medium-high heat 3 minutes. Sprinkle both sides of steaks evenly with pepper. Coat skillet with cooking spray; add steaks. Cook 1 to 2 minutes on each side until fish is medium-rare or desired degree of doneness. Remove steaks from pan; slice each steak crosswise into ¼-inch-thick slices.
3. Combine edamame, cucumber, and green onions; toss gently. Spoon edamame salad onto 4 plates; arrange steak slices beside salads. Drizzle soy sauce mixture evenly over salads and steak slices; sprinkle evenly with cilantro. YIELD: 4 SERVINGS (SERVING SIZE: 1 SLICED TUNA STEAK, ABOUT ¾ CUP EDAMAME SALAD, AND ABOUT 1 TABLESPOON SOY SAUCE MIXTURE).

PER SERVING: Calories 364; Fat 13.1g (sat 2.5g, mono 4.2g, poly 4.8g); Protein 45.8g; Carb 10.9g; Fiber 3.5g; Chol 65mg; Iron 3.2mg; Sodium 461mg; Calc 65mg

SEARED SCALLOPS WITH BACON, TOMATO, AND AVOCADO SALAD

PointsPlus value per serving: 7

HANDS-ON TIME: 13 min. ■ **TOTAL TIME:** 20 min.

Scallops can overcook in the blink of an eye, rendering them tough and unpalatable. Don't step away while these are browning.

1 cup halved grape tomatoes
3 tablespoons coarsely chopped celery leaves
3 tablespoons light red wine vinegar and olive oil dressing
¼ teaspoon freshly ground black pepper, divided
1 avocado, peeled and chopped
3 center-cut bacon slices
20 sea scallops (about 1½ pounds)

1. Combine tomato halves, celery leaves, dressing, ⅛ teaspoon pepper, and avocado in a medium bowl; toss gently to coat. Set aside.
2. Cook bacon in a large nonstick skillet over medium heat until crisp. Remove bacon from pan, reserving 1 teaspoon drippings in pan. Crumble bacon, and set aside.
3. Heat pan over medium-high heat. Pat scallops dry with paper towels; sprinkle evenly with remaining ⅛ teaspoon pepper. Add half of scallops to pan; cook 2 minutes on each side or until golden brown. Remove from pan; keep warm. Repeat procedure with remaining half of scallops.
4. Combine tomato mixture and bacon. Serve salad with scallops. YIELD: 4 SERVINGS (SERVING SIZE: 5 SCALLOPS AND ABOUT ½ CUP SALAD).

PER SERVING: Calories 282; Fat 12.5g (sat 2.2g, mono 6.1g, poly 2.5g); Protein 31.4g; Carb 10.8g; Fiber 4g; Chol 61mg; Iron 0.8mg; Sodium 492mg; Calc 55mg

SEARING SCALLOPS

To get a beautiful crust and great sear on your scallops, a hot pan is essential. It also helps keep food from sticking. Place the pan over the heat and let it get hot, and then add the scallops. With a preheated pan, they'll only need a couple of minutes on each side to brown.

COQUILLES ST. JACQUES

PointsPlus value per serving: 7

HANDS-ON TIME: 8 min. ■ **TOTAL TIME:** 21 min.

No seashell-shaped gratin dishes? No problem. Any single-serving broiler-proof shallow dishes will work.

Cooking spray
½ cup finely chopped onion
1 garlic clove, minced
¼ cup all-purpose flour
1½ pounds bay scallops
1 tablespoon butter
½ cup dry white wine
1 teaspoon thyme leaves
½ teaspoon salt
¼ cup panko (Japanese breadcrumbs)
¼ cup (1 ounce) shredded Gruyère or Swiss cheese

1. Heat a large nonstick skillet over medium heat. Coat pan with cooking spray. Add onion and garlic to pan; sauté 3 minutes or until tender. Remove from pan; set aside.
2. Place flour in a shallow bowl. Pat scallops dry with paper towels. Dredge scallops in flour, shaking off excess.
3. Melt butter in skillet over medium-high heat. Add scallops; sauté 2 minutes or until lightly browned. Add wine, thyme, salt, and onion mixture; cook 30 seconds or until slightly thickened, stirring constantly. Divide mixture evenly among 4 individual gratin dishes.
4. Preheat broiler.
5. Combine panko and cheese; sprinkle evenly over each serving. Place dishes on a baking sheet; broil 1 minute or until cheese melts and panko is golden. Serve immediately. YIELD: 4 SERVINGS (SERVING SIZE: 1 DISH).

PER SERVING: Calories 282; Fat 6.9g (sat 3.3g, mono 1.5g, poly 0.7g); Protein 32.3g; Carb 15.4g; Fiber 0.7g; Chol 72mg; Iron 1mg; Sodium 626mg; Calc 124mg

SHRIMP AND SUCCOTASH SAUTÉ

PointsPlus value per serving: 8

HANDS-ON TIME: 13 min. ▪ **TOTAL TIME:** 23 min.

A versatile option, this skillet meal works as a quick weeknight dinner or as a chilled portable lunch. Serve with a simple green salad dressed with your favorite vinaigrette.

1 tablespoon olive oil, divided
1½ pounds large shrimp, peeled and deveined
1½ cups fresh corn kernels (about 2 ears)
1 cup chopped red bell pepper
1 garlic clove, minced
1 cup frozen shelled edamame (green soybeans), thawed
¼ cup chopped fresh cilantro
½ teaspoon grated fresh lime rind
2 tablespoons fresh lime juice
¼ teaspoon salt
¼ teaspoon freshly ground black pepper

1. Heat a large nonstick skillet over medium–high heat. Add 1½ teaspoons oil; swirl to coat. Add shrimp; sauté 3 minutes or until done. Remove shrimp from pan; keep warm.
2. Add remaining 1½ teaspoons oil to pan; swirl to coat. Add corn, bell pepper, and garlic to pan; sauté 3 minutes. Add edamame; sauté 3 minutes. Stir in cilantro and remaining ingredients; cook 30 seconds or until liquid almost evaporates. Stir in shrimp. Serve warm or chilled. YIELD: 4 SERVINGS (SERVING SIZE: 1⅓ CUPS).

PER SERVING: Calories 325; Fat 8.9g (sat 1.1g, mono 3.7g, poly 3.9g); Protein 41.9g; Carb 19.3g; Fiber 4.4g; Chol 259mg; Iron 6mg; Sodium 412mg; Calc 115mg

SHRIMP SIZE

Shrimp size isn't determined solely by how big they are but how many like-sized unpeeled shrimp it takes to weigh 1 pound. The shell accounts for about one-third of a shrimp's weight, so if you need 1 pound of peeled shrimp, buy 1⅓ pounds unpeeled.

SHRIMP PRIMAVERA ALFREDO

PointsPlus value per serving: 8

HANDS-ON TIME: 6 min. ▪ **TOTAL TIME:** 15 min.

This one-dish dinner of whole-grain pasta, fresh broccoli, and tender sautéed shrimp will leave you feeling satisfied.

6 ounces uncooked whole-grain linguine
3 cups broccoli florets
1 (10-ounce) container light alfredo sauce
¼ cup fat-free, lower-sodium chicken broth
2 teaspoons olive oil
1½ pounds medium shrimp, peeled and deveined
½ teaspoon freshly ground black pepper
¼ teaspoon salt

1. Cook pasta according to package directions, omitting salt and fat. During last 2 minutes of cooking, add broccoli. Drain.
2. While pasta and broccoli cook, combine alfredo sauce and broth in a small saucepan; cook over low heat until warm, stirring occasionally. Add sauce mixture to pasta mixture, tossing to coat.
3. Heat a large nonstick skillet over medium–high heat. Add oil; swirl to coat. Sprinkle shrimp with pepper and salt. Add shrimp to pan; sauté 3 minutes or just until shrimp are done. Toss shrimp with pasta mixture. Serve immediately. YIELD: 6 SERVINGS (SERVING SIZE: ABOUT 1 CUP).

PER SERVING: Calories 313; Fat 8.7g (sat 3.4g, mono 2.6g, poly 1.3g); Protein 31.4g; Carb 28.2g; Fiber 4.7g; Chol 184mg; Iron 4.1mg; Sodium 568mg; Calc 165mg

QUICK CIOPPINO

PointsPlus value per serving: 7

HANDS-ON TIME: 19 min. ▪ **TOTAL TIME:** 19 min.

Pick up a package of refrigerated prechopped onion at the grocery store to shorten this recipe's speedy prep even more.

2 teaspoons olive oil
1 cup chopped onion
½ cup finely chopped fennel bulb
1⅔ cups canned no-salt-added crushed tomatoes
1 cup dry white wine
2 tablespoons tomato paste
1 tablespoon bottled minced roasted garlic
1 (8-ounce) bottle clam juice
48 mussels (about 1½ pounds), scrubbed and debearded
1 (12-ounce) grouper fillet, cut into 2-inch chunks
2 tablespoons chopped fresh parsley

1. Heat a Dutch oven over medium–high heat. Add oil to pan; swirl to coat. Add onion and fennel to pan; sauté 5 minutes or until tender. Add tomatoes and next 4 ingredients; bring to a boil. Reduce heat to medium; add mussels and fish. Cover and cook 5 minutes or until mussel shells open and fish flakes easily when tested with a fork. Remove from heat; discard any unopened shells. Sprinkle with parsley. YIELD: 4 SERVINGS (SERVING SIZE: 1⅓ CUPS STEW, ABOUT 12 MUSSELS, AND 1½ TEA-SPOONS PARSLEY).

PER SERVING: Calories 355; Fat 7.4g (sat 1.3g, mono 2.7g, poly 1.6g); Protein 39.6g; Carb 19.2g; Fiber 3.1g; Chol 81mg; Iron 9.4mg; Sodium 732mg; Calc 128mg

TOMATO-BAKED SHRIMP WITH FETA AND HERBS

PointsPlus value per serving: 4

HANDS-ON TIME: 5 min. ■ TOTAL TIME: 35 min.

Sweet, juicy grape tomatoes create a flavorful cooking liquid for tender shrimp. Serve this dish over orzo or with some crusty bread to soak up the savory sauce.

1 tablespoon olive oil
1 tablespoon fresh lemon juice
¼ teaspoon salt
¼ teaspoon freshly ground black pepper
2 garlic cloves, minced
3 cups grape tomatoes
1½ pounds large shrimp, peeled and deveined
2 ounces crumbled feta cheese (about ½ cup)
2 tablespoons chopped mixed fresh herbs (such as basil, parsley, and oregano)

1. Preheat oven to 450°.
2. Combine first 5 ingredients in a small bowl; stir with a whisk. Place tomatoes in a 13 x 9–inch glass or ceramic baking dish. Pour oil mixture over tomatoes; toss to coat. Bake at 450° for 15 minutes. Stir in shrimp; bake an additional 10 minutes or until shrimp are done. Stir in cheese and herbs. YIELD: 6 SERVINGS (SERVING SIZE: 1 CUP).

PER SERVING: Calories 181; Fat 6.2g (sat 2.1g, mono 2.4g, poly 1.1g); Protein 25g; Carb 5.1g; Fiber 1.1g; Chol 181mg; Iron 2.9mg; Sodium 376mg; Calc 122mg

SHRIMP AND JALAPEÑO CHEESE GRITS

PointsPlus value per serving: 10

HANDS-ON TIME: 10 min. ■ TOTAL TIME: 20 min.

Serve this classic coastal cuisine for dinner alongside a green salad and some crusty French bread.

2 center-cut bacon slices, diced
1½ pounds medium shrimp, peeled and deveined
3 garlic cloves, minced
3 tablespoons fat-free, lower-sodium chicken broth
2¼ cups water
⅔ cup uncooked quick-cooking grits
4 ounces reduced-fat jalapeño cheddar cheese, shredded
1 jalapeño pepper, seeded and minced
¼ cup fat-free milk
⅜ teaspoon salt
¼ teaspoon freshly ground black pepper
Chopped fresh parsley (optional)

1. Cook bacon in a large nonstick skillet over medium-high heat until crisp. Remove bacon from pan, reserving 1 tablespoon drippings in pan. Crumble bacon, and set aside.
2. Add shrimp and garlic to drippings; sauté 1 minute. Add broth; cook 2 minutes or just until shrimp are done. Set aside, and keep warm.
3. While shrimp cooks, bring 2¼ cups water to a boil in a medium saucepan; gradually add grits, stirring constantly. Reduce heat to low; simmer, covered, 5 minutes or until thick, stirring occasionally. Stir in cheese and next 4 ingredients. Cook until thoroughly heated, stirring occasionally.
4. Spoon grits mixture onto each of 4 plates; top evenly with shrimp. Sprinkle evenly with bacon and, if desired, parsley. YIELD: 4 SERVINGS (SERVING SIZE: ¾ CUP SHRIMP AND ¾ CUP GRITS).

PER SERVING: Calories 397; Fat 11.7g (sat 5.2g, mono 2.5g, poly 1.8g); Protein 46.7g; Carb 24.6g; Fiber 0.6g; Chol 280mg; Iron 5.2mg; Sodium 722mg; Calc 316mg

FRESH VS. FROZEN SHRIMP

New technology has made it possible to freeze shrimp immediately after they're caught. Look for the abbreviation IQF (individually quick-frozen) on the label. It's a bit more expensive, but it's the next best option after shrimp fresh off the boat.

MUSSELS IN SAFFRON WINE SAUCE

PointsPlus value per serving: 6

HANDS-ON TIME: 20 min. ■ **TOTAL TIME:** 27 min.

The unique flavor that saffron imparts to the broth pairs perfectly with steamed mussels. Serve with crusty bread to soak up the aromatic liquid.

2 teaspoons olive oil
3 garlic cloves, minced
3 cups chopped tomato
¾ cup dry white wine
1 teaspoon saffron threads, crushed
¼ teaspoon salt
78 mussels (about 3 pounds), scrubbed and debearded
⅓ cup sliced green onions
1 tablespoon thyme leaves
2 tablespoons chopped fresh flat-leaf parsley
½ teaspoon freshly ground black pepper

1. Heat a large Dutch oven over medium-high heat. Add oil to pan; swirl to coat. Add garlic; sauté 30 seconds. Add tomato and next 3 ingredients; cover, reduce heat, and simmer 3 minutes, stirring occasionally.
2. Add mussels, green onions, and thyme to pan; cover and cook 7 minutes or until shells open. Remove from heat; discard any unopened shells.
3. Using a slotted spoon, divide mussels evenly into 6 bowls. Pour broth over mussels, and sprinkle with parsley and pepper. YIELD: 6 SERVINGS (SERVING SIZE: 13 MUSSELS AND ½ CUP BROTH).

PER SERVING: Calories 255; Fat 6.8g (sat 1.2g, mono 2.3g, poly 1.6g); Protein 28g; Carb 14g; Fiber 1.5g; Chol 64mg; Iron 9.6mg; Sodium 755mg; Calc 82mg

SAFFRON

Saffron has a vibrant color and delicate bittersweet flavor. The harvesting process is time-consuming, which is the reason this is one of the world's most expensive spices. It's a delicious investment though, and most recipes don't require much.

GRILLED WHITE PIZZA WITH CLAMS

PointsPlus value per serving: 8

HANDS-ON TIME: 8 min. ■ **TOTAL TIME:** 22 min.

Substitute 1 cup chopped cooked shrimp for the clams, if you prefer.

2 teaspoons olive oil, divided
1½ cups sliced onion
3 garlic cloves, minced
2 teaspoons thyme leaves
¼ teaspoon freshly ground black pepper
1 (13.8-ounce) can refrigerated pizza crust dough
Cooking spray
½ cup light alfredo sauce
2 (6½-ounce) cans chopped clams, drained
½ cup (2 ounces) preshredded part-skim mozzarella cheese
1 tablespoon fresh lemon juice
2 cups baby arugula
¼ teaspoon crushed red pepper (optional)

1. Preheat grill to medium heat.
2. Heat a large nonstick skillet over medium-high heat. Add 1 teaspoon oil; swirl to coat. Add onion to pan; sauté 6 minutes. Add garlic; sauté 1 minute or until onion and garlic are lightly browned. Remove from heat; stir in thyme and black pepper.
3. Unroll dough onto a large baking sheet coated with cooking spray; pat into a 12 x 9–inch rectangle. Lightly spray dough with cooking spray.
4. Place dough on grill rack coated with cooking spray; grill 1 minute or until lightly browned. Turn crust over. Spread alfredo sauce over crust; top with onion mixture, clams, and cheese. Cover and grill 2 minutes or until crust is lightly browned and cheese melts; remove from grill.
5. Combine remaining 1 teaspoon olive oil and lemon juice in a medium bowl; stir well with a whisk. Add arugula, tossing gently to coat. Top pizza with arugula mixture, and sprinkle with red pepper, if desired. Serve immediately. YIELD: 6 SERVINGS (SERVING SIZE: 1 SLICE).

PER SERVING: Calories 313; Fat 8.2g (sat 3g, mono 3.6g, poly 1g); Protein 20.9g; Carb 39.2g; Fiber 1.7g; Chol 42mg; Iron 14.6mg; Sodium 685mg; Calc 165mg

meatless main dishes

Veggie Omelet with Goat Cheese, page 78

Omelets are open to endless interpretations and variations. Dress one up with leftover roasted vegetables, or add ham or turkey, plus a little cheese. Omelets cook quickly, so precook meats and dice vegetables beforehand because you'll have to work fast. Before beginning, preheat a nonstick pan over medium-high heat.

1. Whisk the eggs until slightly frothy, about 20 to 30 seconds. Be careful not to overbeat them. Add oil to the pan, or spray with cooking spray before pouring in the eggs.

2. Gently shake the pan to distribute the eggs. Use a nonstick spatula to lift the edges and allow any uncooked egg to flow underneath. Cook until the egg appears set, not runny.

3. Add ingredients to half of the omelet, and then use the spatula to lift and fold the other half over the fillings. Let the omelet cook another 30 seconds.

4. To remove the omelet from the pan, carefully slide it onto a plate with the folded edge facing out.

VEGGIE OMELET WITH GOAT CHEESE

PointsPlus value per serving: 6   *pictured on page 61*

HANDS-ON TIME: 14 min. ■ **TOTAL TIME:** 14 min.

1½ teaspoons olive oil, divided
½ cup sliced cremini mushrooms
1 tablespoon chopped fresh chives
1 tablespoon water
¼ teaspoon salt
¼ teaspoon freshly ground black pepper
4 large eggs
1 large egg white
½ cup chopped fresh baby spinach
4 drained oil-packed sun-dried tomatoes, finely chopped
2 tablespoons crumbled goat cheese

1. Heat a 10-inch nonstick skillet over medium-high heat. Add ½ teaspoon oil; swirl to coat. Add mushrooms; sauté 3 minutes or just until tender. Remove from pan.

2. Combine chives and next 5 ingredients in a bowl, stirring with a whisk until well blended.

3. Heat remaining 1 teaspoon oil in pan over medium-high heat. Add egg mixture, and cook until edges begin to set (about 1 minute). Slide front edge of spatula between edge of omelet and pan. Gently lift edge of omelet, tilting pan to allow some uncooked egg mixture to come in contact with pan. Repeat procedure on opposite edge of omelet. Continue cooking until center is just set (about 2 minutes).

4. Arrange mushrooms, spinach, tomato, and cheese over half of omelet. Loosen omelet with a spatula, and fold in half; cook 30 seconds. Carefully slide omelet onto a plate; cut omelet in half. YIELD: 2 SERVINGS (SERVING SIZE: ½ OMELET).

PER SERVING: Calories 240; Fat 17.2g (sat 5.8g, mono 7.5g, poly 1.9g); Protein 18g; Carb 4g; Fiber 0.8g; Chol 430mg; Iron 2.6mg; Sodium 542mg; Calc 87mg

ASPARAGUS QUICHE

PointsPlus value per serving: 6

HANDS-ON TIME: 6 min. ■ **TOTAL TIME:** 50 min.

½ (14.1-ounce) package refrigerated pie dough
Cooking spray
1 pound asparagus, cut into ¼-inch-thick slices
½ teaspoon freshly ground black pepper, divided
¼ teaspoon salt, divided
6 ounces goat cheese (about ¾ cup), crumbled
4 large eggs
¾ cup 1% low-fat milk

1. Preheat oven to 375°.

2. Fit dough into a 9-inch pie plate according to package directions.

3. Heat a large skillet over medium-high heat. Coat pan with cooking spray. Add asparagus, ¼ teaspoon pepper, and ⅛ teaspoon salt; sauté 4 minutes or until crisp-tender. Spoon asparagus into prepared pie plate; sprinkle evenly with goat cheese.

4. Combine eggs, milk, remaining ¼ teaspoon pepper, and remaining ⅛ teaspoon salt; pour over asparagus. Bake at 375° for 35 minutes or until almost set in center. Let stand 5 minutes before slicing. YIELD: 8 SERVINGS (SERVING SIZE: 1 SLICE).

PER SERVING: Calories 217; Fat 13.9g (sat 6.8g, mono 4.5g, poly 1.2g); Protein 10g; Carb 14.9g; Fiber 1.2g; Chol 119mg; Iron 2.1mg; Sodium 328mg; Calc 84mg

SUN-DRIED TOMATO STRATA

PointsPlus value per serving: 8   *pictured on page 62*

HANDS-ON TIME: 5 min. ■ **TOTAL TIME:** 1 hr., 25 min.

Layers of Italian bread, tangy cheese, and sweet sun-dried tomatoes bake together to create a casserole perfect for a weekend breakfast or a casual supper.

4 large eggs
1¾ cups 1% low-fat milk
¼ teaspoon salt
¼ teaspoon freshly ground black pepper
½ (16-ounce) loaf Italian bread, cut into 1-inch cubes
1 cup drained oil-packed julienne-cut sun-dried tomatoes
Cooking spray
6 ounces goat cheese with herbs (about ¾ cup), crumbled
¼ cup chopped fresh basil (optional)

1. Combine first 4 ingredients in a large bowl. Add bread cubes and tomatoes; toss gently to combine. Let stand 20 minutes.
2. Preheat oven to 375°.
3. Spoon half of tomato mixture into an 8-inch square glass or ceramic baking dish coated with cooking spray; sprinkle with half of cheese. Top with remaining tomato mixture and cheese. Cover and bake at 375° for 50 minutes. Uncover and bake an additional 10 minutes or until browned. Sprinkle with basil, if desired. Cut into squares. **YIELD: 6 SERVINGS (SERVING SIZE: 1 SQUARE).**

PER SERVING: Calories 291; Fat 14.1g (sat 6.2g, mono 4.8g, poly 1.5g); Protein 14.9g; Carb 28.1g; Fiber 2.1g; Chol 155mg; Iron 2.2mg; Sodium 577mg; Calc 141mg

ROASTING VEGETABLES

Roasting vegetables concentrates their natural sugars, creating a slightly sweet flavor. The high direct heat of this simple method also gives them a beautiful, tasty browned exterior. Be sure to spread the vegetables in a single layer on the baking sheet so that air circulates around all of the pieces. If they're stacked on top of each other, pieces on the bottom will steam rather than roast, creating a softer texture.

ROASTED VEGETABLES OVER PARMESAN POLENTA

PointsPlus value per serving: 5   *pictured on page 63*

HANDS-ON TIME: 8 min. ■ **TOTAL TIME:** 30 min.

Cook the polenta during the last 5 minutes of the vegetable bake time so it will remain soft and creamy.

2 cups presliced mushrooms
1½ cups grape tomatoes
1½ cups (1½-inch) sliced asparagus (about ½ pound)
1 small yellow squash, quartered lengthwise and sliced
1 medium zucchini, quartered lengthwise and sliced
2 tablespoons olive oil
½ teaspoon salt, divided
½ teaspoon freshly ground black pepper, divided
4 cups water
1 cup quick-cooking polenta
2 tablespoons chopped fresh parsley
2 teaspoons chopped fresh thyme
4 ounces shredded Parmigiano-Reggiano cheese (about 1 cup), divided
Chopped fresh thyme (optional)

1. Preheat oven to 450°.
2. Combine first 6 ingredients in a large bowl; spread in a single layer on a large rimmed baking sheet. Sprinkle with ¼ teaspoon salt and ¼ teaspoon pepper. Bake at 450° for 25 minutes, stirring after 15 minutes.
3. Bring 4 cups water to a boil over medium-high heat; gradually add polenta, stirring with a whisk. Reduce heat, and simmer 2 minutes or until thick, stirring constantly with a whisk. Remove from heat; stir in remaining ¼ teaspoon salt, remaining ¼ teaspoon pepper, parsley, thyme, and ¾ cup cheese. Cover and keep warm.
4. Divide polenta among 6 plates; top evenly with roasted vegetables and remaining ¼ cup cheese. Sprinkle with thyme, if desired. **YIELD: 6 SERVINGS (SERVING SIZE: 1 CUP POLENTA, ⅔ CUP VEGETABLES, AND ABOUT 2 TEASPOONS CHEESE).**

PER SERVING: Calories 236; Fat 10.1g (sat 3.4g, mono 4.9g, poly 0.8g); Protein 12.3g; Carb 19.2g; Fiber 4.6g; Chol 14mg; Iron 1.3mg; Sodium 543mg; Calc 300mg

QUINOA WITH OVEN-ROASTED TOMATOES

PointsPlus value per serving: 6

HANDS-ON TIME: 9 min. ■ **TOTAL TIME:** 32 min.

Quinoa (pronounced KEEN-wah) is an excellent source of iron—it supplies your entire daily recommendation in 1 cup.

1½ cups water
¾ cup quinoa
1½ cups grape tomatoes
½ cup thinly sliced red onion
1 teaspoon freshly ground black pepper, divided
½ teaspoon salt, divided
1 garlic clove, chopped
Cooking spray
2 cups chopped fresh baby spinach
1 teaspoon grated fresh lemon rind
1 tablespoon fresh lemon juice
2 ounces feta cheese (about ¼ cup), crumbled

1. Preheat oven to 375°.

2. Bring 1½ cups water to a boil in a medium saucepan. Place quinoa in a fine sieve; place sieve in a large bowl. Cover quinoa with water. Using your hands, rub grains together for 30 seconds; rinse and drain. Repeat procedure twice. Drain well. Stir quinoa into boiling water; cover, reduce heat, and simmer 20 minutes or until liquid is absorbed.

3. While quinoa cooks, place tomatoes, onion, ½ teaspoon pepper, ¼ teaspoon salt, and garlic in a large bowl; toss gently. Line a large rimmed baking sheet with foil. Coat foil with cooking spray. Spread vegetable mixture in a single layer on prepared pan. Bake, uncovered, at 375° for 10 minutes or until tomatoes begin to burst.

4. Place quinoa in a large bowl. Add spinach, and toss until spinach wilts. Stir in lemon rind, lemon juice, remaining ½ teaspoon pepper, and remaining ¼ teaspoon salt. Add tomato mixture and cheese to quinoa mixture. Toss gently. Serve at room temperature or chilled. **YIELD: 3 SERVINGS (SERVING SIZE: 1⅓ CUPS).**

PER SERVING: Calories 240; Fat 7g (sat 3.2g, mono 1.6g, poly 1.6g); Protein 10.2g; Carb 34.9g; Fiber 5g; Chol 17mg; Iron 2.7mg; Sodium 627mg; Calc 155mg

HOW TO PREPARE SPAGHETTI SQUASH

This melon-shaped winter squash is named for its flesh, which separates into spaghetti-like strands after it's cooked.

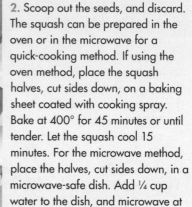

1. Cut each squash in half lengthwise.

2. Scoop out the seeds, and discard. The squash can be prepared in the oven or in the microwave for a quick-cooking method. If using the oven method, place the squash halves, cut sides down, on a baking sheet coated with cooking spray. Bake at 400° for 45 minutes or until tender. Let the squash cool 15 minutes. For the microwave method, place the halves, cut sides down, in a microwave-safe dish. Add ¼ cup water to the dish, and microwave at HIGH for 7 minutes or until tender. Be careful not to overbake the spaghetti squash or the strands will not hold their shape. If the skin is slightly soft when pressed, it's cooked long enough.

3. Cool the squash slightly. Holding the squash in a vertical position with one hand, use a fork to gently scrape out the spaghetti-like flesh, working from the top to the base.

CURRIED CHICKPEAS AND SPAGHETTI SQUASH

PointsPlus value per serving: 6

HANDS-ON TIME: 28 min. ■ **TOTAL TIME:** 44 min.

If you can find it, hot Bengal chutney is a delicious condiment for this dish.

1 (14-ounce) package firm water-packed tofu, drained
2 small spaghetti squash (about 2¾ pounds)
½ cup water, divided
7 teaspoons red curry powder, divided
2 tablespoons olive oil, divided
½ cup chopped onion
1 tablespoon minced seeded serrano chile (1 chile)
2 garlic cloves, minced
1 (15½-ounce) can chickpeas (garbanzo beans), drained
1 cup chopped tomato
½ teaspoon salt
¼ cup chopped fresh cilantro

1. Place tofu between paper towels until barely moist (about 30 minutes). Cut into ½-inch cubes.
2. While tofu stands, cut squash in half lengthwise; discard seeds and membranes. Place 2 squash halves, cut sides down, in a 9-inch microwave-safe pie plate. Add ¼ cup water to dish. Microwave at HIGH 7 minutes or until tender. Cool slightly. Repeat procedure with remaining 2 squash halves and remaining water. Scrape insides of squash halves with a fork to remove spaghetti-like strands to measure 3 cups. Keep warm.
3. Place tofu in a large heavy-duty zip-top plastic bag. Add 4 teaspoons curry powder; seal bag, tossing to coat. Heat a large nonstick skillet over medium-high heat. Add 1 tablespoon oil; swirl to coat. Add tofu to pan; cook 7 minutes or until browned, stirring occasionally. Remove from pan; reduce heat to medium.
4. Add remaining 1 tablespoon oil to pan. Add onion, chile, and garlic to pan; sauté 2 minutes or until tender. Add chickpeas, tomato, salt, and remaining 1 tablespoon curry powder; cook 1 minute or until thoroughly heated and tomato softens. Remove from heat. Add spaghetti squash and tofu, tossing gently to combine. Sprinkle with cilantro. YIELD: 6 SERVINGS (SERVING SIZE: ABOUT 1¼ CUPS).

PER SERVING: Calories 214; Fat 9.6g (sat 1.3g, mono 4.4g, poly 2.5g); Protein 10g; Carb 26g; Fiber 6.1g; Chol 0mg; Iron 2.9mg; Sodium 304mg; Calc 196mg

TWO-BEAN CAKES

PointsPlus value per serving: 6

HANDS-ON TIME: 7 min. ■ **TOTAL TIME:** 23 min.

These hearty bean cakes are quick to put together for a simple dinner.

Cooking spray
1 small onion, chopped (about ¾ cup)
⅔ cup seasoned breadcrumbs
2 teaspoons chopped fresh cilantro
½ teaspoon ground cumin
½ teaspoon ground red pepper
⅛ teaspoon salt
2 large eggs, lightly beaten
1 (16-ounce) can fat-free refried beans
1 (15-ounce) can reduced-sodium black beans, rinsed and drained
1 tablespoon olive oil, divided
6 tablespoons reduced-fat sour cream
6 tablespoons bottled salsa

1. Heat a large nonstick skillet over medium-high heat. Coat pan with cooking spray. Add onion; sauté 2 minutes or until tender.
2. Combine onion, breadcrumbs, and next 7 ingredients in a medium bowl. With moist hands, shape mixture into 12 (2½-inch) cakes. (Mixture will be very moist.)
3. Heat pan over medium heat. Add 1 teaspoon oil to pan; swirl to coat. Add 4 cakes to pan; cook 3 minutes or until browned. Spray uncooked side of each cake with cooking spray; turn and cook 2 to 3 minutes or until browned. Remove from pan; keep warm. Repeat procedure twice with remaining 2 teaspoons oil and remaining 8 cakes. Top cakes with sour cream and salsa. YIELD: 6 SERVINGS (SERVING SIZE: 2 CAKES, 1 TABLESPOON SOUR CREAM, AND 1 TABLESPOON SALSA).

PER SERVING: Calories 248; Fat 6.7g (sat 2.2g, mono 3g, poly 0.9g); Protein 13.1g; Carb 36.5g; Fiber 8.6g; Chol 78mg; Iron 3.7mg; Sodium 639mg; Calc 121mg

SPINACH-CHICKPEA CAKES WITH YOGURT SAUCE

PointsPlus value per serving: 6

HANDS-ON TIME: 12 min. ■ **TOTAL TIME:** 29 min.

You'll find such an abundance of classic Mediterranean flavors in this dish that you'll never miss the meat.

½ cup plain fat-free Greek yogurt
2 tablespoons Major Grey's chutney
1 tablespoon chopped fresh flat-leaf parsley
1 (10-ounce) package frozen chopped spinach
2 (15½-ounce) cans chickpeas (garbanzo beans), rinsed
　　and drained
2 garlic cloves, minced
1 large egg, lightly beaten
½ cup finely chopped onion
1½ teaspoons garam masala
¼ teaspoon freshly ground black pepper
¼ teaspoon ground red pepper
1 tablespoon canola oil, divided

1. Combine first 3 ingredients, stirring well with a whisk. Set aside.
2. Cook spinach in microwave according to package directions; place spinach in a colander, pressing until barely moist. Cool slightly.
3. Place chickpeas in a food processor; process until smooth, scraping sides of bowl occasionally. Combine spinach, chickpeas, garlic, and next 5 ingredients in a large bowl; divide mixture into 8 equal portions, shaping each into a ½-inch-thick patty.
4. Heat a large nonstick skillet over medium heat. Add 1½ teaspoons oil; swirl to coat. Add 4 patties to pan; cook 4 to 5 minutes on each side or until browned. Repeat procedure with remaining 1½ teaspoons oil and patties. Serve warm with yogurt sauce. YIELD: 4 SERVINGS (SERVING SIZE: 2 PATTIES AND 1 TABLESPOON SAUCE).

PER SERVING: Calories 246; Fat 6.5g (sat 0.7g, mono 3.2g, poly 2.2g); Protein 11.8g; Carb 32.9g; Fiber 5.8g; Chol 53mg; Iron 2.2mg; Sodium 411mg; Calc 125mg

WILD MUSHROOM PENNE WITH PUMPKIN CREAM SAUCE

PointsPlus value per serving: 9

HANDS-ON TIME: 5 min. ■ **TOTAL TIME:** 30 min.

Perfect for your fall entertaining menu, this rich pasta entrée will pair nicely with a crisp white wine.

1 (12-ounce) package whole-wheat penne pasta
Cooking spray
3 cups sliced Vidalia or other sweet onion
3 (4-ounce) packages presliced exotic mushroom blend
　　(such as shiitake, cremini, and oyster)
1 (12-ounce) can evaporated fat-free milk
1½ tablespoons cornstarch
1½ tablespoons water
½ cup canned pumpkin
2 teaspoons chopped fresh sage
½ teaspoon salt
½ teaspoon freshly ground black pepper
2 ounces grated fresh Parmesan cheese (about ½ cup)

1. Cook pasta according to package directions, omitting salt and fat. Keep warm.
2. Heat a large nonstick skillet over medium-high heat. Coat pan with cooking spray. Add onion and mushrooms to pan; sauté 5 minutes or until tender. Remove pan from heat, and keep warm.
3. Bring milk to a simmer in a medium saucepan over medium heat (do not boil). Combine cornstarch and 1½ tablespoons water, stirring with a whisk; add to milk. Cook 2 minutes or until thick, stirring constantly with whisk. Remove from heat; stir in pumpkin, sage, salt, and pepper.
4. Add pasta and pumpkin mixture to mushroom mixture in skillet, tossing well to coat. Sprinkle with cheese; serve immediately. YIELD: 6 SERVINGS (SERVING SIZE: ABOUT 1½ CUPS).

PER SERVING: Calories 324; Fat 3.8g (sat 1.8g, mono 0.9g, poly 0.5g); Protein 16.8g; Carb 61.1g; Fiber 8g; Chol 11mg; Iron 2.8mg; Sodium 416mg; Calc 604mg

VEGETABLE BOLOGNESE

PointsPlus value per serving: 8

HANDS-ON TIME: 6 min. ■ **TOTAL TIME:** 23 min.

An abundance of fresh mushrooms adds rich, meaty texture to this hearty main-dish pasta.

1 (12-ounce) package whole-wheat linguine
Cooking spray
2 (8-ounce) packages presliced mushrooms
2 (8-ounce) packages refrigerated prechopped onion, celery, and bell pepper mix
1 cup chopped carrot
1 teaspoon dried Italian seasoning
½ teaspoon salt
½ teaspoon freshly ground black pepper
1 (28-ounce) can no-salt-added crushed tomatoes
½ cup dry red wine
2 ounces grated fresh Parmesan cheese (about ½ cup)

1. Cook pasta according to package directions, omitting salt and fat. Drain, reserving pasta water; keep pasta warm.
2. Heat a large nonstick skillet over medium-high heat. Coat pan with cooking spray. Add mushrooms and next 5 ingredients to pan; sauté 10 minutes or until vegetables are tender. Add tomatoes to pan; cook 1 minute, stirring constantly. Stir in wine. Bring to a boil, reduce heat to medium, and simmer 10 minutes, stirring occasionally.
3. Add pasta to mushroom mixture. Toss gently to coat, adding reserved pasta water as needed to thin sauce to desired consistency. Sprinkle with cheese. Serve immediately. YIELD: 6 SERVINGS (SERVING SIZE: 1 CUP PASTA AND 1 CUP SAUCE).

PER SERVING: Calories 307; Fat 3.7g (sat 1.7g, mono 0.9g, poly 0.6g); Protein 15.1g; Carb 56.2g; Fiber 9.8g; Chol 8mg; Iron 4.1mg; Sodium 381mg; Calc 480mg

RISOTTO

Risottos are typically made with Arborio rice, which contains lots of easily released starch that provides this dish's characteristic creaminess. Bringing the liquid mixture (in this recipe, a combination of broth, water, and salt) to a simmer and keeping it hot is key so that the risotto stays at a simmer with each addition—cold ingredients slow the release of starch. And keep stirring until each portion is absorbed. Constant stirring agitates the grain, causing it to release its starch.

ROASTED MUSHROOM AND SHALLOT RISOTTO

PointsPlus value per serving: 8

HANDS-ON TIME: 36 min. ■ **TOTAL TIME:** 36 min.

Risotto may not be the quickest recipe, but it is definitely worth the effort and time it takes to make it. We gave this creamy, earthy comfort food very high marks in our Test Kitchen.

2 (4-ounce) packages presliced exotic mushroom blend (such as shiitake, cremini, and oyster), quartered
2 large shallots, peeled and sliced lengthwise
4 teaspoons olive oil, divided
¼ teaspoon salt, divided
¼ teaspoon freshly ground black pepper, divided
1 (32-ounce) carton organic vegetable broth
2¼ cups water
1¼ cups Arborio rice or other medium-grain rice
2 ounces grated fresh Parmesan cheese (about ½ cup)
6 tablespoons chopped walnuts, toasted
¼ cup chopped fresh chives (optional)

1. Preheat oven to 450°.
2. Place mushrooms and shallots on a large rimmed baking sheet. Drizzle with 2 teaspoons olive oil; sprinkle with ⅛ teaspoon salt and ⅛ teaspoon pepper, and toss to coat. Bake at 450° for 15 minutes.
3. While vegetables bake, combine broth, 2¼ cups water, and remaining ⅛ teaspoon salt in a medium saucepan; bring to a simmer over medium heat (do not boil). Keep warm over low heat.
4. Heat a Dutch oven over medium heat. Add remaining 2 teaspoons oil; swirl to coat. Add rice. Cook 2 minutes or until rice is lightly toasted, stirring constantly. Stir in 1 cup broth mixture; cook, stirring constantly, until the liquid is nearly absorbed. Add remaining broth mixture, ½ cup at a time, stirring constantly until each portion of broth mixture is absorbed before adding the next (about 25 minutes total).
5. Stir cheese and remaining ⅛ teaspoon pepper into rice mixture. Place rice mixture on each of 6 plates. Top evenly with roasted mushroom mixture and walnuts. Sprinkle with chives, if desired. YIELD: 6 SERVINGS (SERVING SIZE: ¾ CUP RISOTTO, ⅓ CUP MUSHROOM MIXTURE, AND 1 TABLESPOON WALNUTS).

PER SERVING: Calories 281; Fat 11g (sat 2.2g, mono 3.6g, poly 4g); Protein 9.9g; Carb 37.5g; Fiber 2.6g; Chol 7mg; Iron 0.7mg; Sodium 633mg; Calc 142mg

ROASTED SPAGHETTI SQUASH WITH MARINARA

PointsPlus value per serving: 6

HANDS-ON TIME: 7 min. ■ **TOTAL TIME:** 1 hr., 7 min.

Spaghetti squash is a curious vegetable. When you cut it open, it resembles other winter squash, such as acorn and butternut. But after it's cooked, scraping the inside of the squash with a fork releases golden strands that resemble its namesake pasta.

2 small spaghetti squash (about 3½ pounds)
1 (25.5-ounce) jar fat-free roasted garlic pasta sauce
1 tablespoon dried Italian seasoning
2 teaspoons canola oil
1 (12-ounce) package frozen meatless fat-free crumbles
6 tablespoons grated fresh Parmesan cheese

1. Preheat oven to 400°.
2. Place squash, cut sides down, on a baking sheet; bake at 400° for 45 minutes or until tender. Cut squash in half lengthwise; discard seeds and membranes. Cool 15 minutes. Scrape insides of squash halves with a fork to remove spaghetti–like strands to measure 4¾ cups.
3. Combine pasta sauce and Italian seasoning in a large saucepan over medium–high heat. Heat a nonstick skillet over medium heat. Add oil to pan; swirl to coat. Add soy crumbles, and cook 6 minutes or until crumbles are heated through, stirring often. Stir soy crumbles into pasta sauce, cook 2 minutes, tossing to combine.
4. Spoon spaghetti squash evenly onto 6 plates; top with sauce mixture. Sprinkle evenly with cheese.

YIELD: 6 SERVINGS (SERVING SIZE: ¾ CUP SQUASH, ⅔ CUP SAUCE, AND 1 TABLESPOON CHEESE).

PER SERVING: Calories 245; Fat 7.2g (sat 1.3g, mono 2.2g, poly 2.5g); Protein 16.7g; Carb 31.3g; Fiber 8.2g; Chol 5mg; Iron 4mg; Sodium 769mg; Calc 167mg

SPINACH AND MUSHROOM ENCHILADAS

PointsPlus value per serving: 8

HANDS-ON TIME: 11 min. ■ **TOTAL TIME:** 40 min.

No need to head to a restaurant to satisfy your craving for Mexican food. You can have these hearty enchiladas on the table in less than 45 minutes. Our Test Kitchen staff gave this recipe a big thumbs up.

2 teaspoons olive oil
1 cup chopped onion
1 teaspoon ground cumin
¼ teaspoon freshly ground black pepper
1 (8-ounce) package presliced mushrooms
1 jalapeño pepper, seeded and finely chopped
1 garlic clove, minced
2 (6-ounce) packages fresh baby spinach
3 ounces shredded 50%-less-fat jalapeño cheddar cheese (about ¾ cup), divided
1⅓ cups red enchilada sauce, divided
8 (6-inch) corn tortillas
Cooking spray
¼ cup fat-free sour cream
2 tablespoons chopped fresh cilantro

1. Preheat oven to 350°.
2. Heat a large nonstick skillet over medium-high heat. Add oil; swirl to coat. Add onion and next 5 ingredients to pan; sauté 5 minutes or until onion is tender. Add spinach; sauté 2 minutes or until spinach wilts, stirring frequently. Stir in ¼ cup cheese.
3. Heat ⅓ cup enchilada sauce in a medium saucepan over low heat. Dip tortillas in warm sauce using tongs, allowing excess to drain back into pan. Stack tortillas on a plate. Spoon about ⅓ cup mushroom mixture down center of each tortilla; roll up. Place tortillas, seam sides down, in a 13 x 9–inch glass or ceramic baking dish coated with cooking spray. Pour remaining 1 cup sauce evenly over enchiladas; top with remaining ½ cup cheese.
4. Cover and bake at 350° for 20 minutes or until thoroughly heated. Serve with sour cream and cilantro.

YIELD: 4 SERVINGS (SERVING SIZE: 2 ENCHILADAS, 1 TABLESPOON SOUR CREAM, AND 1½ TEASPOONS CILANTRO).

PER SERVING: Calories 296; Fat 9.5g (sat 2.8g, mono 2.9g, poly 1.3g); Protein 15g; Carb 45.9g; Fiber 6.8g; Chol 13mg; Iron 3.4mg; Sodium 736mg; Calc 276mg

CHEESY SQUASH AND RED ONION QUESADILLAS

PointsPlus value per serving: *7*

HANDS-ON TIME: 8 min. ■ **TOTAL TIME:** 37 min.

These quesadillas are loaded with fresh vegetables accented with creamy goat cheese.

⅓ cup light sour cream
1 teaspoon chopped fresh thyme
2 medium-sized yellow squash
1 large zucchini
1 large red onion
Cooking spray
¼ teaspoon freshly ground black pepper
4 ounces goat cheese
4 (8-inch) 96% fat-free whole-wheat tortillas

1. Combine sour cream and thyme in a small bowl; cover and chill until ready to serve.
2. Cut yellow squash and zucchini in half lengthwise and then crosswise into ¼-inch-thick slices. Cut onion lengthwise into quarters; cut crosswise into ¼-inch-thick slices.
3. Heat a large nonstick skillet over medium-high heat. Coat pan with cooking spray. Add vegetables to pan; sauté 6 minutes or until crisp-tender. Sprinkle with pepper.
4. Spread 1 ounce cheese on half of each tortilla; top each with ¾ cup vegetable mixture. Fold tortillas in half.
5. Wipe pan dry with paper towels; heat pan over medium heat. Coat pan with cooking spray. Place 2 tortillas, folded sides together, in pan. Cook 2 minutes or until lightly browned; turn, keeping folded sides in center of pan. Cook 2 minutes or until lightly browned and cheese melts. Remove from pan, and keep warm. Repeat procedure with remaining 2 tortillas. Serve warm with sour cream mixture. YIELD: 4 SERVINGS (SERVING SIZE: 1 QUESADILLA AND ABOUT 1 TABLESPOON SOUR CREAM MIXTURE).

PER SERVING: Calories 279; Fat 10.2g (sat 5.5g, mono 2.2g, poly 0.4g); Protein 13.2g; Carb 36.2g; Fiber 5.7g; Chol 13mg; Iron 2.8mg; Sodium 480mg; Calc 226mg

TEMPEH-MUSHROOM QUESADILLAS

PointsPlus value per serving: *7*

HANDS-ON TIME: 8 min. ■ **TOTAL TIME:** 19 min.

Tempeh is a soy-based meat substitute that easily absorbs flavors and keeps its shape. We sliced it for these quesadillas, but you can crumble it instead.

1 (8-ounce) package organic soy tempeh
Cooking spray
1 (8-ounce) package presliced mushrooms
1 (6-ounce) package fresh baby spinach
⅓ cup light creamy alfredo pasta sauce
¼ teaspoon freshly ground black pepper
4 (7½-inch) whole-wheat tortillas
1 ounce preshredded part-skim mozzarella cheese
    (about ¼ cup)

1. Cut tempeh into 16 (¼-inch-thick) slices. Heat a large nonstick skillet over medium-high heat. Coat pan with cooking spray. Add tempeh; cook 3 minutes or until browned, turning once. Remove from pan; keep warm.
2. Heat pan over medium-high heat. Coat pan with cooking spray. Add mushrooms to pan; cook 2 minutes or until browned, stirring often. Add spinach; cook 2 minutes or until spinach wilts. Drain; return mixture to pan. Stir in alfredo sauce and pepper.
3. Divide mixture evenly over half of each tortilla; top each with 4 slices tempeh and 1 tablespoon cheese. Fold tortillas in half.
4. Wipe pan dry with paper towels; heat pan over medium heat. Coat pan with cooking spray. Place 2 tortillas, folded sides together, in pan. Cook 1 to 2 minutes or until lightly browned; turn, keeping folded sides in center of pan. Cook 1 to 2 minutes or until lightly browned. Remove from pan, and keep warm. Repeat procedure with remaining 2 tortillas. Cut each quesadilla into 2 triangles. YIELD: 4 SERVINGS (SERVING SIZE: 1 QUESADILLA).

PER SERVING: Calories 290; Fat 8.3g (sat 2.1g, mono 3g, poly 1.8g); Protein 18.9g; Carb 34.6g; Fiber 8.1g; Chol 7mg; Iron 4mg; Sodium 456mg; Calc 136mg

TEMPEH

Tempeh has an assertive tangy, nutty flavor which it obtains from the fermentation process used to make it. It's rich in high-quality protein, fiber, and calcium, and it can also provide significant amounts of iron.

BROCCOLI-FETA CALZONES

PointsPlus value per serving: 8

HANDS-ON TIME: 8 min. ■ **TOTAL TIME:** 26 min.

Substitute 1½ cups chopped cooked fresh broccoli for the frozen, if you prefer. The food processor is key for getting the filling to a smooth consistency.

⅔ cup part-skim ricotta cheese
1 large egg yolk
4 ounces crumbled feta cheese (about 1 cup)
½ teaspoon freshly ground black pepper
1 (10-ounce) package frozen chopped broccoli, thawed and drained
1 pound refrigerated fresh pizza dough
Cooking spray
1 large egg white, lightly beaten
Pasta sauce (optional)

1. Preheat oven to 450°.
2. Place ricotta and egg yolk in a food processor; process until smooth. Combine ricotta mixture, feta cheese, pepper, and broccoli in a medium bowl.
3. Divide dough into 6 equal portions. Roll each portion into a 6-inch circle on a lightly floured surface. Place ⅓ cup broccoli mixture onto half of each circle. Fold dough over filling; seal by rolling edges toward center and crimping. Cut a small slit in the center of each calzone to allow steam to escape. Place calzones on a large baking sheet coated with cooking spray; brush with egg white.
4. Bake at 450° for 18 minutes or until golden brown. Serve with warm pasta sauce, if desired. **YIELD: 6 SERVINGS** (SERVING SIZE: 1 CALZONE).

PER SERVING: Calories 312; Fat 9.2g (sat 5.3g, mono 2.9g, poly 0.9g); Protein 14.8g; Carb 44.5g; Fiber 2.8g; Chol 60mg; Iron 3.1mg; Sodium 731mg; Calc 199mg

ROASTED ASPARAGUS AND TOMATO PIZZA

PointsPlus value per serving: 8

HANDS-ON TIME: 13 min. ■ **TOTAL TIME:** 25 min.

Roasted asparagus, cherry tomatoes, and pesto turn simple pizza into a mouthwatering weeknight meal.

½ pound asparagus spears, trimmed
2 cups small cherry tomatoes
Cooking spray
½ cup part-skim ricotta cheese
2 tablespoons commercial pesto
1 pound refrigerated fresh pizza dough
2 ounces preshredded part-skim mozzarella cheese (about ½ cup)
1 ounce crumbled goat cheese (about ¼ cup)

1. Preheat oven to 500°.
2. Place asparagus and tomatoes on a large rimmed baking sheet coated with cooking spray. Coat vegetables with cooking spray. Bake at 500° for 10 minutes. Cool slightly. Cut asparagus into 1-inch pieces.
3. While vegetables bake, combine ricotta cheese and pesto in a small bowl. Roll dough into a 12-inch circle; place on a baking sheet coated with cooking spray. Spread pesto mixture on crust. Top with vegetables, and sprinkle with mozzarella cheese and goat cheese.
4. Bake at 500° for 12 minutes or until crust is golden and cheeses melt. Cut pizza into wedges. **YIELD: 6 SERVINGS** (SERVING SIZE: 1 WEDGE).

PER SERVING: Calories 299; Fat 9.4g (sat 3.9g, mono 4.6g, poly 0.9g); Protein 13.3g; Carb 41.6g; Fiber 2.7g; Chol 15mg; Iron 2.7mg; Sodium 687mg; Calc 158mg

meats

Kung Pao Pork, page 93

SMOTHERED MUSHROOM AND ONION STEAKS

PointsPlus value per serving: 9

HANDS-ON TIME: 18 min. ▪ **TOTAL TIME:** 18 min.

This is comfort food at its best. Serve with mashed potatoes and a tossed green salad for an easy weeknight supper.

Cooking spray
1 cup sliced onion
1 (8-ounce) package presliced mushrooms
¼ teaspoon freshly ground black pepper
1 tablespoon olive oil
4 (4-ounce) boneless top sirloin steaks
2 teaspoons reduced-sodium Montreal steak seasoning
4 (0.6-ounce) slices reduced-fat Swiss cheese

1. Heat a large nonstick skillet over medium-high heat. Coat pan with cooking spray. Add onion and mushrooms; sauté 5 minutes or just until vegetables are tender. Stir in pepper. Remove mixture from pan; set aside, and keep warm.
2. Heat pan over medium-high heat. Add oil to pan; swirl to coat. Sprinkle steaks evenly with steak seasoning; add to pan. Cook 3 minutes on each side or until desired degree of doneness. Spoon vegetable mixture evenly over steaks; top each with 1 cheese slice. Cover and cook 1 minute or until cheese melts. YIELD: 4 SERVINGS (SERVING SIZE: 1 STEAK AND ¾ CUP VEGETABLE MIXTURE).

PER SERVING: Calories 347; Fat 22.1g (sat 8.3g, mono 9.7g, poly 1.1g); Protein 31.3g; Carb 5.7g; Fiber 0.6g; Chol 63mg; Iron 1.9mg; Sodium 361mg; Calc 237mg

THYME-PEPPERCORN BEEF FILETS WITH PORT

PointsPlus value per serving: 6

HANDS-ON TIME: 2 min. ▪ **TOTAL TIME:** 17 min.

We used larger cuts of steak and then cut them in half after cooking to achieve greater flavor and moistness.

1 tablespoon chopped fresh thyme
2 teaspoons coarsely ground black pepper
¼ teaspoon salt
2 (8-ounce) beef tenderloin steaks, trimmed
        (1¼ inches thick)
½ cup ruby port or other sweet red wine
½ cup fat-free, lower-sodium beef broth
1 tablespoon butter

1. Combine first 3 ingredients; sprinkle both sides of steaks with thyme mixture, pressing mixture into steaks.
2. Heat a large nonstick skillet over medium-high heat. Add steaks; cook 5 to 6 minutes on each side or until desired degree of doneness. Remove steaks from pan; cut steaks in half vertically, and keep warm.
3. Add port and broth to pan, scraping pan to loosen browned bits. Bring to a boil; cook until reduced by half (about 4 minutes). Remove from heat; add butter, stirring with a whisk until butter melts. Spoon sauce over steaks. YIELD: 4 SERVINGS (SERVING SIZE: ½ STEAK AND 2 TABLESPOONS SAUCE).

PER SERVING: Calories 229; Fat 10.3g (sat 4.6g, mono 3.7g, poly 0.4g); Protein 25.7g; Carb 2.9g; Fiber 0.3g; Chol 84mg; Iron 2mg; Sodium 289mg; Calc 36mg

BEEF FAJITA SOFT TACOS

PointsPlus value per serving: 10

HANDS-ON TIME: 10 min. ▪ **TOTAL TIME:** 21 min.

You can use fat-free flour tortillas if you have those on hand. The ***PointsPlus*** value per serving will be the same.

1 (1-pound) flank steak, trimmed
Cooking spray
1 (8-ounce) package refrigerated presliced bell pepper
1 medium onion, thinly sliced
1 tablespoon chili powder
1 tablespoon fresh lime juice
8 (6-inch) flour tortillas
3 tablespoons fat-free sour cream
3 tablespoons chopped fresh cilantro

1. Cut steak diagonally across grain into thin slices. Heat a large nonstick skillet over medium-high heat. Coat pan with cooking spray. Add steak slices to pan; sauté 3 to 4 minutes or until desired degree of doneness. Remove from pan; keep warm.
2. Add bell pepper and onion to pan; sauté 5 minutes or just until tender. Add steak slices, chili powder, and lime juice to vegetables in pan, tossing to coat.
3. Spoon steak mixture evenly into tortillas; top evenly with sour cream and cilantro. YIELD: 4 SERVINGS (SERVING SIZE: 2 TACOS, ABOUT 2 TEASPOONS SOUR CREAM, AND ABOUT 2 TEASPOONS CILANTRO).

PER SERVING: Calories 394; Fat 11.6g (sat 3.7g, mono 4.8g, poly 1.4g); Protein 31.1g; Carb 40g; Fiber 4.2g; Chol 39mg; Iron 4.4mg; Sodium 476mg; Calc 138mg

FLAT-IRON STEAKS WITH SUN-DRIED TOMATO–BASIL BUTTER

PointsPlus value per serving: 7

HANDS-ON TIME: 11 min. ■ **TOTAL TIME:** 21 min.

Flat-iron steak, also known as a "top blade steak," is perfect for grilling in a stove top grill pan or cast-iron skillet. For the best results, we recommend not cooking this cut beyond medium.

½ teaspoon kosher salt
½ teaspoon freshly ground black pepper
1 (1-pound) flat-iron steak, trimmed (½ to 1 inch thick)
2 teaspoons canola oil
3 tablespoons light stick butter, softened
2 tablespoons chopped sun-dried tomatoes, packed without oil
2 tablespoons chopped fresh basil
1 tablespoon grated fresh Parmigiano-Reggiano cheese

1. Combine salt and pepper; rub evenly over both sides of steak. Heat a 10-inch cast-iron skillet over medium-high heat. Add oil to pan; swirl to coat. Add steak to pan; cook 6 minutes on each side or until desired degree of doneness. Let stand 10 minutes. Cut steak diagonally across grain into thin slices.
2. While steak stands, combine butter, tomato, basil, and cheese in a medium bowl. Serve butter mixture over steak slices. **YIELD: 4 SERVINGS (SERVING SIZE: 3 OUNCES STEAK AND 1 TABLESPOON BUTTER MIXTURE).**

PER SERVING: Calories 255; Fat 16.6g (sat 6.6g, mono 7.7g, poly 1.3g); Protein 24.7g; Carb 2g; Fiber 0.3g; Chol 77mg; Iron 2.8mg; Sodium 442mg; Calc 28mg

COMPOUND BUTTER

Compound butters are an ideal way to dress up a meal—they're easy to prepare, can be made ahead, and can be adjusted to suit any tastes. Allow stick butter to soften at room temperature for 20 to 30 minutes so the herbs and additional seasonings will blend easily and thoroughly. If you have any butter leftover, transfer it to a sheet of wax paper. Fold the edge of the paper over the butter, and roll it into a log. Twist the ends of the wax paper in opposite directions to seal. The compound butter will stay fresh in the refrigerator for about three weeks.

CHILE-LIME FLANK STEAK

PointsPlus value per serving: 5

HANDS-ON TIME: 5 min. ■ **TOTAL TIME:** 8 hrs., 25 min.

Toss some bell pepper and onion on the grill with the steak, and serve with warm flour tortillas for an easy supper with very little cleanup.

¼ cup chopped fresh cilantro, divided
3 tablespoons fresh lime juice
1 tablespoon olive oil
1 teaspoon ground cumin
1 teaspoon ancho chile powder
½ teaspoon salt
4 garlic cloves, minced
2 jalapeño peppers, seeded and minced (¼ cup)
1 (1½-pound) flank steak, trimmed
Cooking spray

1. Combine 2 tablespoons cilantro, lime juice, and next 6 ingredients in a large zip-top plastic bag; seal and shake well. Add steak to bag; seal. Marinate in refrigerator 8 hours, turning bag occasionally.
2. Preheat grill to high heat.
3. Remove steak from bag, discarding marinade. Place steak on grill rack coated with cooking spray; grill 5 minutes on each side or until desired degree of doneness. Remove steak from grill, and let stand 10 minutes. Cut steak diagonally across grain into thin slices; sprinkle with remaining 2 tablespoons cilantro. Serve immediately. **YIELD: 6 SERVINGS (SERVING SIZE: 3 OUNCES STEAK).**

PER SERVING: Calories 190; Fat 8.8g (sat 2.7g, mono 4g, poly 0.5g); Protein 24.8g; Carb 1.9g; Fiber 0.4g; Chol 37mg; Iron 2mg; Sodium 265mg; Calc 36mg

FLAT-IRON STEAK AU POIVRE WITH COGNAC SAUCE

PointsPlus value per serving: 6

HANDS-ON TIME: 18 min. ■ **TOTAL TIME:** 18 min.

This flavor combination of creamy, fragrant cognac sauce and pepper-crusted steak is a French classic that we have deliciously lightened.

2 tablespoons black peppercorns
1 (1-pound) flat-iron steak
½ teaspoon salt
1 tablespoon butter
1 teaspoon olive oil
¼ cup cognac
¾ cup 1% low-fat milk

1. Coarsely crush peppercorns with a cast–iron skillet or a mortar and pestle. Sprinkle both sides of steak with crushed peppercorns and salt, pressing into steak.
2. Heat a large skillet over medium heat. Add butter and oil to pan; swirl to coat. Add steak to pan; cook 4 minutes on each side or until desired degree of doneness. Remove steak from pan.
3. Pour cognac into one side of skillet. Ignite cognac with a long match; let flames die down. Return pan to medium heat; gradually stir in milk. Bring to a boil, stirring constantly. Reduce heat, and cook 5 minutes or until mixture thickens slightly. Cut steak diagonally across grain into thin slices; pour cognac mixture over steak slices. Serve immediately. YIELD: 4 SERVINGS (SERVING SIZE: 3 OUNCES STEAK AND 1 TABLESPOON SAUCE).

PER SERVING: Calories 257; Fat 12.6g (sat 5.7g, mono 5g, poly 0.6g); Protein 25.6g; Carb 2.3g; Fiber 0g; Chol 50mg; Iron 1.8mg; Sodium 397mg; Calc 84mg

TEX-MEX MEAT LOAF

PointsPlus value per serving: 7   *pictured on page 131*

HANDS-ON TIME: 13 min. ■ **TOTAL TIME:** 1 hr., 13 min.

Pair this southwestern favorite with Mexican rice and guacamole salad. Spoon fresh salsa over each serving for an extra kick of flavor.

⅔ cup chopped seeded poblano or Anaheim chile
½ cup chopped onion
⅓ cup chopped fresh cilantro
1 teaspoon salt
2 teaspoons roasted ground cumin
2 teaspoons bottled minced roasted garlic
¾ teaspoon chipotle chile powder
4 taco shells (about 1½ ounces), finely crushed
2 egg whites, lightly beaten
1 (15-ounce) can black beans, rinsed and drained
2 pounds ground round
Cooking spray

1. Preheat oven to 375°.
2. Combine first 10 ingredients in a large bowl. Crumble beef over chile mixture, stirring just until blended.
3. Shape meat mixture into a 9 x 5–inch loaf pan coated with cooking spray. Bake at 375° for 50 minutes or until meat loaf registers 160°. Let meat loaf stand 10 minutes in pan. Remove from pan; cut into 10 slices. YIELD: 10 SERVINGS (SERVING SIZE: 1 SLICE).

PER SERVING: Calories 257; Fat 15.2g (sat 5.6g, mono 6.3g, poly 1.1g); Protein 19.6g; Carb 8.7g; Fiber 1.7g; Chol 62mg; Iron 2.5mg; Sodium 390mg; Calc 32mg

GROUND BEEF

When shopping, you'll find lots of ground beef choices. Here are some common terms and what they mean:

- **Ground hamburger:** Ground from the trimmings of any cut of beef. Fat can be added, and total fat content can be up to 30 percent.
- **Ground beef:** Like hamburger, but no *added* fat.
- **Ground chuck:** Beef ground from the shoulder section known as the chuck that contains about 15 to 20 percent fat.
- **Ground round:** From the round (rump to hind leg), about 10 to 15 percent fat.
- **Ground sirloin:** Lean ground sirloin contains about 8 to 10 percent fat.
- **Lean ground beef:** This cut is even leaner, containing 8 percent fat or less.

CLASSIC LASAGNA

PointsPlus value per serving: 8

HANDS-ON TIME: 30 min. ■ **TOTAL TIME:** 1 hr., 15 min.

¾ pound ground beef, extra lean
1½ cups chopped onion
4 garlic cloves, minced
⅓ cup dry red wine
1 teaspoon sugar
½ teaspoon salt
¼ teaspoon crushed red pepper
3 (14.5-ounce) cans no-salt-added diced tomatoes
    with basil, garlic, and oregano, undrained
1 (6-ounce) can no-salt-added tomato paste
¼ cup chopped fresh basil
2 tablespoons chopped fresh oregano
1 (15-ounce) carton fat-free ricotta cheese
1 large egg white
Cooking spray
12 cooked lasagna noodles
4 ounces finely shredded 6-cheese Italian blend cheese
    (about 1 cup)
Basil leaves (optional)

1. Cook beef in a large nonstick skillet over medium heat 5 minutes or until browned, stirring to crumble. Drain beef well, and return to pan. Add onion and garlic; sauté 5 minutes. Stir in wine and next 5 ingredients. Bring to a boil; cover, reduce heat, and simmer 10 minutes. Uncover and simmer 1 to 2 minutes or until slightly thick.
2. Combine basil and next 3 ingredients in a small bowl.
3. Spread ½ cup tomato mixture in bottom of a 13 x 9–inch glass or ceramic baking dish coated with cooking spray. Arrange 4 noodles over tomato mixture; top noodles with 2¼ cups tomato mixture, half of ricotta cheese mixture, and ⅓ cup Italian blend cheese. Repeat layers, ending with noodles. Spread remaining 2 cups tomato mixture over noodles, and sprinkle with remaining ⅓ cup Italian blend cheese.
4. Cover and bake at 350° for 35 minutes. Uncover and bake an additional 10 minutes. Let stand 5 minutes before serving. Garnish with basil leaves, if desired. **YIELD: 9 SERVINGS (SERVING SIZE: ⅑ OF LASAGNA).**

PER SERVING: Calories 305; Fat 5.5g (sat 2.5g, mono 1.7g, poly 0.5g); Protein 21.3g; Carb 41.1g; Fiber 3.3g; Chol 37mg; Iron 3.7mg; Sodium 373mg; Calc 210mg

BEEF STROGANOFF MEATBALLS

PointsPlus value per serving: 9

HANDS-ON TIME: 26 min. ■ **TOTAL TIME:** 35 min.

Adding canola oil to the meatballs helps keep this lean cut of beef moist and tender.

2½ cups uncooked medium egg noodles
1 pound ground beef, extra lean
⅓ cup Italian-seasoned panko (Japanese breadcrumbs)
2 tablespoons canola oil, divided
½ teaspoon salt
¼ teaspoon freshly ground black pepper
1 large egg
1 (8-ounce) package presliced mushrooms
¾ cup fat-free milk
1 (10.75-ounce) can condensed 30% reduced-sodium 98%
    fat-free cream of mushroom soup, undiluted
2 tablespoons chopped fresh parsley

1. Cook pasta according to package directions, omitting salt and fat. Drain; keep warm.
2. While noodles cook, combine beef, panko, 1 tablespoon oil, and next 3 ingredients in a large bowl. Shape mixture into 25 (1-inch) meatballs with moist hands.
3. Heat 1 teaspoon oil in a large nonstick skillet over medium-high heat. Add mushrooms; sauté 8 minutes or until browned. Remove mushrooms from pan, and keep warm.
4. Add 2 teaspoons oil to pan; swirl to coat. Heat oil over medium-high heat. Add meatballs; cook 6 minutes, browning on all sides.
5. Combine milk and soup, stirring with a whisk. Fold in mushrooms. Pour mushroom mixture over meatballs. Cover; reduce heat to medium-low, and cook 8 minutes or until meatballs are done. Serve over noodles, and sprinkle with parsley. **YIELD: 5 SERVINGS (SERVING SIZE: 5 MEATBALLS, ABOUT ½ CUP SAUCE, AND ABOUT ½ CUP NOODLES).**

PER SERVING: Calories 351; Fat 13g (sat 2.7g, mono 6.1g, poly 3g); Protein 27.1g; Carb 31.3g; Fiber 2.2g; Chol 126mg; Iron 2.9mg; Sodium 548mg; Calc 65mg

BEER-BRAISED HONEY-LIME BRISKET

PointsPlus value per serving: 8

HANDS-ON TIME: 14 min. ■ **TOTAL TIME:** 8 hr., 14 min.

Beef brisket needs long, slow cooking to tenderize the meat, making it a perfect candidate for a slow cooker. Be sure to buy an unseasoned brisket instead of a corned beef brisket, which is cured in a seasoned brine and can be high in sodium.

2 tablespoons salt-free fiesta-lime seasoning blend
½ teaspoon salt
1 (3-pound) flat-cut beef brisket, trimmed
1 tablespoon canola oil
1 cup dark Mexican beer
3 garlic cloves, sliced
2 medium onions, sliced
3 tablespoons honey
2 tablespoons fresh lime juice
Chopped fresh cilantro (optional)

1. Combine seasoning blend and salt; rub evenly over both sides of brisket. Heat a large nonstick skillet over medium-high heat. Add oil to pan; swirl to coat. Add brisket; cook 3 minutes on each side or until browned. Transfer brisket to a 5-quart electric slow cooker.
2. Add beer to pan; bring to a boil, scraping pan to loosen browned bits. Pour beer mixture over brisket in slow cooker; top with garlic and onion. Cover and cook on LOW for 8 hours or until brisket is tender.
3. Remove brisket and onion from slow cooker with a slotted spoon. Skim fat from cooking liquid; discard fat. Combine ½ cup cooking liquid, honey, and lime juice in a small bowl, stirring with a whisk. Cut brisket diagonally across grain into thin slices; serve with sauce. Sprinkle with cilantro, if desired. YIELD:8 SERVINGS (SERVING SIZE: 3 OUNCES BRISKET, 3 TABLESPOONS ONION, AND 1½ TABLESPOONS SAUCE).

PER SERVING: Calories 273; Fat 8.3g (sat 2.6g, mono 3.9g, poly 0.8g); Protein 37.1g; Carb 10.1g; Fiber 0.5g; Chol 70mg; Iron 3.4mg; Sodium 274mg; Calc 37mg

LEMON-THYME GRILLED LAMB CHOPS

PointsPlus value per serving: 6

HANDS-ON TIME: 13 min. ■ **TOTAL TIME:** 21 min.

Spraying the chops with cooking spray helps the aromatic coating adhere to the meat. Expect to see a small amount of the rub fall off the chops.

1½ tablespoons chopped fresh thyme
1 tablespoon fresh lemon juice
1 teaspoon grated fresh lemon rind
¼ teaspoon salt
¼ teaspoon freshly ground black pepper
3 garlic cloves, minced
8 (3-ounce) lamb loin chops, trimmed
Cooking spray

1. Preheat grill to medium-high heat.
2. Combine first 6 ingredients in a small bowl. Spray both sides of chops with cooking spray; rub thyme mixture evenly over both sides of chops. Spray rub mixture with cooking spray. Place chops on a grill rack coated with cooking spray; grill 4 minutes on each side or until a thermometer registers 145° (medium-rare). YIELD:4 SERVINGS (SERVING SIZE: 2 CHOPS).

PER SERVING: Calories 251; Fat 10.3g (sat 3.6g, mono 4.2g, poly 1g); Protein 35.8g; Carb 1.5g; Fiber 0.3g; Chol 112mg; Iron 3.5mg; Sodium 264mg; Calc 30mg

LAMB LOIN CHOPS

These versatile chops are affordable and quick-cooking, making them ideal for weeknight meals. Simple seasonings (as in this recipe) work well, or you can marinate overnight so the flavor permeates. For best flavor, grill them, or sear and roast at high heat.

MOLASSES GRILLED PORK TENDERLOIN WITH HORSERADISH SAUCE

PointsPlus value per serving: 6

HANDS-ON TIME: 6 min. ■ **TOTAL TIME:** 8 hr., 34 min.

Our Test Kitchen staff prefers to use unsulphured molasses in our testing due to its thicker consistency and sweeter taste than its sulphured counterpart.

3 tablespoons lower-sodium soy sauce
2 tablespoons molasses
1 teaspoon canola oil
½ teaspoon freshly ground black pepper
2 garlic cloves, crushed
1 (1-pound) pork tenderloin, trimmed
Cooking spray
½ cup light mayonnaise
1 tablespoon fat-free milk
1 tablespoon prepared horseradish
1 teaspoon grated fresh onion
¼ teaspoon freshly ground black pepper

1. Combine first 5 ingredients in a large zip-top plastic bag. Add pork to bag; seal. Marinate in refrigerator at least 8 hours and up to 24 hours, turning bag occasionally. Remove pork from bag, discarding marinade.
2. Preheat grill to medium-high heat.
3. Place pork on grill rack coated with cooking spray; cover and grill 16 to 18 minutes or until a thermometer registers 145° (medium-rare), turning occasionally. Remove pork from grill; cover and let stand 10 minutes.
4. While pork stands, combine mayonnaise and remaining ingredients, stirring well. Cut pork into ½-inch-thick slices; serve with horseradish sauce. YIELD: 4 SERVINGS (SERVING SIZE: 3 OUNCES PORK AND 2 TABLESPOONS SAUCE).

PER SERVING: Calories 232; Fat 12.6g (sat 2.3g, mono 3.5g, poly 5.7g); Protein 24.2g; Carb 3.8g; Fiber 0.2g; Chol 84mg; Iron 1.2mg; Sodium 327mg; Calc 16mg

KUNG PAO PORK

PointsPlus value per serving: 7   *pictured on page 129*

HANDS-ON TIME: 13 min. ■ **TOTAL TIME:** 13 min.

Serve this classic stir-fry over ½ cup of steamed brown or white rice—it'll add a *PointsPlus* value per serving of 3.

¾ cup water
3 tablespoons lower-sodium soy sauce
2 teaspoons cornstarch
1¼ teaspoons crushed red pepper
1 teaspoon brown sugar
½ teaspoon ground ginger paste
2 tablespoons dark sesame oil, divided
1 cup chopped onion
⅔ cup coarsely chopped red bell pepper
⅔ cup coarsely chopped yellow bell pepper
⅔ cup coarsely chopped green bell pepper
2 garlic cloves, minced
1 (1-pound) pork tenderloin, trimmed and cut into
    1-inch pieces
2 tablespoons chopped unsalted, dry-roasted peanuts

1. Combine first 6 ingredients in a bowl, stirring with a whisk until sugar dissolves.
2. Heat a large nonstick skillet over medium-high heat. Add 1 tablespoon oil to pan; swirl to coat. Add onion and bell pepper; stir-fry 3 minutes or until crisp-tender. Add garlic; stir-fry 30 seconds. Remove vegetables from pan; keep warm.
3. Add 1 tablespoon oil to pan; swirl to coat. Add pork; stir-fry 4 minutes or until browned. Return vegetables to pan. Stir soy sauce mixture into pork mixture. Bring to a boil; cook 1 minute or until sauce thickens, stirring constantly. Remove from heat; sprinkle with peanuts. YIELD: 4 SERVINGS (SERVING SIZE: ABOUT 1 CUP).

PER SERVING: Calories 275; Fat 13.6g (sat 2.7g, mono 5.7g, poly 4.5g); Protein 26.5g; Carb 12.2g; Fiber 2.5g; Chol 74mg; Iron 1.8mg; Sodium 358mg; Calc 34mg

SMOKED PORK QUESADILLAS

PointsPlus value per serving: 8

HANDS-ON TIME: 17 min. ■ **TOTAL TIME:** 17 min.

2 tablespoons spicy barbecue sauce
2 tablespoons reduced-fat ranch dressing
4 (8-inch) 96% fat-free whole-wheat tortillas
3 ounces reduced-fat shredded sharp cheddar cheese
    (about ¾ cup)
1 cup (5 ounces) pulled smoked pork
½ cup frozen whole-kernel corn, thawed
2 tablespoons chopped fresh cilantro
Cooking spray
¼ cup reduced-fat sour cream (optional)

1. Combine barbecue sauce and ranch dressing in a small bowl; spread evenly over tortillas. Top half of each tortilla evenly with cheese, pork, corn, and cilantro; fold in half.
2. Heat a large nonstick skillet over medium–high heat. Coat pan with cooking spray. Place 2 tortillas, folded sides together, in pan; coat tops with cooking spray. Cook 1 to 2 minutes on each side or until lightly browned and cheese melts. Remove from pan, and keep warm. Repeat procedure with remaining tortillas. Serve with sour cream, if desired. YIELD: 4 SERVINGS (SERVING SIZE: 1 QUESADILLA).

PER SERVING: Calories 296; Fat 13.1g (sat 5.3g, mono 4.5g, poly 1.3g); Protein 18.3g; Carb 26.5g; Fiber 1.2g; Chol 48mg; Iron 1.3mg; Sodium 513mg; Calc 364mg

GRILLED PORK CHOPS WITH PEACH-MANGO CHUTNEY

PointsPlus value per serving: 8

HANDS-ON TIME: 6 min. ■ **TOTAL TIME:** 16 min.

While the grill is hot, go ahead and throw on some asparagus spears and fresh corn on the cob to serve alongside this summery supper entrée.

4 (6-ounce) bone-in center-cut pork chops (about
    ¾ inch thick), trimmed
¼ teaspoon salt
¼ teaspoon freshly ground black pepper
2 large peeled peaches, halved and pitted
Cooking spray
1 jalapeño pepper, seeded
½ cup mango chutney
2 teaspoons fresh lime juice

1. Preheat grill to medium–high heat.
2. Sprinkle pork evenly with salt and black pepper. Place pork and peach halves, cut sides down, on grill rack coated with cooking spray. Grill peach halves 3 minutes on each side or until browned and tender. Grill pork 5 minutes on each side or until done. Remove pork and peach halves from grill; keep pork warm. Cut each peach half into 3 wedges.
3. With food processor on, drop jalapeño through food chute; process until minced. Add peach wedges, mango chutney, and lime juice, processing just until combined. Serve chutney over pork. YIELD: 4 SERVINGS (SERVING SIZE: 1 CHOP AND ½ CUP CHUTNEY).

PER SERVING: Calories 332; Fat 11.8g (sat 3.8g, mono 4.7g, poly 1.6g); Protein 26.9g; Carb 26.9g; Fiber 1.4g; Chol 87mg; Iron 1.1mg; Sodium 477mg; Calc 30mg

SAUSAGE AND MUSHROOM PIZZA

PointsPlus value per serving: 8

HANDS-ON TIME: 4 min. ■ **TOTAL TIME:** 20 min.

This meaty pie will be on the table way before the pizza delivery guy could arrive. Feel free to substitute a hotter, spicier sausage if you'd like some heat.

4 ounces mild Italian pork sausage
1½ cups sliced cremini mushrooms
⅓ cup thinly sliced onion
1 (9.7-ounce) golden wheat pizza crust
½ cup spicy red pepper pasta sauce
4 ounces preshredded part-skim mozzarella cheese
    (about 1 cup)

1. Preheat oven to 450°.
2. Remove casings from sausage. Cook sausage in a large nonstick skillet over medium–high heat 5 minutes or until browned, stirring to crumble. Drain well; return to pan. Add mushrooms and onion; cook 3 minutes or until vegetables are lightly browned and tender.
3. Place crust on a baking sheet. Spread pasta sauce evenly over crust, leaving a 1-inch border. Spoon sausage mixture evenly over sauce; sprinkle with cheese. Bake at 450° for 8 minutes or until cheese melts. YIELD: 5 SERVINGS (SERVING SIZE: 2 SLICES).

PER SERVING: Calories 290; Fat 12.9g (sat 5.9g, mono 5.5g, poly 1g); Protein 15.9g; Carb 30.7g; Fiber 5.3g; Chol 25mg; Iron 0.5mg; Sodium 669mg; Calc 194mg

poultry

Chicken with Mushroom and Herb Sauce, page 98

HERBED BUTTERMILK "FRIED" CHICKEN

PointsPlus value per serving: 8

HANDS-ON TIME: 12 min. ■ **TOTAL TIME:** 24 hr., 36 min.

Our grandmothers would attest to the fact that marinating chicken up to a day in buttermilk yields the juiciest, most tender fried chicken. We agree—this "fried" chicken earned very high marks. If you can't find cracker meal on the baking aisle of your supermarket, just pulse 10 saltine crackers in a blender or food processor until finely ground.

1 cup low-fat buttermilk
3 tablespoons chopped fresh mixed herbs (such as parsley, basil, thyme, and tarragon)
2 garlic cloves, minced
1 small onion, sliced (1 cup)
2 bone-in chicken breast halves (about 1 pound), skinned
2 chicken drumsticks (about ½ pound), skinned
2 chicken thighs (about ½ pound), skinned
⅓ cup all-purpose flour
⅓ cup cracker meal
½ teaspoon salt
½ teaspoon freshly ground black pepper
1 tablespoon butter
1 tablespoon olive oil

1. Combine first 4 ingredients in a large zip-top plastic bag. Add chicken; seal and marinate in refrigerator 24 hours, turning bag occasionally.
2. Preheat oven to 425°.
3. Combine flour and cracker meal in a shallow dish. Remove chicken from bag, discarding marinade; sprinkle chicken evenly with salt and pepper. Dredge chicken in flour mixture, shaking off excess.
4. Heat a large ovenproof skillet over medium-high heat. Add butter and oil to pan; swirl to coat. Heat pan until butter melts. Add chicken to pan, meaty sides down; cook 4 to 5 minutes or until golden brown. Turn chicken. Transfer pan to oven. Bake at 425° for 20 minutes or until a thermometer registers 165°. YIELD: 4 SERVINGS (SERVING SIZE: 1 BREAST HALF OR 1 EACH DRUMSTICK AND THIGH).

PER SERVING: Calories 331; Fat 10.6g (sat 3.6g, mono 4.6g, poly 1.3g); Protein 34.7g; Carb 22.3g; Fiber 1.2g; Chol 105mg; Iron 2.4mg; Sodium 492mg; Calc 96mg

LEMON-JALAPEÑO ROAST CHICKEN

PointsPlus value per serving: 6

HANDS-ON TIME: 11 min. ■ **TOTAL TIME:** 1 hr., 26 min.

1 (3-pound) whole chicken
Cooking spray
⅓ cup green pepper sauce
3 tablespoons fresh lemon juice
2 garlic cloves, minced
1 jalapeño pepper, seeded and minced
1 cup dry white wine
2 tablespoons butter
4 lemon wedges (optional)
2 tablespoons chopped fresh cilantro (optional)

1. Preheat oven to 400°.
2. Remove and discard giblets and neck from chicken. Remove skin; trim excess fat. Tie ends of legs together with twine. Lift wing tips up and over back; tuck under chicken. Place chicken, breast side up, on a broiler pan coated with cooking spray.
3. Combine pepper sauce and next 3 ingredients; pour into cavity and over chicken. Bake at 400° for 1 hour or until a thermometer registers 165°, basting occasionally with pan drippings. Transfer chicken to a platter; cover and let stand 10 minutes.
4. Remove any charred bits from pan. Add wine to pan drippings, scraping pan to loosen browned bits. Pour wine mixture into a small saucepan; bring to a boil over medium heat. Cook until mixture is reduced to ⅔ cup, stirring occasionally. Add butter, stirring with a whisk until melted.
5. Cut chicken into quarters. Serve chicken with wine mixture. Garnish with lemon wedges and cilantro, if desired. YIELD: 4 SERVINGS (SERVING SIZE: 1 BREAST HALF OR 1 LEG QUARTER AND 3 TABLESPOONS WINE MIXTURE).

PER SERVING: Calories 286; Fat 10.8g (sat 4.8g, mono 3g, poly 1.5g); Protein 35.8g; Carb 2.9g; Fiber 0.3g; Chol 128mg; Iron 2.1mg; Sodium 292mg; Calc 29mg

ROAST CHICKEN

The most critical step when preparing roast chicken is cooking it to the proper internal temperature. Insert a meat thermometer into a meaty part of the leg (avoiding the bone). When the temperature reaches 165°, pull the bird from the oven. Let it rest for 10 minutes so the juices will redistribute throughout the meat.

SUN-DRIED TOMATO AND GOAT CHEESE–TOPPED CHICKEN

PointsPlus value per serving: 6

HANDS-ON TIME: 7 min. ▪ **TOTAL TIME:** 24 min.

So quick and full of flavor, this quick entrée will become a favorite go-to for easy weeknight suppers.

4 (6-ounce) skinless, boneless chicken breast halves
¼ teaspoon freshly ground black pepper
⅛ teaspoon salt
1 teaspoon olive oil
2 ounces crumbled goat cheese (about ½ cup)
¼ cup chopped fresh basil
¼ cup sun-dried tomato pesto
¼ teaspoon grated fresh lemon rind

1. Sprinkle chicken evenly with pepper and salt. Heat a large nonstick skillet over medium-high heat. Add oil to pan; swirl to coat. Add chicken; cook 8 to 10 minutes on each side or until chicken is done.
2. Combine goat cheese and remaining ingredients in a small bowl. Top each breast half with 2 heaping tablespoons goat cheese mixture; cover and cook 1 to 2 minutes or until cheese melts. YIELD: 4 SERVINGS (SERVING SIZE: 1 TOPPED CHICKEN BREAST HALF).

PER SERVING: Calories 259; Fat 7.5g (sat 3g, mono 2.6g, poly 0.9g); Protein 42.8g; Carb 2.3g; Fiber 0.3g; Chol 105mg; Iron 1.9mg; Sodium 394mg; Calc 44mg

CREAMY CHICKEN AND RICE CASSEROLE

PointsPlus value per serving: 8

HANDS-ON TIME: 12 min. ▪ **TOTAL TIME:** 55 min.

Traditional chicken and rice casserole clocks in with a *PointsPlus* value per serving of 18. This lightened version offers the same hearty comfort with significantly fewer calories and less saturated fat and sodium.

2 (8.8-ounce) packages butter-and-garlic flavored instant rice
Cooking spray
1½ pounds skinless, boneless chicken breast, cut into bite-sized pieces
¾ cup fat-free sour cream
½ teaspoon freshly ground black pepper
1 (10¾-ounce) can condensed reduced-fat, reduced-sodium cream of mushroom soup, undiluted
⅔ cup crushed multigrain crackers

1. Prepare rice according to package directions.
2. Preheat oven to 350°.
3. Heat a large nonstick skillet over medium-high heat; coat pan with cooking spray. Add chicken; sauté 6 to 8 minutes or until browned. Stir in prepared rice, sour cream, pepper, and soup.
4. Coat an 8-inch square glass or ceramic baking dish with cooking spray. Spoon chicken mixture into prepared baking dish; sprinkle evenly with cracker crumbs. Spray crumbs liberally with cooking spray. Bake at 350° for 35 minutes or until bubbly. YIELD: 6 SERVINGS (SERVING SIZE: 1¼ CUPS).

PER SERVING: Calories 338; Fat 5.7g (sat 1.4g, mono 2g, poly 1.5g); Protein 31.3g; Carb 37.2g; Fiber 2g; Chol 71mg; Iron 1.9mg; Sodium 771mg; Calc 101mg

CHICKEN WITH MUSHROOM AND HERB SAUCE

PointsPlus value per serving: 6   *pictured on page 131*

HANDS-ON TIME: 10 min. ■ **TOTAL TIME:** 29 min.

Substitute ¼ teaspoon dried thyme if fresh isn't available.

½ cup fat-free, lower-sodium chicken broth
½ teaspoon chopped fresh thyme
1 (10.75-ounce) can condensed 30% reduced-sodium, 98% fat-free cream of mushroom soup, undiluted
4 (6-ounce) skinless, boneless chicken breast halves
¼ teaspoon freshly ground black pepper
⅛ teaspoon salt
1 teaspoon olive oil
1 (8-ounce) package presliced mushrooms
Chopped thyme (optional)

1. Combine first 3 ingredients in a medium bowl. Sprinkle chicken with pepper and salt.
2. Heat a large nonstick skillet over medium–high heat. Add oil to pan; swirl to coat. Add chicken; cook 3 to 4 minutes on each side or until browned. Remove chicken from pan.
3. Add mushrooms to pan; sauté 2 minutes. Reduce heat to medium; return chicken to pan. Pour soup mixture over chicken and mushrooms. Cover and cook 11 minutes or until mushrooms are tender and chicken is done, stirring once. Transfer chicken to a platter. Pour mushroom mixture over chicken. Garnish with thyme sprigs, if desired. YIELD: 4 SERVINGS (SERVING SIZE: 1 CHICKEN BREAST HALF AND ABOUT ⅓ CUP SAUCE).

PER SERVING: Calories 254; Fat 4.6g (sat 1g, mono 1.6g, poly 1.2g); Protein 41.7g; Carb 8.3g; Fiber 0.7g; Chol 102mg; Iron 1.4mg; Sodium 538mg; Calc 22mg

GRILLED CHICKEN WITH MANGO–BLACK BEAN SALSA

PointsPlus value per serving: 6

HANDS-ON TIME: 16 min. ■ **TOTAL TIME:** 26 min.

This taste of the tropics couldn't be any easier. Serve with fresh watermelon. If you'd like some heat in the salsa, leave the seeds in the jalapeño.

1 cup chopped peeled mango
½ cup canned lower-sodium black beans, rinsed and drained
¼ cup chopped red onion
2 tablespoons chopped fresh cilantro
1 tablespoon fresh lime juice
1 jalapeño pepper, seeded and finely chopped
4 (6-ounce) skinless, boneless chicken breast halves
¼ teaspoon freshly ground black pepper
¼ teaspoon salt-free fiesta-lime seasoning blend
⅛ teaspoon salt
Cooking spray

1. Preheat grill to medium–high heat.
2. Combine first 6 ingredients in a small bowl; set aside.
3. Sprinkle chicken evenly on both sides with pepper, seasoning blend, and salt. Coat chicken on both sides with cooking spray. Place chicken on grill rack coated with cooking spray, and grill 5 minutes on each side or until chicken is done.
4. Cut chicken diagonally across grain into ¼-inch-thick slices. Serve mango salsa over chicken. YIELD: 4 SERVINGS (SERVING SIZE: 1 SLICED CHICKEN BREAST HALF AND 6 TABLESPOONS SALSA).

PER SERVING: Calories 240; Fat 2.5g (sat 0.6g, mono 0.7g, poly 0.5g); Protein 40.9g; Carb 12.8g; Fiber 2.6g; Chol 99mg; Iron 1.8mg; Sodium 225mg; Calc 37mg

CHICKEN FETTUCCINE WITH WALNUT-FETA PESTO SAUCE

PointsPlus value per serving: 8

HANDS-ON TIME: 12 min. ■ **TOTAL TIME:** 17 min.

Toss the remaining pesto sauce with cooked tortellini for a quick lunch.

4 (6-ounce) skinless, boneless chicken breast halves
1 tablespoon salt-free garlic and herb seasoning blend
⅛ teaspoon salt
Cooking spray
2 garlic cloves, peeled
2 cups loosely packed basil leaves
¼ cup chopped walnuts, toasted
1 cup plain fat-free yogurt
1 (4-ounce) package crumbled feta cheese
½ teaspoon grated fresh lemon rind
3 cups hot cooked fettuccine (about 6 ounces uncooked pasta)

1. Preheat grill to high heat.
2. Sprinkle chicken evenly on both sides with seasoning blend and salt. Coat chicken on both sides with cooking spray. Place chicken on grill rack coated with cooking spray; cook 5 minutes on each side or until chicken is done. Remove from grill; cover and let stand 5 minutes.
3. While chicken grills, drop garlic through food chute with food processor on; process until minced. Add basil and walnuts; process until finely chopped. Add yogurt, cheese, and rind; process until smooth. Combine 1 cup pesto mixture and fettuccine; toss to coat. Reserve remaining pesto mixture for another use.
4. Cut chicken diagonally across grain into ½-inch-thick slices. Combine chicken and pasta mixture, tossing to coat. **YIELD: 6 SERVINGS (SERVING SIZE: ABOUT ¾ CUP).**

PER SERVING: Calories 332; Fat 9.2g (sat 3.6g, mono 2g, poly 3.2g); Protein 35.6g; Carb 26.4g; Fiber 1.5g; Chol 83mg; Iron 2.5mg; Sodium 359mg; Calc 192mg

LEMON RIND

Grated fresh lemon rind adds a wonderful brightness to a variety of dishes. When grating lemon rind, make sure you only remove the yellow skin. If you've reached the layer of white beneath (called the pith) and grate some more, you'll end up with a bitter finish to your dish.

PEANUTTY CHICKEN LETTUCE CUPS

PointsPlus value per serving: 7

HANDS-ON TIME: 17 min. ■ **TOTAL TIME:** 17 min.

Peanut sauce combines the classic Thai flavors of garlic, soy, chiles, and peanuts, lending a distinct Asian flair to this recipe.

4 (6-ounce) skinless, boneless chicken breast halves
1 tablespoon sesame oil
1½ cups thinly sliced onion
1½ cups (¼-inch-thick) red bell pepper strips
Cooking spray
3 tablespoons peanut sauce
12 large Boston or iceberg lettuce leaves
2 tablespoons chopped unsalted, dry-roasted peanuts

1. Cut each chicken breast crosswise into ½-inch-thick slices. Heat a large nonstick skillet over medium-high heat. Add oil to pan; swirl to coat. Add half of chicken; cook 2 minutes on each side or until browned. Remove chicken from pan; keep warm. Repeat procedure with remaining half of chicken.
2. Reduce heat to medium. Add onion and bell pepper to pan; coat vegetables with cooking spray. Sauté 5 minutes or until tender. Remove pan from heat; add chicken and peanut sauce to pan, tossing to coat.
3. Place ⅓ cup chicken mixture in center of each lettuce leaf; sprinkle evenly with peanuts. Serve immediately.
YIELD: 4 SERVINGS (SERVING SIZE: 3 LETTUCE CUPS).

PER SERVING: Calories 313; Fat 10.2g (sat 1.8g, mono 4g, poly 3.2g); Protein 42.5g; Carb 11.1g; Fiber 2.3g; Chol 99mg; Iron 2.1mg; Sodium 304mg; Calc 49mg

CHICKEN CORDON BLEU

PointsPlus value per serving: 6

HANDS-ON TIME: 7 min. ■ **TOTAL TIME:** 32 min.

Serve this dish with roasted potatoes and steamed green beans.

3 tablespoons reduced-fat mayonnaise
2 teaspoons Dijon mustard
1 garlic clove, minced
4 (4-ounce) chicken cutlets
¼ teaspoon freshly ground black pepper
⅛ teaspoon salt
2 (1-ounce) slices ⅓-less-fat Swiss cheese, cut in half
2 (1-ounce) slices 33%-less-sodium ham, cut in half
⅓ cup dry breadcrumbs
Cooking spray

1. Preheat oven to 375°.
2. Combine first 3 ingredients in a small bowl. Sprinkle both sides of cutlets evenly with pepper and salt. Spread 2 teaspoons mayonnaise mixture over one side of each cutlet; top each with 1 cheese slice and 1 ham slice. Roll up cutlets jelly-roll fashion.
3. Spread remaining mayonnaise mixture over chicken; coat with breadcrumbs. Place rolls, seam sides down, in an 8-inch square glass or ceramic baking dish coated with cooking spray. Coat rolls with cooking spray. Bake at 375° for 25 minutes or until browned and chicken is done. YIELD: 4 SERVINGS (SERVING SIZE: 1 CHICKEN ROLL).

PER SERVING: Calories 241; Fat 6.6g (sat 2.2g, mono 1.9g, poly 1.7g); Protein 34.7g; Carb 10g; Fiber 0.5g; Chol 79mg; Iron 1.4mg; Sodium 508mg; Calc 166mg

CHICKEN CUTLETS MARSALA

PointsPlus value per serving: 7

HANDS-ON TIME: 14 min. ■ **TOTAL TIME:** 19 min.

The flour coating on the cutlets combines with the sweet Marsala wine to create a rich, rosemary-scented sauce.

Cooking spray
2 (8-ounce) packages presliced cremini mushrooms
2 teaspoons chopped fresh rosemary
½ teaspoon salt, divided
½ teaspoon freshly ground black pepper, divided
4 (4-ounce) chicken cutlets
¼ cup all-purpose flour
4 teaspoons olive oil
½ cup sweet Marsala wine

1. Heat a large nonstick skillet over medium heat. Coat pan with cooking spray. Add mushrooms to pan; sauté 8 minutes or until browned and tender. Stir in rosemary, ¼ teaspoon salt, and ¼ teaspoon pepper. Remove mushroom mixture from pan; set aside, and keep warm.
2. Sprinkle cutlets evenly with remaining ¼ teaspoon salt and remaining ¼ teaspoon pepper. Place flour in a shallow dish. Dredge cutlets in flour, shaking off excess flour.
3. Heat pan over medium heat. Add oil to pan; swirl to coat. Add cutlets to pan; cook 1 to 2 minutes on each side or until browned. Add wine; cover and cook 3 minutes. Remove from heat; stir in mushroom mixture. YIELD: 4 SERVINGS (SERVING SIZE: 1 CUTLET AND ½ CUP MUSHROOM MIXTURE).

PER SERVING: Calories 268; Fat 6.3g (sat 1g, mono 3.6g, poly 0.9g); Protein 29.9g; Carb 14.4g; Fiber 1g; Chol 66mg; Iron 1.8mg; Sodium 378mg; Calc 38mg

BREADED CHICKEN CUTLETS WITH SUN-DRIED TOMATO AIOLI

PointsPlus value per serving: 7   *pictured on page 135*

HANDS-ON TIME: 5 min. ■ **TOTAL TIME:** 13 min.

Panko (also known as Japanese breadcrumbs) are much crisper than traditional breadcrumbs. They mimic the delicious crunchy texture of fried foods with less fat. The aioli is a delicious accompaniment, but these cutlets are tasty on their own.

4 (4-ounce) chicken cutlets
¼ teaspoon salt
¼ teaspoon freshly ground black pepper
1 large egg, lightly beaten
¾ cup Italian-seasoned panko (Japanese breadcrumbs)
1 tablespoon olive oil
⅓ cup light mayonnaise
3 tablespoons chopped drained oil-packed sun-dried
    tomatoes
1 tablespoon chopped fresh basil

1. Sprinkle chicken evenly with salt and pepper. Place egg in a shallow dish; place panko in another shallow dish. Dip chicken in egg; dredge in panko.
2. Heat a large nonstick skillet over medium heat. Add oil to pan; swirl to coat. Add chicken to pan; cook 4 minutes on each side or until done.
3. Combine mayonnaise, tomatoes, and basil in a small bowl; serve with chicken. **YIELD: 4 SERVINGS (SERVING SIZE: 1 CUTLET AND 1½ TABLESPOONS AIOLI).**

PER SERVING: Calories 296; Fat 13.6g (sat 2.3g, mono 5.2g, poly 5g); Protein 29.3g; Carb 11.5g; Fiber 0.4g; Chol 126mg; Iron 1.5mg; Sodium 454mg; Calc 24mg

CHICKEN CUTLETS

These lean pieces of chicken are ideal for weeknight dinners because they're thin and cook quickly. They're perfect for broiling, sautéing, grilling, and pan-frying (as in this recipe). If you only have chicken breasts in your fridge, you can make your own cutlets. Place one chicken breast on a cutting board, and, using a sharp knife, cut the breast in half horizontally with the knife parallel to the cutting board. Using a meat mallet or small heavy skillet, pound each half to a ¼-inch-thickness.

PARMESAN-CRUSTED CHICKEN TENDERS

PointsPlus value per serving: 6

HANDS-ON TIME: 6 min. ■ **TOTAL TIME:** 26 min.

¾ cup Italian-seasoned panko (Japanese breadcrumbs)
2 ounces grated fresh Parmesan cheese (about ½ cup)
1 teaspoon dried thyme
1 large egg white, lightly beaten
8 chicken breast tenders (about 1 pound)
¼ teaspoon freshly ground black pepper
⅛ teaspoon salt
Cooking spray

1. Preheat oven to 400°.
2. Combine first 3 ingredients in a shallow dish. Place egg white in a bowl. Sprinkle chicken with pepper and salt. Dip chicken in egg white; dredge in panko mixture. Place chicken on a baking sheet coated with cooking spray. Coat chicken with cooking spray.
3. Bake at 400° for 10 minutes; turn chicken over, and coat with cooking spray. Bake an additional 10 minutes or until golden brown. **YIELD: 4 SERVINGS (SERVING SIZE: 2 CHICKEN TENDERS).**

PER SERVING: Calories 226; Fat 5.1g (sat 2.5g, mono 1.5g, poly 0.6g); Protein 33.6g; Carb 12.2g; Fiber 1.7g; Chol 79mg; Iron 1.5mg; Sodium 454mg; Calc 161mg

On average, 1 tablespoon of peanut butter has 100 calories and 8 grams of total fat. While the amount of fat may seem high, the majority of it is good-for-your-heart unsaturated fat. One tablespoon also contains 4 grams of high-quality protein. Be sure to go for the real deal. Reduced-fat spreads offer little calorie savings, and you're losing healthy fats in the switch. Plus, the full-fat varieties trump reduced-fat flavor.

Be certain to check the ingredient list, too, and make sure it doesn't contain partially hydrogenated fats, which indicates the product contains unhealthy trans fats that have been linked to an increased risk of heart disease. Fully hydrogenated fats are OK.

MALAYSIAN PIZZAS

PointsPlus value per serving: 9

HANDS-ON TIME: 5 min. ■ **TOTAL TIME:** 22 min.

Be sure to cook the spicy peanut sauce in a skillet; the extra surface area allows the sauce to thicken quickly. While the sauce thickens, get the pizza toppings ready to go on the crusts, and dinner will be ready in minutes.

- ½ cup rice vinegar
- 3 tablespoons brown sugar
- 3 tablespoons lower-sodium soy sauce
- 2 tablespoons water
- 2 tablespoons ginger spice blend paste
- 4 teaspoons crunchy peanut butter
- ½ teaspoon crushed red pepper
- 1½ teaspoons minced garlic
- 1⅓ cups chopped cooked chicken breast
- 4 (6-inch) pitas
- 2 ounces shredded 6-cheese Italian blend cheese (about ½ cup)
- ¼ cup sliced green onions

1. Preheat oven to 450°.
2. Bring first 8 ingredients to a boil in an 8-inch non-stick skillet over medium-high heat. Cook 6 minutes or until thick, stirring frequently. (Mixture will be consistency of syrup.) Add chicken to sauce, stirring to coat.
3. Place pitas on a large baking sheet. Spread about ⅓ cup chicken mixture over each pita. Sprinkle 2 tablespoons cheese over each pizza.

4. Bake at 450° for 8 minutes or until thoroughly heated and lightly browned around edges. Sprinkle with green onions. YIELD: 4 SERVINGS (SERVING SIZE: 1 PIZZA).

PER SERVING: Calories 357; Fat 8.1g (sat 3g, mono 3g, poly 1.3g); Protein 27.2g; Carb 43.3g; Fiber 1.7g; Chol 50mg; Iron 3.6mg; Sodium 616mg; Calc 161mg

SMOKED CHICKEN–PESTO PIZZA

PointsPlus value per serving: 7   *pictured on page 130*

HANDS-ON TIME: 7 min. ■ **TOTAL TIME:** 22 min.

The tomatoes will release some moisture as they cook, so be sure to place them on top to avoid a soggy crust. Substitute rotisserie chicken or smoked turkey for the smoked chicken, if you like.

- 1 pound refrigerated fresh pizza dough
- Cooking spray
- 3 tablespoons commercial pesto
- ½ pound shredded smoked chicken
- 4 ounces shredded part-skim mozzarella cheese (about 1 cup)
- 1 cup grape tomatoes, halved
- 2 tablespoons chopped fresh basil

1. Preheat oven to 450°.
2. Roll dough into a 12-inch circle; place on a baking sheet coated with cooking spray. Spread pesto over crust, leaving a ½-inch border. Top with chicken, cheese, and tomato.
3. Bake at 450° for 15 minutes or until crust is golden brown. Sprinkle pizza with basil. Cut pizza into 8 wedges. YIELD: 8 SERVINGS (SERVING SIZE: 1 WEDGE).

PER SERVING: Calories 269; Fat 7.5g (sat 1.8g, mono 2.8g, poly 1.5g); Protein 18.6g; Carb 31.7g; Fiber 1.4g; Chol 31mg; Iron 2.3mg; Sodium 522mg; Calc 124mg

CHICKEN CHILAQUILES VERDES

PointsPlus value per serving: 7

HANDS-ON TIME: 9 min. ■ **TOTAL TIME:** 45 min.

Chilaquiles is a traditional Mexican dish in which green or red salsa is poured over crispy tortilla triangles. Shredded chicken is sometimes thrown into the mix, as in this recipe.

8 (6-inch) corn tortillas, quartered
1½ cups salsa verde
⅓ cup light sour cream
2 teaspoons olive oil
¾ cup chopped onion
2 cups shredded skinless, boneless rotisserie
    chicken breast
½ teaspoon chili powder
½ teaspoon ground cumin
Cooking spray
4 ounces reduced-fat shredded jalapeño cheddar
    cheese (about 1 cup)
Chopped fresh cilantro (optional)

1. Preheat oven to 375°.
2. Place tortillas on a large baking sheet. Bake at 375° for 15 minutes or until crisp.
3. While tortillas bake, combine salsa verde and sour cream in a small bowl; set aside.
4. Heat a large nonstick skillet over medium-high heat. Add oil to pan; swirl to coat. Add onion, and sauté 3 minutes or until tender. Stir in chicken, chili powder, and cumin.
5. Place half of tortillas in an 11 x 7–inch glass or ceramic baking dish coated with cooking spray. Top with half of chicken mixture, half of salsa verde mixture, and ½ cup cheese. Repeat layers with remaining tortillas, chicken mixture, salsa verde mixture, and ½ cup cheese. Bake at 375° for 25 minutes or until browned. Sprinkle with cilantro, if desired. Serve immediately. **YIELD: 6 SERVINGS (SERVING SIZE: ⅙ OF CHILAQUILES).**

PER SERVING: Calories 286; Fat 9.5g (sat 3.4g, mono 2.5g, poly 1g); Protein 21.9g; Carb 26.7g; Fiber 1.7g; Chol 54mg; Iron 0.6mg; Sodium 677mg; Calc 166mg

MEXICAN CHICKEN SPAGHETTI

PointsPlus value per serving: 7

HANDS-ON TIME: 10 min. ■ **TOTAL TIME:** 20 min.

2 cups fresh pico de gallo
1 cup fresh corn kernels (about 2 ears)
1 tablespoon finely chopped seeded
    jalapeño pepper
1 tablespoon extra-virgin olive oil
1 tablespoon fresh lime juice
½ teaspoon ground cumin
⅛ teaspoon kosher salt
1 (15-ounce) can no-salt-added black beans,
    rinsed and drained
2 cups hot cooked angel hair (about 4 ounces
    uncooked pasta)
2 cups chopped cooked chicken breast
½ cup chopped fresh cilantro
4 ounces crumbled queso fresco cheese
    (about 1 cup)

1. Combine first 8 ingredients in a large bowl; toss gently. Let stand 10 minutes. Add pasta, chicken, cilantro, and cheese; toss well. **YIELD: 6 SERVINGS (SERVING SIZE: 1⅓ CUPS).**

PER SERVING: Calories 285; Fat 6.4g (sat 1.9g, mono 3g, poly 0.9g); Protein 22.9g; Carb 32.2g; Fiber 3.8g; Chol 46mg; Iron 2.9mg; Sodium 614mg; Calc 89mg

HOW TO DE-KERNEL CORN

To de-kernel corn, cut about ½ inch from the top of each ear to create a flat base on which to stand the cob while removing the kernels. Stand the cob upright on a plate or in a bowl to catch the kernels, and use a sharp knife to cut off the kernels.

LINGUINE WITH CHICKEN RAGÙ

PointsPlus value per serving: 8

HANDS-ON TIME: 6 min. ■ **TOTAL TIME:** 15 min.

6 ounces uncooked linguine
Cooking spray
¾ pound skinless, boneless chicken thighs, cut into
　　½-inch pieces
1 cup chopped onion
3 garlic cloves, minced
¼ cup dry white wine
1¾ cups canned crushed tomatoes
¼ teaspoon freshly ground black pepper
⅛ teaspoon salt
2 tablespoons chopped fresh basil
1 ounce grated fresh Parmesan cheese (about ¼ cup)

1. Cook pasta according to package directions, omitting salt and fat. Drain.
2. While pasta cooks, heat a large nonstick skillet over medium-high heat. Coat pan with cooking spray. Add chicken to pan; cook 6 minutes or until done, stirring occasionally. Remove chicken from pan; keep warm.
3. Add onion and garlic to pan; sauté 2 minutes or just until onion is tender. Add wine, scraping pan to loosen browned bits. Add chicken, tomatoes, pepper, and salt; cook 1 minute or until heated through. Stir in basil. Spoon chicken mixture over pasta, and sprinkle with cheese. YIELD: 4 SERVINGS (SERVING SIZE: ¾ CUP PASTA, ¾ CUP SAUCE, AND 1 TABLESPOON CHEESE).

PER SERVING: Calories 352; Fat 6.2g (sat 2.3g, mono 1.7g, poly 1.2g); Protein 27.6g; Carb 43.9g; Fiber 3.9g; Chol 77mg; Iron 3.8mg; Sodium 426mg; Calc 147mg

ONE-DISH SOUTHWESTERN CHICKEN

PointsPlus value per serving: 7

HANDS-ON TIME: 5 min. ■ **TOTAL TIME:** 19 min.

Boneless, skinless chicken thighs are just about the best buy in the meat case. They have lots of flavor and stay moist when cooked.

2 teaspoons olive oil
1 tablespoon salt-free Southwest chipotle
　　seasoning blend
8 (3-ounce) skinless, boneless chicken thighs, trimmed
1 (15-ounce) can black beans, rinsed and drained
1 (14.5-ounce) can diced tomatoes with green pepper
　　and onion, undrained
¼ cup chopped fresh cilantro

1. Heat a large nonstick skillet over medium-high heat. Add oil to pan; swirl to coat. Sprinkle seasoning blend evenly over chicken. Add chicken to pan; cook 3 minutes. Reduce heat to medium; turn chicken, and cook 3 minutes. Add beans and tomatoes; cover and simmer 8 minutes or until chicken is done. Sprinkle with cilantro. YIELD: 4 SERVINGS (SERVING SIZE: 2 THIGHS AND ½ CUP TOMATO MIXTURE).

PER SERVING: Calories 316; Fat 9.2g (sat 2g, mono 3.7g, poly 2g); Protein 37.7g; Carb 18g; Fiber 4.5g; Chol 141mg; Iron 3.2mg; Sodium 491mg; Calc 73mg

MAPLE-CHIPOTLE DRUMSTICKS

PointsPlus value per serving: 5

HANDS-ON TIME: 7 min. ■ **TOTAL TIME:** 27 min.

Wait to brush on the sweet sauce until the chicken is almost done. The sugary syrup will burn if cooked too long.

¼ cup maple syrup
3 tablespoons cider vinegar
2 teaspoons finely chopped chipotle chiles, canned
　　in adobo sauce
8 chicken drumsticks (about 2 pounds), skinned
¼ teaspoon salt
¼ teaspoon freshly ground black pepper
Cooking spray
2 tablespoons chopped fresh cilantro

1. Preheat grill to medium-high heat.
2. Combine first 3 ingredients in a small saucepan, stirring with a whisk. Bring to a boil; cook until reduced to ⅓ cup (about 2 minutes). Reserve 2 tablespoons sauce mixture.
3. Sprinkle chicken evenly with salt and black pepper; coat chicken with cooking spray. Place chicken on grill rack coated with cooking spray; grill 15 minutes. Turn chicken, and brush with sauce mixture; grill 5 minutes or until done. Remove chicken from grill, and brush with reserved 2 tablespoons sauce; sprinkle evenly with cilantro. YIELD: 4 SERVINGS (SERVING SIZE: 2 DRUMSTICKS).

PER SERVING: Calories 208; Fat 4.5g (sat 1.1g, mono 1.5g, poly 1.1g); Protein 26.2g; Carb 13.9g; Fiber 0.3g; Chol 98mg; Iron 1.6mg; Sodium 289mg; Calc 29mg

GREEK BRAISED CHICKEN THIGHS

PointsPlus value per serving: 9   *pictured on page 133*

HANDS-ON TIME: 10 min. ■ **TOTAL TIME:** 1 hr., 53 min.

The rich sauce paired with moist chicken thighs creates a phenomenal one-dish meal that earned one of our Test Kitchen's highest ratings. Use kitchen shears to chop the stewed tomatoes right in the can. Garnish with additional chopped fresh oregano, if you'd like.

¼ cup fresh lemon juice
1 teaspoon salt-free Greek seasoning
1 teaspoon paprika
½ teaspoon freshly ground black pepper
⅛ teaspoon salt
8 bone-in chicken thighs (about 2 pounds), skinned
2 teaspoons canola oil, divided
1 cup chopped onion
3 garlic cloves, minced
2 (14.5-ounce) cans no-salt-added stewed
    tomatoes with onions, celery, and green
    peppers, undrained and chopped
⅓ cup tomato paste
¼ cup sliced pitted kalamata olives (10 olives)
2 tablespoons chopped fresh oregano

1. Combine first 5 ingredients in a large heavy-duty zip-top plastic bag. Add chicken to bag; seal. Marinate in refrigerator at least 1 hour, turning once. Remove chicken from marinade, reserving marinade. Pat chicken dry.
2. Heat a Dutch oven over high heat. Add 1 teaspoon oil to pan; swirl to coat. Add half of chicken to pan; cook 3 minutes on each side or until browned. Remove chicken from pan, and keep warm. Repeat procedure with remaining oil and chicken.
3. Add onion and garlic to pan; sauté 3 minutes. Stir in reserved marinade, tomatoes, and next 3 ingredients. Return chicken to pan. Bring to a boil. Cover, reduce heat, and simmer 30 minutes or until chicken is tender.
YIELD: 4 SERVINGS (SERVING SIZE: 2 CHICKEN THIGHS AND ABOUT 1¼ CUPS SAUCE).

PER SERVING: Calories 362; Fat 16.2g (sat 3.6g, mono 7.6g, poly 3.6g); Protein 29.9g; Carb 26g; Fiber 5.3g; Chol 97mg; Iron 2.9mg; Sodium 421mg; Calc 81mg

THAI CHICKEN PATTIES

PointsPlus value per serving: 5

HANDS-ON TIME: 9 min. ■ **TOTAL TIME:** 33 min.

Serve these Asian-inspired patties over rice vermicelli or rice noodles instead of napa cabbage, if you'd like—½ cup has a **PointsPlus** value per serving of 2.

1 teaspoon dark sesame oil
¼ cup finely chopped green onions
¼ cup finely chopped carrot
¼ cup finely chopped celery
2 garlic cloves, minced
1½ pounds ground chicken
1 cup cooked long-grain rice
3 tablespoons lower-sodium soy sauce
1 teaspoon ground ginger paste
Cooking spray
3 cups thinly shredded napa (Chinese) cabbage
3 tablespoons Bangkok padang peanut sauce
2 tablespoons finely chopped unsalted, dry-roasted
    peanuts

1. Heat a large nonstick skillet over medium-high heat. Add oil to pan; swirl to coat. Add green onions, carrot, and celery to pan; sauté 3 to 4 minutes or until tender. Add garlic; sauté 1 minute.
2. Transfer vegetable mixture to a large bowl; stir in chicken and next 3 ingredients. Divide mixture into 16 equal portions, shaping each into a 2-inch patty.
3. Heat pan over medium-high heat. Coat pan with cooking spray. Add 8 patties to pan; cook 5 minutes on each side or until done. Repeat procedure with remaining 8 patties. Place cabbage on a large platter. Place patties on cabbage; drizzle evenly with peanut sauce, and sprinkle evenly with peanuts. YIELD: 8 SERVINGS (SERVING SIZE: 2 PATTIES, ABOUT ⅓ CUP CABBAGE, ABOUT 1 TEASPOON PEANUT SAUCE, AND ¾ TEASPOON PEANUTS).

PER SERVING: Calories 189; Fat 9.6g (sat 2.3g, mono 4.3g, poly 2.1g); Protein 15.8g; Carb 10.2g; Fiber 1g; Chol 56mg; Iron 0.4mg; Sodium 300mg; Calc 33mg

APPLE CHICKEN SAUSAGE WITH KRAUT

PointsPlus value per serving: 5

HANDS-ON TIME: 18 min. ■ **TOTAL TIME:** 18 min.

Ideal for a chilly fall evening, this hearty German-inspired one-skillet meal is sure to warm you up.

Cooking spray
1 (12-ounce) package chicken apple sausage, cut into ½-inch pieces
1 medium onion, vertically sliced
1 cup fat-free, lower-sodium chicken broth
¼ cup Dijon mustard
1 (25-ounce) jar refrigerated sauerkraut, drained
3 cups cooked medium egg noodles
2 tablespoons chopped fresh flat-leaf parsley (optional)

1. Heat a large nonstick skillet over medium–high heat. Coat pan with cooking spray. Add sausage and onion to pan; sauté 4 minutes or until sausage is lightly browned. Reduce heat to medium.
2. Combine broth and mustard in a small bowl; add to sausage mixture. Bring to a boil; cook 4 minutes, stirring occasionally. Add sauerkraut; cook 1 minute, stirring constantly. Stir in noodles, tossing to combine. Sprinkle with parsley, if desired. YIELD: 8 SERVINGS (SERVING SIZE: 1 CUP).

PER SERVING: Calories 177; Fat 7.7g (sat 2.2g, mono 3.2g, poly 0.5g); Protein 9.4g; Carb 17.9g; Fiber 1.9g; Chol 58mg; Iron 0.8mg; Sodium 866mg; Calc 9mg

ROSEMARY ROASTED TURKEY TENDERLOINS

PointsPlus value per serving: 5

HANDS-ON TIME: 12 min. ■ **TOTAL TIME:** 59 min.

Basting the tenderloins with the rosemary-scented apple juice mixture keeps the turkey tender, juicy, and flavorful.

2 (12-ounce) turkey tenderloins
⅜ teaspoon salt
¼ teaspoon freshly ground black pepper
Cooking spray
½ cup fat-free, lower-sodium chicken broth
⅓ cup frozen apple juice concentrate, thawed
2 tablespoons chopped fresh rosemary
1 garlic clove, minced

1. Preheat oven to 425°.
2. Sprinkle turkey evenly with salt and pepper. Place turkey on a foil-lined broiler pan coated with cooking spray.
3. Combine broth and remaining ingredients in a small bowl; reserve half of mixture. Brush remaining half of broth mixture evenly over turkey.
4. Bake at 425° for 37 minutes or until a thermometer registers 165°, basting occasionally with remaining broth mixture. Let stand 10 minutes. Cut each tenderloin into 8 slices. YIELD: 4 SERVINGS (SERVING SIZE: 4 SLICES).

PER SERVING: Calories 195; Fat 2.6g (sat 0.7g, mono 0.4g, poly 0.6g); Protein 42.2g; Carb 2.9g; Fiber 0.2g; Chol 68mg; Iron 2.3mg; Sodium 376mg; Calc 7mg

TURKEY CUTLETS WITH CHERRY-PORT SAUCE

PointsPlus value per serving: 6

HANDS-ON TIME: 19 min. ■ **TOTAL TIME:** 19 min.

Frozen pitted dark sweet cherries that have been thawed can stand in for the fresh cherries in this recipe.

12 (¼-inch-thick) turkey breast cutlets (1½ pounds)
¼ teaspoon salt
¼ teaspoon freshly ground black pepper
4 teaspoons olive oil, divided
⅓ cup sliced shallots
1 cup sweet fresh cherries, pitted and halved
½ cup fat-free, lower-sodium chicken broth
½ cup ruby port or other sweet red wine

1. Sprinkle cutlets evenly with salt and pepper. Heat a large nonstick skillet over medium–high heat. Add 1 teaspoon oil to pan; swirl to coat. Add 4 cutlets to pan; cook 1 minute on each side or until done. Remove cutlets from pan; cover and keep warm. Repeat procedure with 2 teaspoons oil and remaining 8 cutlets.
2. Heat pan over medium heat. Add remaining 1 teaspoon oil to pan; swirl to coat. Add shallots to pan; sauté 2 minutes or until tender. Add cherries, broth, and port, scraping pan to loosen browned bits. Bring mixture to a boil; cook 6 minutes or until mixture is thickened and reduced to 1 cup. YIELD: 4 SERVINGS (SERVING SIZE: 3 CUTLETS AND ¼ CUP SAUCE).

PER SERVING: Calories 278; Fat 5.3g (sat 0.7g, mono 3.4g, poly 0.6g); Protein 42.9g; Carb 10.5g; Fiber 0.8g; Chol 68mg; Iron 2.6mg; Sodium 357mg; Calc 12mg

Mojito Fruit Salad, page 108

MOJITO FRUIT SALAD

PointsPlus value per serving: 3   *pictured on page 139*

HANDS-ON TIME: 10 min. ▪ **TOTAL TIME:** 10 min.

Mangoes and strawberries also make a nice addition to this fruit salad with all the flavors of a favorite Cuban cocktail.

2 tablespoons sugar
3 tablespoons fresh lime juice
3 tablespoons white rum
1½ cups (1-inch) cubed honeydew melon
1½ cups (1-inch) cubed peeled papaya
1½ cups (1-inch) cubed pineapple
1½ cups (1-inch) cubed seeded watermelon
½ cup chopped fresh mint

1. Combine first 3 ingredients in a large bowl; stir well with a whisk. Add fruit and mint, tossing gently to coat. Serve immediately, or cover and chill up to 3 hours. YIELD: 6 SERVINGS (SERVING SIZE: 1 CUP).

PER SERVING: Calories 97; Fat 0.2g (sat 0.1g, mono 0g, poly 0.1g); Protein 1g; Carb 20.1g; Fiber 1.9g; Chol 0mg; Iron 0.4mg; Sodium 11mg; Calc 25mg

CARAMELIZED ONION AND PEAR SALAD

PointsPlus value per serving: 4

HANDS-ON TIME: 15 min. ▪ **TOTAL TIME:** 35 min.

The slight sweetness of the caramelized onions pairs well with the tangy flavor of the Gorgonzola cheese. To add another sweet element to this salad, try swapping the regular walnuts for candied walnuts.

Cooking spray
1 cup vertically sliced onion (1 small)
3 tablespoons pear nectar
1 tablespoon champagne or white wine vinegar
1 tablespoon olive oil
¼ teaspoon freshly ground black pepper
⅛ teaspoon salt
1 (6-ounce) package fresh baby spinach
1⅓ cups Bartlett pear slices
¼ cup chopped walnuts, toasted
1 ounce crumbled Gorgonzola cheese (about ¼ cup)

1. Heat a large nonstick skillet over medium-low heat. Coat pan with cooking spray. Add onion to pan. Heavily coat onion with cooking spray; cook 30 minutes or until very tender and caramelized, stirring frequently.
2. Combine pear nectar and next 4 ingredients in a small bowl, stirring with a whisk. Divide spinach among 4 plates. Top each evenly with pear, onion, walnuts, and cheese. Drizzle dressing over salads. YIELD: 4 SERVINGS (SERVING SIZE: 1 CUP SPINACH, ½ CUP PEAR, 2 TABLESPOONS ONION, 1 TABLESPOON WALNUTS, 1 TABLESPOON CHEESE, AND ABOUT 1 TABLESPOON DRESSING).

PER SERVING: Calories 164; Fat 10.5g (sat 2.4g, mono 3.5g, poly 3.9g); Protein 4g; Carb 16.5g; Fiber 4.6g; Chol 6mg; Iron 1.7mg; Sodium 239mg; Calc 84mg

CARAMELIZED ONIONS

Caramelizing breaks down the natural sugars in onion and adds rich texture and depth. Don't be tempted to crank the heat when cooking the onions. To get the translucence and meltingly tender texture that makes them so delicious, the onions need to cook on lower heat for a long time—sometimes up to an hour. Stir more frequently as the onions darken. Serve them on a burger with goat cheese and pesto, or add them to sandwiches and salads.

GRILLED BOK CHOY AND RADICCHIO SALAD WITH CITRUS-HONEY VINAIGRETTE

PointsPlus value per serving: 6

HANDS-ON TIME: 14 min. ■ **TOTAL TIME:** 22 min.

A citrusy-sweet vinaigrette balances out the inherent bitterness of the bok choy and radicchio in this warm salad. Serve it with grilled pork chops.

3 tablespoons olive oil
3 tablespoons fresh orange juice
1 tablespoon honey
¼ teaspoon freshly ground black pepper
⅛ teaspoon salt
1 head bok choy, cut in half lengthwise
1 head radicchio, quartered and cored
½ teaspoon freshly ground black pepper
1 tablespoon olive oil
Cooking spray
2 large navel oranges, each cut into 6 wedges

1. Preheat grill to medium–high heat.
2. Combine first 5 ingredients in a small bowl, stirring with a whisk until well blended. Set aside.
3. Sprinkle bok choy and radicchio with ½ teaspoon pepper; drizzle with 1 tablespoon oil. Place vegetables on grill rack coated with cooking spray; grill 10 minutes, turning once. Add orange wedges to grill rack; grill 4 minutes, turning once. Remove vegetables from grill rack; peel and coarsely chop. Combine bok choy, radicchio, orange, and vinaigrette in a large bowl; toss well to combine. Serve immediately. YIELD: 4 SERVINGS (SERVING SIZE: 1 CUP).

PER SERVING: Calories 214; Fat 14g (sat 2g, mono 9.9g, poly 1.7g); Protein 4.2g; Carb 21.4g; Fiber 3.8g; Chol 0mg; Iron 1.9mg; Sodium 186mg; Calc 198mg

BOK CHOY

This cabbage, originally from China, is fast cooking and packed with vitamins A and C. Low in calories and widely available year-round, strong, firm stalks and dark green, crispy leaves have the most flavor.

PANZANELLA

PointsPlus value per serving: 5

HANDS-ON TIME: 14 min. ■ **TOTAL TIME:** 14 min.

Panzanella, or "bread salad," is the perfect way to use leftover bread. Use a serrated knife to cut the bread. With its scalloped, toothlike edge, this knife is ideal for cutting through foods with a hard exterior and a softer interior. The teeth of the blade catch and rip the bread as the knife smoothly slices through it. If your bread is not really dry or stale, spread the cubes in a single layer and toast them in the oven, or leave them out overnight to dry out. You'll make this summer salad again and again.

2 tablespoons olive oil
2 tablespoons red wine vinegar
½ teaspoon freshly ground black pepper
5 cups (1-inch) cubes day-old French bread, toasted
½ cup torn basil leaves
2 tablespoons drained capers
2 large ripe tomatoes, chopped (3 cups)
1 yellow bell pepper, cut into ½-inch pieces (1 cup)
½ English cucumber, halved lengthwise and thinly sliced (1¼ cups)
½ medium-sized red onion, thinly sliced (1 cup)

1. Combine first 3 ingredients in a large bowl, stirring with a whisk. Add bread cubes and remaining ingredients, tossing gently to coat. Serve immediately, or cover and chill up to 30 minutes. YIELD: 5 SERVINGS (SERVING SIZE: 2 CUPS).

PER SERVING: Calories 173; Fat 6.6g (sat 0.9g, mono 4g, poly 0.9g); Protein 4.4g; Carb 25g; Fiber 2.7g; Chol 0mg; Iron 1.7mg; Sodium 337mg; Calc 49mg

GRILLED ROMAINE WITH TOMATO DRESSING

PointsPlus value per serving: 2

HANDS-ON TIME: 4 min. ■ **TOTAL TIME:** 4 min.

Grilling the romaine brings out a slight sweetness that is balanced by the bright tang of the tomato dressing in this highly rated recipe.

1 (24.2-ounce) package romaine hearts
Olive oil–flavored cooking spray
½ teaspoon salt, divided
½ teaspoon freshly ground black pepper, divided
1½ cups chopped plum tomato, divided
2 tablespoons white wine vinegar
1 tablespoon chopped fresh basil
2 teaspoons olive oil
½ teaspoon Dijon mustard
¼ teaspoon sugar
½ small garlic clove, minced
3 tablespoons crumbled blue cheese

1. Preheat grill to medium-high heat.
2. Cut romaine hearts in half lengthwise. Coat cut sides of romaine with cooking spray; sprinkle evenly with ¼ teaspoon salt and ¼ teaspoon pepper. Place cut sides down on grill rack coated with cooking spray. Grill 1 to 2 minutes on each side or until slightly charred. Arrange 1 romaine half on each of 6 plates.
3. Place ¾ cup tomato in a blender; process until smooth. Strain mixture through a sieve into a bowl, reserving juice. Discard solids. Add remaining ¾ cup chopped tomato, remaining ¼ teaspoon salt, remaining ¼ teaspoon pepper, vinegar, and next 5 ingredients to juice in bowl; stir well.
4. Spoon tomato dressing evenly over each romaine half; sprinkle evenly with blue cheese. YIELD: 6 SERVINGS (SERVING SIZE: ½ ROMAINE HEART, 2 TABLESPOONS DRESSING, AND 1½ TEASPOONS CHEESE).

PER SERVING: Calories 61; Fat 3g (sat 1g, mono 1.4g, poly 0.2g); Protein 2.8g; Carb 6.6g; Fiber 2g; Chol 3mg; Iron 1.7mg; Sodium 275mg; Calc 83mg

POACHED SALMON SALAD WITH HORSERADISH-DILL DRESSING

PointsPlus value per serving: 6

HANDS-ON TIME: 4 min. ■ **TOTAL TIME:** 2 hr., 24 min.

1 lemon, halved
6 cups water
3 tablespoons chopped fresh dill, divided
½ teaspoon freshly ground black pepper
2 (6-ounce) skin-on salmon fillets
⅓ cup light mayonnaise
2½ tablespoons fat-free milk
1½ teaspoons prepared horseradish
6 cups mixed salad greens
1 cup (¼-inch-thick) slices cucumber
½ cup sliced red onion

1. Squeeze 4 teaspoons juice from 1 lemon half; cut remaining half into slices.
2. Bring 6 cups water, 2 tablespoons dill, pepper, 2 teaspoons lemon juice, and lemon slices to a boil in a Dutch oven; reduce heat, and simmer, uncovered, 10 minutes.
3. Add fish to poaching liquid. Simmer, uncovered, 10 minutes. Remove fish from poaching liquid with a slotted spoon; discard liquid. Place fish in a bowl; cover and refrigerate 2 hours or until thoroughly chilled. Remove skin from fish, and break into large chunks.
4. While fish chills, combine mayonnaise, milk, horseradish, remaining 1 tablespoon dill, and remaining 2 teaspoons lemon juice in a large bowl, stirring with a whisk until blended. Add greens, cucumber, and onion; toss gently to coat. Divide salad mixture evenly among 4 plates; top evenly with fish. YIELD: 4 SERVINGS (SERVING SIZE: 1¾ CUPS SALAD MIXTURE AND 2 OUNCES FISH).

PER SERVING: Calories 237; Fat 12.8g (sat 2g, mono 3.6g, poly 5.7g); Protein 21.1g; Carb 9.8g; Fiber 2.6g; Chol 61mg; Iron 1.7mg; Sodium 243mg; Calc 36mg

MEDITERRANEAN TUNA PASTA SALAD

PointsPlus value per serving: 6

HANDS-ON TIME: 13 min. ■ **TOTAL TIME:** 13 min.

This Mediterranean-inspired salad capitalizes on the convenience of canned tuna. Albacore tuna often costs more but is meatier and more satisfying than other varieties.

6 ounces uncooked farfalle (bow tie pasta)
¼ cup olive oil
2 tablespoons fresh lemon juice
1½ teaspoons grated fresh lemon rind
1 teaspoon honey
¼ teaspoon freshly ground black pepper
⅛ teaspoon salt
1 (12-ounce) can albacore tuna in water, drained and flaked
1 cup halved grape tomatoes
½ cup pitted halved kalamata olives
¼ cup chopped fresh parsley
2 cups packed sliced fresh baby spinach

1. Cook pasta according to package directions, omitting salt and fat. Drain and rinse with cold water; drain.
2. While pasta cooks, combine olive oil and next 5 ingredients in a large bowl, stirring with a whisk. Add pasta, tuna, and next 3 ingredients; toss gently to coat. Chill until ready to serve. Add spinach; toss well, and serve immediately. YIELD: 8 SERVINGS (SERVING SIZE: ABOUT 1 CUP).

PER SERVING: Calories 210; Fat 9.7g (sat 1.3g, mono 6.8g, poly 1.2g); Protein 11.5g; Carb 19.3g; Fiber 1.4g; Chol 19mg; Iron 1.1mg; Sodium 350mg; Calc 18mg

GRILLED SHRIMP AND ORZO SALAD WITH SUN-DRIED TOMATO VINAIGRETTE

PointsPlus value per serving: 10   *pictured on page 135*

HANDS-ON TIME: 26 min. ■ **TOTAL TIME:** 26 min.

Prepare the orzo salad a day ahead, omitting the spinach. Grill the shrimp, and toss the spinach with the orzo mixture just before serving.

1 cup uncooked orzo (rice-shaped pasta)
1¼ pounds shrimp, peeled and deveined
Cooking spray
24 asparagus spears
¼ cup sherry vinegar
3 tablespoons olive oil
½ teaspoon freshly ground black pepper
¼ teaspoon salt
½ cup finely chopped sun-dried tomatoes, packed without oil (about 17)
2 cups bagged prewashed baby spinach
½ cup drained canned chopped artichoke hearts (about 3 hearts)
¼ cup chopped red onion
4 ounces crumbled goat cheese (about 1 cup)

1. Preheat grill to medium-high heat.
2. Cook pasta according to package directions, omitting salt and fat. Drain and rinse with cold water; drain.
3. While pasta cooks, thread shrimp evenly onto 6 metal skewers. Place skewers on grill rack coated with cooking spray; grill 2 to 3 minutes on each side or until done.
4. Snap off tough ends of asparagus; chop asparagus. Combine vinegar and next 3 ingredients; stir with a whisk. Stir in asparagus and tomatoes. Add pasta, spinach, artichoke, and onion, tossing to coat. Divide pasta mixture evenly among 6 plates. Top evenly with shrimp; sprinkle with cheese. YIELD: 6 SERVINGS (SERVING SIZE: 1 CUP SALAD, ABOUT 5 SHRIMP, AND ABOUT 2½ TABLESPOONS CHEESE).

PER SERVING: Calories 379; Fat 14.1g (sat 5.2g, mono 6.4g, poly 1.3g); Protein 27g; Carb 36.3g; Fiber 3.6g; Chol 155mg; Iron 6.1mg; Sodium 509mg; Calc 119mg

ORZO

Shaped like a large grain of rice, orzo is easy to prepare and virtually unlimited in its uses. It tastes light and fresh when paired with a vinaigrette and simple roasted vegetables, but it's a serious comfort-food contender when used in warm soups or combined with bubbly cheese.

SHRIMP SALAD

PointsPlus value per serving: 5

HANDS-ON TIME: 11 min. ■ **TOTAL TIME:** 11 min.

Quick, easy, and light—this salad is a perfect dish for a summer lunch.

¾ **cup light mayonnaise**
1½ **tablespoons fresh lemon juice**
4 **teaspoons chopped fresh tarragon**
½ **teaspoon Dijon mustard**
¼ **teaspoon freshly ground black pepper**
⅛ **teaspoon salt**
3 **cups coarsely chopped cooked shrimp**
½ **cup chopped celery**
½ **cup chopped red onion**
12 **Bibb lettuce leaves**
1½ **cups sliced cherry tomatoes**

1. Combine first 6 ingredients in a large bowl, stirring until blended. Stir in shrimp, celery, and onion. Cover and chill until ready to serve.
2. Place lettuce leaves on each of 6 plates; top evenly with shrimp salad and tomatoes. YIELD: 6 SERVINGS (SERVING SIZE: ½ CUP SHRIMP MIXTURE, ¼ CUP TOMATOES, AND 2 LETTUCE LEAVES).

PER SERVING: Calories 197; Fat 10.9g (sat 1.8g, mono 2.6g, poly 5.7g); Protein 17.5g; Carb 6.7g; Fiber 1.2g; Chol 163mg; Iron 3mg; Sodium 484mg; Calc 56mg

GRILLED FAJITA STEAK SALAD

PointsPlus value per serving: 6   *pictured on page 132*

HANDS-ON TIME: 20 min. ■ **TOTAL TIME:** 34 min.

Smoky grilled steak and vegetables top a bed of crisp greens and showcase a creamy avocado dressing. For even quicker preparation, choose a bottled lime dressing.

1 **(1-pound) flank steak, trimmed**
1 **tablespoon salt-free Southwest chipotle seasoning blend**
½ **teaspoon salt, divided**
Cooking spray
1 **onion, cut into ½-inch-thick slices**
1 **(7-ounce) package mini bell peppers**
¼ **cup mashed peeled avocado (½ large)**
¼ **cup reduced-fat sour cream**
1 **tablespoon water**
1 **tablespoon fresh lime juice**
2 **teaspoons chopped fresh cilantro**
6 **cups chopped romaine lettuce**

1. Preheat grill to medium-high heat.
2. Sprinkle steak evenly with chipotle seasoning and ¼ teaspoon salt.
3. Place steak on grill rack coated with cooking spray. Grill steak 6 minutes on each side or until desired degree of doneness. Let stand 10 minutes.
4. While steak stands, coat onion and bell peppers with cooking spray. Place onion on grill rack; grill 3 minutes. Add bell peppers to grill rack. Grill 3 minutes. Turn onion and peppers over; grill 3 minutes or until peppers are tender. Remove peppers from grill. Grill onion an additional 3 minutes or until tender. Cut onion slices into quarters. Cut peppers in half lengthwise; discard seeds and membranes. Cut peppers into ¼-inch-wide strips. Place onion and pepper strips in a bowl; toss. Cut steak diagonally across grain into thin slices.
5. Combine avocado, next 4 ingredients, and remaining ¼ teaspoon salt in a small bowl, stirring with a whisk. Divide lettuce among 4 plates. Top with steak and grilled vegetables; drizzle with dressing. YIELD: 4 SERVINGS (SERVING SIZE: 1½ CUPS LETTUCE, 3 OUNCES STEAK, ½ CUP VEGETABLE MIXTURE, AND 2 TABLESPOONS DRESSING).

PER SERVING: Calories 242; Fat 10.7g (sat 3.9g, mono 3.6g, poly 0.6g); Protein 27.1g; Carb 9.7g; Fiber 3.8g; Chol 45mg; Iron 2.8mg; Sodium 376mg; Calc 89mg

GRILLED LAMB SALAD

PointsPlus value per serving: 9

HANDS-ON TIME: 10 min. ■ **TOTAL TIME:** 14 min.

Grilling the lamb adds a subtle smokiness and creates a delicious brown crust.

- 1 (6-ounce) carton plain fat-free Greek yogurt
- 2 tablespoons red wine vinegar
- 1 tablespoon salt-free Greek seasoning, divided
- 1 cup coarsely shredded seeded peeled cucumber
- ¾ pound boneless leg of lamb, cut into 1½-inch cubes
- Cooking spray
- 2 (10-ounce) packages Italian blend salad greens
- 2 cups halved grape tomatoes
- ½ cup thinly sliced red onion
- ½ cup whole-wheat pita chips, lightly crushed

1. Combine yogurt, red wine vinegar, and 1½ teaspoons Greek seasoning, stirring with a whisk. Stir in cucumber. Cover and chill.
2. Sprinkle lamb with remaining 1½ teaspoons Greek seasoning, tossing to coat. Heat a large skillet over medium-high heat. Coat pan with cooking spray. Add lamb to pan. Cook 3 minutes or until desired degree of doneness, turning occasionally to brown on all sides.
3. Divide salad greens among 4 plates. Top each with tomato, onion, and lamb. Drizzle salads with yogurt dressing, and sprinkle with pita chips. YIELD: 4 SERVINGS (SERVING SIZE: ABOUT 2 CUPS SALAD GREENS, ½ CUP TOMATO, 2 TABLESPOONS ONION, 2¼ OUNCES LAMB, ¼ CUP YOGURT DRESSING, AND 2 TABLESPOONS PITA CHIPS).

PER SERVING: Calories 341; Fat 19.6g (sat 7.8g, mono 8.4g, poly 1.6g); Protein 22.3g; Carb 17.8g; Fiber 3.9g; Chol 60mg; Iron 3mg; Sodium 187mg; Calc 105mg

LAMB

Boneless leg of lamb is simple to cook and easy to serve. When shopping for this cut, you may find "butterflied" lamb, which is a boneless cut that's been cut in half down the center but not completely through. It's a term that's often used interchangeably with "boneless;" either will do for this recipe. Fresh lamb is preferable although frozen lamb is readily available and a good option. Look for a cut that is firm with good marbling and solid white fat.

ROTISSERIE CHICKEN

Picking up one of these at the grocery store can be a weekday lifesaver. Use it to make a salad, a main dish, or as a base for quick chicken salad sandwiches. You can also sprinkle it into tortillas with cheese, vegetables, and salsa for easy weeknight quesadillas. Avoid seasoned options. A plain chicken will offer the most versatility and also be lower in sodium.

COBB SALAD LETTUCE CUPS

PointsPlus value per serving: 8

HANDS-ON TIME: 9 min. ■ **TOTAL TIME:** 9 min.

Traditional Cobb salad ingredients are tossed together and served in buttery Boston lettuce cups for a twist on the classic. This recipe garnered a top rating from our Test Kitchen.

- 2 tablespoons red wine vinegar
- 1 tablespoon olive oil
- ¼ teaspoon freshly ground black pepper
- 1½ cups chopped rotisserie chicken breast
- ¾ cup chopped seeded tomato
- 1½ ounces crumbled blue cheese (about ⅓ cup)
- 4 center-cut bacon slices, cooked and crumbled
- 2 hard-cooked large eggs, chopped
- 1 peeled avocado, chopped
- 8 Boston lettuce leaves

1. Combine first 3 ingredients in a medium bowl, stirring with a whisk. Add chicken and next 5 ingredients; toss to coat. Spoon about ½ cup chicken mixture onto each lettuce leaf. YIELD: 4 SERVINGS (SERVING SIZE: 2 LETTUCE CUPS).

PER SERVING: Calories 306; Fat 20.7g (sat 5.9g, mono 10.4g, poly 2.7g); Protein 25.3g; Carb 6.6g; Fiber 4g; Chol 172mg; Iron 1.2mg; Sodium 520mg; Calc 95mg

To avoid browning, be sure to cut an avocado only as soon as you need it. If necessary, squeeze lemon juice over the fruit to prevent discoloration.

1. Gently hold the avocado in place by using one hand on one side. Use a long, sharp knife to make a continuous, lengthwise cut all the way around the seed, rotating the knife around the seed.

2. Gently twist the two halves in opposite directions to separate, placing the half without the seed to the side.

3. Use a spoon to carefully scoop out the seed, or place the avocado half on a cutting board and cautiously tap the seed with the knife blade to wedge the blade just below the surface of the seed. Adjust pressure as necessary. Slowly twist the knife so that the seed is freed from the avocado. Discard seed.

4. Use a smaller knife to carefully make cuts in a crosshatch pattern on the interior of each avocado half (be sure not to cut through the peel).

5. Use a spoon to scoop the sliced pieces out of the peel.

AVOCADO CHICKEN SALAD WITH CHIPOTLE DRESSING

PointsPlus value per serving: 7

HANDS-ON TIME: 15 min. ■ **TOTAL TIME:** 15 min.

Spicy chipotle chile powder and cool, creamy ranch dressing complement each other in this main-dish salad. Romaine grows in heads, ranging from dark green outer leaves to yellowish green leaves at the heart. It offers a signature crunch from the center vein that runs along each leaf.

6 cups chopped romaine lettuce
2 cups shredded cooked chicken
1 cup fresh corn kernels (about 2 ears)
1 cup grape tomatoes, halved
1 diced peeled avocado
⅓ cup light ranch dressing
1 teaspoon fresh lime juice
¼ teaspoon chipotle chile powder

1. Combine first 4 ingredients in a large bowl. Divide mixture evenly among 4 plates; top evenly with avocado.

2. Combine dressing, lime juice, and chile powder in a small bowl; drizzle evenly over salads. **YIELD: 4 SERVINGS (SERVING SIZE: 2 CUPS SALAD AND 4 TEASPOONS DRESSING).**

PER SERVING: Calories 281; Fat 13.4g (sat 1.8g, mono 4.8g, poly 2.4g); Protein 25.6g; Carb 17.1g; Fiber 4.4g; Chol 65mg; Iron 2.1mg; Sodium 272mg; Calc 46mg

ORANGE CHICKEN SALAD

PointsPlus value per serving: 4

HANDS-ON TIME: 7 min. ■ **TOTAL TIME:** 7 min.

Edamame (green soybeans) are packed with healthy components. A ½-cup serving contains 4 grams of fiber and 3 grams of fat—all of which is the heart-healthy monounsaturated and polyunsaturated kind. They're also high in soy protein, which may help reduce cholesterol. Plus, the beans are an excellent source of potassium, a mineral that helps prevent muscle cramps by regulating the balance of fluid in the body.

> 6 cups shredded napa (Chinese) cabbage
> 2 cups shredded cooked chicken
> 1 cup frozen shelled edamame (green soybeans), thawed
> ½ cup orange sections (2 oranges)
> ¼ cup sliced almonds, toasted
> ½ cup chow mein noodles (optional)
> ¼ cup light Asian dressing with ginger and soy

1. Place first 5 ingredients and, if desired, chow mein noodles in a large bowl; toss well. Drizzle with dressing; toss gently to coat. YIELD: 6 SERVINGS (SERVING SIZE: 1½ CUPS).

PER SERVING: Calories 182; Fat 5.3g (sat 0.6g, mono 2.3g, poly 2g); Protein 20.1g; Carb 13.7g; Fiber 3.8g; Chol 40mg; Iron 1.6mg; Sodium 177mg; Calc 111mg

CITRUS-FENNEL SALAD

PointsPlus value per serving: 1

HANDS-ON TIME: 13 min. ■ **TOTAL TIME:** 13 min.

A mandoline is a handy tool for this recipe. Cutting the fennel into thin slices allows other ingredients to coat the fennel, mellowing its strong anise flavor.

> 3 tablespoons fresh lemon juice
> 2 tablespoons fresh orange juice
> 1 tablespoon white wine vinegar
> 1 teaspoon chopped fresh thyme
> 1 teaspoon grated fresh orange rind
> ¼ teaspoon kosher salt
> ¼ teaspoon freshly ground black pepper
> 2 tablespoons extra-virgin olive oil
> 3 cups thinly sliced fennel bulb (about 1 large bulb)
> 1 cup orange sections (2 large oranges)
> ½ cup sliced red onion
> 1 tablespoon chopped fennel fronds (optional)

1. Combine first 7 ingredients in a large bowl, stirring with a whisk. Add oil, stirring with whisk until blended. Add fennel, orange, and onion; toss gently to combine. Chill until ready to serve. Sprinkle with chopped fennel fronds, if desired. YIELD: 9 SERVINGS (SERVING SIZE: ABOUT ½ CUP).

PER SERVING: Calories 52; Fat 3.2g (sat 0.4g, mono 2.4g, poly 0.3g); Protein 0.7g; Carb 6g; Fiber 1.6g; Chol 0mg; Iron 0.3mg; Sodium 69mg; Calc 25mg

HOW TO PREPARE FENNEL

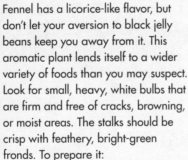

Fennel has a licorice-like flavor, but don't let your aversion to black jelly beans keep you away from it. This aromatic plant lends itself to a wider variety of foods than you may suspect. Look for small, heavy, white bulbs that are firm and free of cracks, browning, or moist areas. The stalks should be crisp with feathery, bright-green fronds. To prepare it:

1. Trim the stalks about an inch above the bulb.
2. Trim about ½ inch off the root end.
3. To slice it, stand the bulb on the root end and cut vertically.
4. You can also use the stalks in place of celery in soups. The fronds can be used as a garnish, or chop them and use them as you would other herbs like dill or parsley.

APPLE AND CABBAGE SALAD

PointsPlus value per serving: 4

HANDS-ON TIME: 7 min. ■ **TOTAL TIME:** 7 min.

Agave nectar adds a touch of sweetness to the dressing, balancing the tart flavor of the vinegar.

- 3 tablespoons olive oil
- 1 tablespoon cider vinegar
- 1 teaspoon agave nectar
- ¼ teaspoon salt
- ¼ teaspoon freshly ground black pepper
- 3½ cups chopped Granny Smith apple (about 1¼ pounds)
- 2 cups shredded red cabbage
- ½ cup golden raisins
- ⅓ cup chopped walnuts, toasted

1. Combine first 5 ingredients in large bowl, stirring until blended. Add apple and remaining ingredients; toss to coat. Cover and chill until ready to serve. **YIELD: 8 SERVINGS (SERVING SIZE: ABOUT ¾ CUP).**

PER SERVING: Calories 136; Fat 8.3g (sat 0.9g, mono 4.5g, poly 2.4g); Protein 2g; Carb 16.1g; Fiber 1.7g; Chol 0mg; Iron 0.5mg; Sodium 80mg; Calc 19mg

GOLDEN RAISINS

Golden raisins come from the same grape as dark raisins— the Thompson seedless grape—but they're sprayed with sulphur dioxide to prevent darkening and are not dried as long. Raisins add a burst of sweetness to any salad.

BUTTERNUT SQUASH SLAW

PointsPlus value per serving: 4

HANDS-ON TIME: 13 min. ■ **TOTAL TIME:** 3 hr., 13 min.

While not a traditional base for slaw, the butternut squash in this recipe stands in beautifully when shredded. It not only adds color, but also vitamins A and C and a sweet, nutty flavor. When roasted, this squash finds even more uses in soups, salads, or even inside a cheesy baked pasta dotted with rosemary. For the best flavor, let the slaw marinate in the refrigerator overnight so the flavors can fully develop.

- 2 tablespoons honey
- 4 teaspoons cider vinegar
- 2 teaspoons fresh lemon juice
- 1 teaspoon ground cumin
- ½ teaspoon salt
- ¼ teaspoon freshly ground black pepper
- 3 tablespoons extra-virgin olive oil
- 4 cups shredded peeled butternut squash (about 1¼ pounds)
- 2 cups matchstick-cut unpeeled Granny Smith apple (1 large)
- ⅔ cup thinly sliced red onion
- ½ cup dried sweet cherries, coarsely chopped

1. Combine first 7 ingredients in a large bowl, stirring with a whisk. Add squash, apple, onion, and cherries, stirring well to coat. Cover and chill 3 hours or overnight. **YIELD: 8 SERVINGS (SERVING SIZE: ABOUT ¾ CUP).**

PER SERVING: Calories 144; Fat 5.4g (sat 0.8g, mono 3.8g, poly 0.8g); Protein 1.5g; Carb 24.4g; Fiber 3.1g; Chol 0mg; Iron 0.8mg; Sodium 153mg; Calc 46mg

GREEK SMASHED POTATO SALAD

PointsPlus value per serving: 3

HANDS-ON TIME: 8 min. ■ **TOTAL TIME:** 28 min.

This potato salad is destined to be a hit at your next cookout.

    1½ pounds red potatoes, cut into 2-inch cubes
        (about 4 medium)
    2 tablespoons olive oil
    4 teaspoons red wine vinegar
    2 teaspoons chopped fresh oregano
    2 teaspoons Dijon mustard
    ½ teaspoon honey
    ½ teaspoon freshly ground black pepper
    ¼ teaspoon salt
    ¼ cup sliced green onions
    1 ounce crumbled feta cheese (about ¼ cup)
    ¼ cup pitted kalamata olives, quartered

1. Place potato in a medium saucepan; cover with water. Bring to a boil. Reduce heat; simmer 15 minutes or until tender. Drain. Coarsely mash potato.
2. Combine oil and next 6 ingredients in a small bowl, stirring with a whisk until blended. Add oil mixture, green onions, cheese, and olives to mashed potatoes; stir well. Cover and chill until ready to serve. YIELD: 8 SERVINGS (SERVING SIZE: ⅔ CUP).

PER SERVING: Calories 119; Fat 5.7g (sat 1.3g, mono 3.6g, poly 0.6g); Protein 2.4g; Carb 15.1g; Fiber 1.6g; Chol 4mg; Iron 0.8mg; Sodium 235mg; Calc 38mg

ROASTED SWEET POTATO SALAD

PointsPlus value per serving: 5

HANDS-ON TIME: 7 min. ■ **TOTAL TIME:** 42 min.

Honey-laced balsamic vinaigrette complements the caramelized sweet potatoes and shallots and slightly bitter arugula, keeping all the flavors in perfect harmony.

    2 small peeled sweet potatoes, cut into 1-inch pieces
    3 small shallots, peeled and quartered
    Cooking spray
    ¼ teaspoon salt
    ¼ teaspoon freshly ground black pepper
    2 tablespoons olive oil, divided
    2 tablespoons white balsamic vinegar
    1 tablespoon honey
    4 cups loosely packed arugula
    2 tablespoons chopped walnuts, toasted

1. Preheat oven to 425°.
2. Arange sweet potato and shallots in a single layer on a large rimmed baking sheet coated with cooking spray. Sprinkle evenly with salt and pepper; drizzle with 2 teaspoons oil. Toss to coat.
3. Bake at 425° for 25 minutes or until tender and browned, stirring once. Cool 10 minutes.
4. While vegetables cool, combine remaining 4 teaspoons oil, vinegar, and honey in a small bowl, stirring with a whisk. Divide arugula among 4 plates; top each with sweet potato mixture and walnuts. Drizzle with dressing. YIELD: 4 SERVINGS (SERVING SIZE: 1 CUP ARUGULA, ½ CUP SWEET POTATO MIXTURE, 1½ TEASPOONS WALNUTS, AND ABOUT 1 TABLESPOON DRESSING).

PER SERVING: Calories 194; Fat 9.3g (sat 1.2g, mono 5.3g, poly 2.5g); Protein 2.9g; Carb 26.7g; Fiber 3.1g; Chol 0mg; Iron 1.2mg; Sodium 204mg; Calc 69mg

CHICKPEA AND ROASTED RED PEPPER SALAD

PointsPlus value per serving: 3

HANDS-ON TIME: 7 min. ■ **TOTAL TIME:** 7 min.

2 tablespoons fresh lemon juice
2 teaspoons olive oil
¼ teaspoon freshly ground black pepper
⅛ teaspoon salt
1 garlic clove, crushed
1 (15-ounce) can no-salt-added chickpeas (garbanzo
    beans), rinsed and drained
⅔ cup chopped bottled roasted red bell peppers
½ cup chopped seeded cucumber
¼ cup chopped fresh parsley
2 tablespoons chopped pitted kalamata olives
2 ounces crumbled feta cheese (about ½ cup)

1. Combine first 5 ingredients in a large bowl, stirring with a whisk. Add chickpeas and remaining ingredients, tossing to coat. Serve immediately, or chill until ready to serve. **YIELD: 6 SERVINGS (SERVING SIZE: ½ CUP).**

PER SERVING: Calories 101; Fat 4.7g (sat 1.7g, mono 2.2g, poly 0.5g); Protein 4.1g; Carb 10.6g; Fiber 2.1g; Chol 8mg; Iron 0.8mg; Sodium 258mg; Calc 80mg

BLACK-EYED PEA SALAD

PointsPlus value per serving: 3

HANDS-ON TIME: 7 min. ■ **TOTAL TIME:** 7 min.

Cover and chill this salad for several hours before serving to allow the flavors to meld. Keep the seeds in the jalapeño if you'd like some heat.

2 tablespoons red wine vinegar
4 teaspoons olive oil
2 teaspoons honey
¼ teaspoon salt
¼ teaspoon freshly ground black pepper
¾ cup chopped red bell pepper
½ cup chopped red onion
2 tablespoons chopped fresh parsley
2 tablespoons minced seeded jalapeño pepper (1 large)
2 (15.8-ounce) cans black-eyed peas, rinsed and drained

1. Combine first 5 ingredients in a large bowl, stirring with a whisk. Add bell pepper and remaining ingredients, tossing to coat. Cover and refrigerate until ready to serve. **YIELD: 6 SERVINGS (SERVING SIZE: ABOUT ⅔ CUP).**

PER SERVING: Calories 123; Fat 3.6g (sat 0.6g, mono 2.2g, poly 0.6g); Protein 5.1g; Carb 17.9g; Fiber 4g; Chol 0mg; Iron 1.2mg; Sodium 277mg; Calc 27mg

HOW TO SEED A JALAPEÑO PEPPER

Hot peppers such as jalapeños, serranos, and habaneros add both depth and heat to a recipe. To tame some of the heat, remove the seeds and membranes where the capsaicin (the source of the fire) is found. Wash your hands thoroughly immediately after working with hot peppers to avoid accidental eye or face contact.

1. Using a sharp knife, cut off the stem of the pepper. Slice the chile in half lengthwise. Cut each half lengthwise to create four strips.
2. Place each strip, skin side down, on a work surface, and slide the knife against the pepper to remove the membrane and seeds. Remove as many seeds and membranes as you like to decrease or increase the level of heat in a dish.

BLACK BEAN–MANGO QUINOA SALAD

PointsPlus value per serving: 7

HANDS-ON TIME: 17 min. ■ **TOTAL TIME:** 32 min.

Make this salad ahead to have on hand for portable lunches throughout the week. If you can't find prewashed quinoa, you'll need to rinse the quinoa first to remove the bitter-tasting coating (called saponin) that keeps birds and other seed-eating animals from eating it in the wild. Place the quinoa in a fine sieve, and place the sieve in a larger bowl. Cover the quinoa with water, and rub the grains together with your hands for 30 seconds. Rinse and drain. Repeat the procedure twice, and then drain well.

    2 cups water
    1 cup uncooked prewashed quinoa
    ¼ teaspoon salt
    2 tablespoons olive oil
    2 tablespoons fresh lime juice
    1 small garlic clove, minced
    ¼ teaspoon freshly ground black pepper
    ¼ teaspoon ground cumin
    1½ cups chopped peeled ripe mango (about 2 large)
    ½ cup sliced green onions
    2 tablespoons chopped fresh cilantro
    1 (15-ounce) can black beans, rinsed and drained
    5 tablespoons queso fresco

1. Combine 2 cups water, quinoa, and salt in a medium saucepan; bring to a boil. Cover, reduce heat, and simmer 15 minutes or until liquid is absorbed. Remove from heat; fluff with a fork.
2. Combine olive oil and next 4 ingredients in a large bowl; stir well with a whisk. Add quinoa, mango, green onions, cilantro, and black beans; toss well. Sprinkle with cheese. YIELD: 5 SERVINGS (SERVING SIZE: 1 CUP SALAD AND 1 TABLESPOON CHEESE).

PER SERVING: Calories 277; Fat 9.2g (sat 1.8g, mono 5g, poly 1.9g); Protein 9.9g; Carb 39.4g; Fiber 5.9g; Chol 5mg; Iron 2.6mg; Sodium 254mg; Calc 95mg

DOLMAS SALAD

PointsPlus value per serving: 5   *pictured on page 134*

HANDS-ON TIME: 8 min. ■ **TOTAL TIME:** 23 min.

Look for preserved grape leaves in well-stocked supermarkets and Middle Eastern markets. This salad incorporates all the wonderful flavors of stuffed grape leaves with much less time and effort. Serve with lamb chops or Greek-seasoned chicken.

    1 (3½-ounce) bag boil-in-bag brown rice
    ¼ cup dried currants
    ½ cup chopped bottled large grape leaves (5 large)
    ¼ cup finely chopped shallot (1 large)
    1 ounce crumbled feta cheese (about ¼ cup)
    2 tablespoons pine nuts, toasted
    ¼ teaspoon freshly ground black pepper
    ¼ cup fresh lemon juice (about 2 lemons)
    2 tablespoons extra-virgin olive oil

1. Cook rice according to package directions, omitting salt and fat. Add currants to boiling water during last minute of cooking. Drain.
2. Combine rice, currants, grape leaves, and next 4 ingredients in a large bowl. Combine lemon juice and oil in a small bowl, stirring with a whisk. Pour dressing over salad; toss well to coat. Serve warm or at room temperature. YIELD: 4 SERVINGS (SERVING SIZE: ½ CUP).

PER SERVING: Calories 192; Fat 12.1g (sat 2.3g, mono 6.7g, poly 2.3g); Protein 3g; Carb 19.2g; Fiber 1.1g; Chol 6mg; Iron 0.8mg; Sodium 206mg; Calc 51mg

BUCKWHEAT NOODLE STIR-FRY SALAD

PointsPlus value per serving: 8   *pictured on page 64*

HANDS-ON TIME: 20 min. ■ **TOTAL TIME:** 22 min.

5 ounces uncooked soba (buckwheat noodles)
⅓ cup light sesame-ginger dressing
¼ cup minced fresh cilantro
½ pound asparagus spears
1 (14-ounce) package water-packed firm tofu,
        drained and cut into ¾-inch cubes
1 tablespoon dark sesame oil
1 cup red bell pepper strips
3 green onions, diagonally cut into 3-inch pieces
1 (8-ounce) package presliced portobello mushrooms
1 tablespoon black sesame seeds
Chopped fresh cilantro (optional)

1. Cook soba noodles according to package directions; rinse and drain well.
2. While noodles cook, combine dressing and ¼ cup cilantro in a large bowl. Snap off tough ends of asparagus. Cut asparagus into 2½-inch pieces. Pat tofu between paper towels until barely moist.
3. Heat a large nonstick skillet over medium–high heat. Add oil to pan; swirl to coat. Add tofu to pan; cook 4 to 5 minutes or until browned, turning once. Drain tofu on a plate lined with paper towels.
4. Add asparagus, bell pepper, green onions, and mushrooms to pan; cook 5 minutes, stirring constantly. Add vegetables and noodles to dressing mixture; toss well until coated. Add tofu, and toss gently; sprinkle with sesame seeds and, if desired, chopped cilantro. YIELD: 4 SERVINGS (SERVING SIZE: ABOUT 1⅔ CUPS).

PER SERVING: Calories 318; Fat 11.5g (sat 1.3g, mono 3.3g, poly 4.2g); Protein 16.1g; Carb 39.2g; Fiber 4g; Chol 0mg; Iron 3mg; Sodium 462mg; Calc 237mg

SOBA

Soba, which is the Japanese word for "buckwheat," is a thin noodle that can be served chilled or hot. It's a perfect blank slate, blending seamlessly with countless seasonings and sauces; also, 100% buckwheat is an easy whole-grain option, requiring little effort to get in a daily serving.

ASIAN PASTA SALAD

PointsPlus value per serving: 2

HANDS-ON TIME: 10 min. ■ **TOTAL TIME:** 1 hr., 10 min.

Cilantro, with its distinctive grassy flavor, can sometimes be difficult to distinguish from flat-leaf parsley. To make sure you're buying the right herb, press a leaf between your fingers. You should be able to quickly detect the more pungent, distinct smell of the cilantro.

½ (6.75-ounce) package uncooked rice sticks
        (rice-flour noodles)
¼ cup seasoned rice vinegar
2 tablespoons sugar
2 tablespoons chopped fresh cilantro
2 tablespoons fresh lime juice
1 tablespoon minced peeled fresh ginger
1 tablespoon fish sauce
1 teaspoon chili paste with garlic
1 cup frozen shelled edamame (green soybeans),
        thawed
1 cup shredded napa (Chinese) cabbage
1 cup matchstick-cut cucumber
½ cup matchstick-cut carrots

1. Soften rice sticks according to package directions.
2. Combine vinegar and next 6 ingredients in a large bowl; stir with a whisk. Add rice sticks, edamame, cabbage, cucumber, and carrots; toss gently to coat. Cover and chill at least 1 hour or until ready to serve.
YIELD: 8 SERVINGS (SERVING SIZE: ½ CUP).

PER SERVING: Calories 94; Fat 0.9g (sat 0g, mono 0.3g, poly 0.4g); Protein 2.9g; Carb 19.2g; Fiber 1.5g; Chol 0mg; Iron 1.1mg; Sodium 285mg; Calc 21mg

sandwiches

Grilled Eggplant Sandwiches, page 123

CARAMELIZED ONION GRILLED CHEESE

PointsPlus value per serving: 6

HANDS-ON TIME: 26 min. ■ **TOTAL TIME:** 26 min.

Cooking spray
1 medium onion, vertically sliced
2 teaspoons balsamic vinegar
2¼ ounces grated fontina cheese
2¼ ounces shredded Gruyère cheese
8 (½-ounce) very thin slices 100% whole-wheat bread
2 cups loosely packed arugula

1. Heat a medium nonstick skillet over medium–high heat. Coat pan with cooking spray. Add onion to pan; spray onion generously with cooking spray. Sauté 5 minutes. Reduce heat to low; cook 13 minutes or until golden brown, stirring occasionally. Add balsamic vinegar; cook 30 seconds, stirring constantly. Remove onion from pan; wipe pan clean with a paper towel.
2. Combine cheeses in a small bowl; divide evenly among 4 slices of bread. Top each with 2 tablespoons onion, ½ cup arugula, and 1 bread slice.
3. Heat pan over medium heat. Coat both sides of sandwiches with cooking spray. Add sandwiches to pan; cook 2 minutes on each side or until browned and cheese melts. Serve immediately. **YIELD: 4 SERVINGS (SERVING SIZE: 1 SANDWICH).**

PER SERVING: Calories 215; Fat 11.7g (sat 6.4g, mono 3g, poly 1.2g); Protein 11.9g; Carb 16.3g; Fiber 2.5g; Chol 36mg; Iron 1mg; Sodium 330mg; Calc 310mg

GREEN CHILE–PORTOBELLO MELTS

PointsPlus value per serving: 6

HANDS-ON TIME: 6 min. ■ **TOTAL TIME:** 22 min.

For an even bigger flavor boost, grill the portobello caps and toast the buns on the grill.

⅓ cup refrigerated fresh no-salt-added salsa
¼ cup cilantro leaves, chopped and divided
1 (4.5-ounce) can chopped green chiles, drained
4 (4-inch) portobello caps
Cooking spray
4 (0.75-ounce) slices reduced-fat Monterey Jack cheese with jalapeño peppers
4 (1½-ounce) whole-wheat hamburger buns
4 (⅛-inch-thick) slices red onion

1. Preheat oven to 425°.

2. Combine salsa, 2 tablespoons cilantro, and chiles; set aside.
3. Place portobello caps on a foil-lined baking sheet coated with cooking spray. Coat portobello caps with cooking spray. Bake at 425° for 10 minutes. Turn and bake an additional 5 minutes or until tender.
4. Spoon 2 tablespoons salsa mixture onto each portobello cap; top each with 1 cheese slice. Bake 1 minute or until cheese melts. Place 1 portobello cap on bottom half of each bun; top each with 1 onion slice and 1½ teaspoons cilantro. Cover with top halves of buns. **YIELD: 4 SERVINGS (SERVING SIZE: 1 SANDWICH).**

PER SERVING: Calories 231; Fat 6.9g (sat 3.4g, mono 1.8g, poly 1.1g); Protein 11.2g; Carb 29.7g; Fiber 4.7g; Chol 15mg; Iron 1.6mg; Sodium 495mg; Calc 55mg

EGG SALAD SANDWICHES

PointsPlus value per serving: 8

HANDS-ON TIME: 19 min. ■ **TOTAL TIME:** 19 min.

⅓ cup light mayonnaise
1 tablespoon Dijon mustard
1½ teaspoons red wine vinegar
⅛ teaspoon salt
⅛ teaspoon freshly ground black pepper
¼ cup finely chopped celery
2 tablespoons finely chopped red onion
5 hard-cooked large eggs, chopped
8 (1-ounce) slices whole-wheat bread, toasted
1⅓ cups trimmed watercress

1. Combine first 5 ingredients in a large bowl. Stir in celery and onion. Add chopped egg, stirring gently.
2. Spoon egg salad evenly onto 4 bread slices; top evenly with watercress and remaining bread slices. **YIELD: 4 SERVINGS (SERVING SIZE: 1 SANDWICH).**

PER SERVING: Calories 312; Fat 15.1g (sat 3.5g, mono 4.7g, poly 3.9g); Protein 15.7g; Carb 27.4g; Fiber 4.1g; Chol 240mg; Iron 2.2mg; Sodium 678mg; Calc 111mg

HOW TO HARD-COOK EGGS

To prevent your hard-cooked eggs from ending up with rubbery whites and chalky yolks (and that green coating on the yolk), follow these steps: Place the eggs in a saucepan, and cover with an inch or two of cold water; place the pan over high heat. Once the water reaches a full boil, remove the pan from the heat, cover, and let the eggs stand for 10 minutes.

SMOKED SALMON PANINI

PointsPlus value per serving: 6

HANDS-ON TIME: 16 min. ▪ **TOTAL TIME:** 16 min.

Spicy arugula and tangy tomatoes cut through the richness of the smoked salmon and cream cheese in these hearty grilled sandwiches. If you don't have a panini press, see page 128 for cooking tips.

½ (18-ounce) loaf ciabatta bread
4 ounces ⅓-less-fat cream cheese (about ½ cup)
½ teaspoon smoked paprika
10 ounces thinly sliced smoked salmon
1½ cups arugula
3 plum tomatoes, thinly sliced (about 2 cups)

1. Preheat panini press.
2. Cut bread in half horizontally; cut diagonally into 12 (½-inch-thick) slices. Combine cream cheese and paprika in a small bowl; spread 2 teaspoons mixture over each bread slice.
3. Layer salmon, arugula, and tomato evenly over cream cheese mixture on 6 bread slices. Place remaining 6 bread slices on top with cream cheese mixture facing in.
4. Place half of sandwiches on panini press; cook 4 minutes or until golden brown. Repeat procedure with remaining half of sandwiches. Serve immediately. YIELD: 6 SERVINGS (SERVING SIZE: 1 SANDWICH).

PER SERVING: Calories 229; Fat 8.1g (sat 3.4g, mono 3.2g, poly 0.9g); Protein 14.2g; Carb 26g; Fiber 1.3g; Chol 24mg; Iron 2mg; Sodium 739mg; Calc 32mg

BISON BURGERS WITH GOAT CHEESE MAYO

PointsPlus value per serving: 10   *pictured on page 137*

HANDS-ON TIME: 7 min. ▪ **TOTAL TIME:** 14 min.

1 pound ground bison
2 teaspoons canola oil
½ teaspoon freshly ground black pepper
¼ teaspoon salt
Cooking spray
4 (1.8-ounce) white whole-wheat hamburger buns
¼ cup light mayonnaise
1 tablespoon commercial pesto
2 tablespoons goat cheese
4 (¼-inch-thick) slices tomato
1 cup arugula

1. Preheat grill to medium-high heat.
2. Combine first 4 ingredients. Divide bison mixture into 4 equal portions, shaping each into a ½-inch-thick patty. Place patties on grill rack coated with cooking spray. Grill 3 to 4 minutes on each side or until a thermometer registers 160°.
3. Place buns, cut sides down, on grill rack; grill 1 minute or until lightly toasted.
4. Combine mayonnaise, pesto, and goat cheese in a small bowl. Spread about 1 tablespoon mayonnaise mixture on bottom half of each bun; add burgers, tomato slices, and arugula. Cover with bun tops. YIELD: 4 SERVINGS (SERVING SIZE: 1 BURGER).

PER SERVING: Calories 381; Fat 21g (sat 6.1g, mono 7.4g, poly 4.8g); Protein 30.1g; Carb 23.9g; Fiber 5.5g; Chol 72mg; Iron 6.3mg; Sodium 637mg; Calc 292mg

BLACK AND BLUE WRAPS

PointsPlus value per serving: 9   *pictured on page 139*

HANDS-ON TIME: 21 min. ▪ **TOTAL TIME:** 21 min.

1 (¾-pound) flank steak, trimmed
½ teaspoon freshly ground black pepper, divided
¼ teaspoon salt
Cooking spray
1¼ cups thinly sliced red onion (1 medium)
2 cups arugula
4 (8-inch) whole-wheat flour tortillas
2½ ounces crumbled blue cheese (about ⅔ cup)
2 tablespoons commercial balsamic glaze

1. Sprinkle both sides of steak evenly with ¼ teaspoon pepper and salt. Heat a large nonstick skillet over medium-high heat. Coat both sides of steak with cooking spray. Add steak to pan; cook 5 minutes on each side or until desired degree of doneness. Remove steak from pan; let stand 5 minutes.
2. While steak stands, add onion to pan; sauté 5 minutes or until tender. Stir in remaining ¼ teaspoon pepper.
3. Cut steak diagonally across grain into thin slices. Place ½ cup arugula on each tortilla. Divide steak slices evenly among tortillas. Top each with 2 tablespoons onion and about 2½ tablespoons blue cheese. Drizzle each evenly with balsamic glaze. Roll up; secure with wooden picks. YIELD: 4 SERVINGS (SERVING SIZE: 1 WRAP).

PER SERVING: Calories 334; Fat 13.7g (sat 6.8g, mono 4.5g, poly 0.5g); Protein 26.7g; Carb 24g; Fiber 1.5g; Chol 47mg; Iron 2.2mg; Sodium 671mg; Calc 211mg

FLAT-IRON HOT MELTS

PointsPlus value per serving: 10

HANDS-ON TIME: 10 min. ■ **TOTAL TIME:** 26 min.

1 (8-ounce) flat-iron steak, trimmed
¼ teaspoon salt
¼ teaspoon freshly ground black pepper
Cooking spray
1 cup refrigerated presliced onion
¼ cup light mayonnaise
1 tablespoon chopped fresh cilantro
1 tablespoon chopped fresh flat-leaf parsley
1 garlic clove, minced
8 (0.8-ounce) slices Italian bread
2 ounces shredded Havarti cheese

1. Heat a grill pan over medium-high heat. Sprinkle steak evenly with salt and pepper. Coat steak on both sides with cooking spray. Add steak and onion to pan; cook steak 2 minutes on each side or until desired degree of doneness and onion is tender. Remove steak and onion from pan; let steak stand 5 minutes. Cut steak diagonally across grain into thin slices.
2. Combine mayonnaise and next 3 ingredients in a bowl. Preheat panini press.
3. Spread 1 tablespoon mayonnaise mixture on each of 4 bread slices; top each with one-fourth of steak, one-fourth of onion, ½ ounce cheese, and 1 bread slice.
4. Coat sandwiches with cooking spray; place on panini press. Cook 2 minutes or until golden and cheese melts. **YIELD: 4 SERVINGS (SERVING SIZE: 1 SANDWICH).**

PER SERVING: Calories 385; Fat 23.9g (sat 8.3g, mono 5.7g, poly 1.9g); Protein 17.5g; Carb 23.2g; Fiber 0.6g; Chol 57mg; Iron 2.5mg; Sodium 561mg; Calc 115mg

CHEESY CHILI DOGS

PointsPlus value per serving: 7

HANDS-ON TIME: 3 min. ■ **TOTAL TIME:** 9 min.

¼ pound ground round
½ cup chopped onion
¼ cup tomato sauce
1 tablespoon water
1 teaspoon chili powder
1 teaspoon lower-sodium Worcestershire sauce
¼ teaspoon freshly ground black pepper
4 (1.75-ounce) fat-free hot dogs
4 (1.6-ounce) white whole-wheat hot dog buns
2 ounces reduced-fat shredded sharp cheddar cheese
    (about ½ cup)

1. Cook beef and ½ cup onion in a large nonstick skillet over medium-high heat 4 minutes or until browned, stirring to crumble. Stir in tomato sauce and next 4 ingredients; cook 1 minute or until mixture thickens.
2. Heat hot dogs according to package directions. Place one hot dog into each bun. Spoon ¼ cup chili mixture over each hot dog, and sprinkle each with 2 tablespoons cheese. **YIELD: 4 SERVINGS (SERVING SIZE: 1 CHILI DOG).**

PER SERVING: Calories 248; Fat 8.9g (sat 3.5g, mono 2.8g, poly 1.3g); Protein 19.5g; Carb 29.5g; Fiber 4.8g; Chol 39mg; Iron 3.8mg; Sodium 878mg; Calc 478mg

CHIPOTLE PORK BURGERS

PointsPlus value per serving: 10

HANDS-ON TIME: 6 min. ■ **TOTAL TIME:** 17 min.

The chipotle flavors in this burger are mild. Use 1 tablespoon (or more) of the minced chipotle if you'd like more heat.

1 pound lean ground pork
2 teaspoons minced chipotle chile, canned in adobo sauce
1½ teaspoons adobo sauce, divided
Cooking spray
4 (1.8-ounce) white whole-wheat hamburger buns
½ small ripe peeled avocado
3 tablespoons light mayonnaise
2 teaspoons chopped fresh cilantro
4 (¼-inch-thick) slices tomato

1. Preheat grill to 400°.
2. Combine pork, chipotle chile, and ½ teaspoon adobo sauce in a medium bowl. Divide mixture into 4 equal portions, shaping each into a ½-inch-thick patty.
3. Place patties on grill rack coated with cooking spray; grill 5 minutes on each side or until done. Grill buns, cut sides down, 1 minute or until toasted.
4. Place avocado in a small bowl; mash with a fork until smooth. Stir in mayonnaise, cilantro, and remaining 1 teaspoon adobo sauce. Spread avocado mixture evenly over cut sides of bun tops. Place patties on bottom halves of buns; top each patty with 1 tomato slice and bun top. **YIELD: 4 SERVINGS (SERVING SIZE: 1 BURGER).**

PER SERVING: Calories 353; Fat 18.4g (sat 5.4g, mono 2.5g, poly 3.4g); Protein 28g; Carb 24.8g; Fiber 6g; Chol 89mg; Iron 3.1mg; Sodium 421mg; Calc 256mg

SLOPPY TERIYAKIS

PointsPlus value per serving: 8

HANDS-ON TIME: 11 min. ■ **TOTAL TIME:** 19 min.

1 pound lean ground pork
2 teaspoons grated peeled fresh ginger
2 garlic cloves, minced
¾ cup water
⅓ cup lower-sodium soy sauce
3 tablespoons brown sugar
3 tablespoons sherry
2 tablespoons cornstarch
⅓ cup sliced green onions
6 (1½-ounce) sandwich buns with sesame seeds
1 cup packaged angel hair coleslaw

1. Heat a large nonstick skillet over medium–high heat. Add pork, ginger, and garlic to pan; cook 6 minutes or until pork is browned, stirring to crumble. Drain well; return pork mixture to pan.
2. Combine ¾ cup water and next 4 ingredients in a small bowl. Add to pork mixture; cook 1 minute or until sauce thickens, stirring constantly. Remove from heat; stir in green onions.
3. Spoon ⅓ cup pork mixture onto bottom half of each bun; top each sandwich evenly with slaw and tops of buns. Serve immediately. **YIELD: 6 SERVINGS (SERVING SIZE: 1 SANDWICH).**

PER SERVING: Calories 301; Fat 9.5g (sat 3.6g, mono 3.5g, poly 1.3g); Protein 20.6g; Carb 31.9g; Fiber 1.4g; Chol 57mg; Iron 1.3mg; Sodium 597mg; Calc 56mg

PORK LOIN SANDWICHES WITH TOMATO CHUTNEY AIOLI

PointsPlus value per serving: 8

HANDS-ON TIME: 4 min. ■ **TOTAL TIME:** 31 min.

Stir together mayonnaise and sun-dried tomato chutney for a no-fuss aioli to dress this hearty sandwich.

1 (1-pound) pork tenderloin, trimmed
1½ teaspoons onion and herb salt-free seasoning blend
Cooking spray
¼ cup light mayonnaise
2 tablespoons sun-dried tomato chutney
4 (1.8-ounce) white whole-wheat hamburger buns, toasted
1 cup loosely packed arugula

1. Preheat oven to 400°.
2. Sprinkle tenderloin evenly with seasoning blend. Heat a large ovenproof skillet over medium-high heat. Coat pan with cooking spray. Add pork to pan; cook 3 minutes or until browned on all sides.
3. Transfer pan to oven. Bake at 400° for 19 minutes or until a thermometer registers 145° (medium-rare). Let stand 5 minutes. Cut into 4 slices.
4. Combine mayonnaise and chutney in a small bowl. Place 1 tenderloin slice on bottom half of each bun; top each with ¼ cup arugula. Spread 1½ tablespoons chutney mixture on cut side of each bun top; place each on arugula. **YIELD: 4 SERVINGS (SERVING SIZE: 1 SANDWICH).**

PER SERVING: Calories 289; Fat 9.6g (sat 2.1g, mono 2.3g, poly 4.1g); Protein 29g; Carb 25.7g; Fiber 5.1g; Chol 79mg; Iron 1.2mg; Sodium 479mg; Calc 315mg

BASIC BANH MI SANDWICHES

PointsPlus value per serving: 10

HANDS-ON TIME: 20 min. ■ **TOTAL TIME:** 24 min.

This sandwich is a Vietnamese classic, and it has some kick. You can tone down the heat by seeding the jalapeño.

8 (2-ounce) boneless center-cut loin pork chops (¼ inch thick)
½ teaspoon five-spice powder
Cooking spray
2 tablespoons canola oil
1 teaspoon fish sauce
½ teaspoon lower-sodium soy sauce
4 (2-ounce) oblong French rolls
½ cup Italian giardiniera, drained and coarsely chopped
1 jalapeño pepper, sliced
24 thin slices English cucumber (about ½ cup)
¼ cup cilantro leaves
2 tablespoons light mayonnaise

1. Preheat oven to 350°.
2. Place plastic wrap over pork; pound to ⅛-inch thickness using a meat mallet or small heavy skillet. Sprinkle pork evenly with five-spice powder.
3. Heat a large nonstick skillet over medium-high heat. Coat pan with cooking spray. Add half of pork to pan; cook 2 minutes on each side or until done. Repeat procedure with cooking spray and remaining pork.
4. Combine oil, fish sauce, and soy sauce in a small bowl. Place rolls directly on oven rack. Bake at 350° for 5 minutes or until thoroughly heated and crusty.

5. Split rolls in half horizontally. Brush fish sauce mixture evenly over cut sides of roll bottoms. Place 2 pork chops on bottom half of each roll; top each with 2 tablespoons giardiniera, 3 jalapeño slices, 6 cucumber slices, and 1 tablespoon cilantro leaves. Spread cut sides of each roll top with 1½ teaspoons mayonnaise. Cover sandwiches with roll tops. Serve immediately. YIELD: 4 SERVINGS (SERVING SIZE: 1 SANDWICH).

PER SERVING: Calories 395; Fat 17.7g (sat 3.2g, mono 8.2g, poly 4.5g); Protein 26.5g; Carb 30.8g; Fiber 2g; Chol 69mg; Iron 2.4mg; Sodium 667mg; Calc 78mg

BUFFALO CHICKEN SANDWICHES WITH BLUE CHEESE–CELERY SLAW

PointsPlus value per serving: 8

HANDS-ON TIME: 9 min. ■ TOTAL TIME: 19 min.

These grilled sandwiches offer all the flavors of a platter of buffalo wings but with less fat and sodium and fewer calories. (A serving of traditional wings can have a *PointsPlus* value of 17 and more than 1,700mg of sodium.)

¼ cup light mayonnaise
2 teaspoons white vinegar
2 tablespoons crumbled blue cheese
1½ cups packaged angel hair coleslaw
½ cup sliced celery
¼ cup bottled wing sauce, divided
4 (4-ounce) skinless, boneless chicken breast halves
Cooking spray
4 (1.8-ounce) white whole-wheat hamburger buns

1. Preheat grill to high heat.
2. Combine mayonnaise and vinegar in a medium bowl, stirring with a whisk. Stir in cheese. Add slaw and celery; toss gently to coat.
3. Brush 2 tablespoons wing sauce evenly over chicken. Place chicken on grill rack coated with cooking spray; grill 5 minutes on each side or until chicken is done.
4. Place 1 chicken breast on bottom half of each bun; drizzle chicken evenly with remaining 2 tablespoons sauce. Top each sandwich with ⅓ cup slaw and bun tops. YIELD: 4 SERVINGS (SERVING SIZE: 1 SANDWICH).

PER SERVING: Calories 338; Fat 9.7g (sat 2.3g, mono 2.4g, poly 4g); Protein 31.3g; Carb 30.9g; Fiber 3.9g; Chol 74mg; Iron 1.9mg; Sodium 852mg; Calc 96mg

BBQ CHICKEN BURGERS

PointsPlus value per serving: 9

HANDS-ON TIME: 19 min. ■ TOTAL TIME: 22 min.

We use ground chicken in this recipe (as opposed to ground chicken *breast*). Using a combination of dark and light meat adds flavor and produces a juicier burger than white meat alone. Covering the pan while cooking ensures these burgers will be cooked through with a good sear on the outside.

2 tablespoons cider vinegar
1 tablespoon olive oil
1 teaspoon sugar
¼ teaspoon salt, divided
¼ teaspoon freshly ground black pepper, divided
2 cups packaged coleslaw
½ cup chopped onion
Cooking spray
1 pound ground chicken
4 (1.8-ounce) white whole-wheat hamburger buns
¼ cup barbecue sauce

1. Combine vinegar, oil, sugar, ⅛ teaspoon salt, and ⅛ teaspoon pepper in a medium bowl, stirring with a whisk until blended. Add coleslaw; toss to combine.
2. Heat a large nonstick skillet over medium-high heat. Add onion to pan; coat onion with cooking spray. Sauté 3 minutes or until tender. Remove from heat; cool 3 minutes.
3. Combine onion, chicken, remaining ⅛ teaspoon salt, and remaining ⅛ teaspoon pepper in a medium bowl. Divide chicken mixture into 4 equal portions, shaping each into a ½-inch-thick patty.
4. Heat pan over medium heat. Coat one side of patties with cooking spray. Add patties to pan, sprayed sides down; cook 5 minutes. Coat patties with cooking spray; turn. Cover and cook 5 minutes or until done. Place 1 patty on bottom half of each bun; top each with about ⅓ cup coleslaw mixture, 1 tablespoon barbecue sauce, and bun tops. YIELD: 4 SERVINGS (SERVING SIZE: 1 BURGER).

PER SERVING: Calories 328; Fat 14.6g (sat 3.5g, mono 6g, poly 2.9g); Protein 24g; Carb 31.1g; Fiber 6g; Chol 75mg; Iron 2.9mg; Sodium 600mg; Calc 267mg

WHITE WHOLE-WHEAT BREAD

This is not an oxymoron. There is an albino variety of wheat that has the appearance and texture of white bread with the nutritional benefits of whole grains.

CHICKEN FAJITA WRAPS

PointsPlus value per serving: 7

HANDS-ON TIME: 14 min. ▪ **TOTAL TIME:** 14 min.

1 pound skinless, boneless chicken breast, cut into
    ½-inch strips
½ teaspoon salt-free Southwest chipotle seasoning blend
¼ teaspoon freshly ground black pepper
Cooking spray
1 (10-ounce) container refrigerated bell pepper strips
¼ cup prepared guacamole
6 (8-inch) flour tortillas
3 ounces preshredded reduced-fat 4-cheese
    Mexican-blend cheese (about ¾ cup)
¼ cup refrigerated fresh salsa

1. Sprinkle chicken evenly with chipotle seasoning and black pepper. Heat a large nonstick skillet over medium-high heat. Coat pan with cooking spray. Add chicken to pan; stir-fry 3 minutes. Add bell pepper; stir-fry 5 minutes or until chicken is done.
2. Spread 2 teaspoons guacamole evenly over each tortilla. Top each evenly with chicken mixture, 2 tablespoons cheese, and 2 teaspoons salsa; roll up. YIELD: 6 SERVINGS (SERVING SIZE: 1 WRAP).

PER SERVING: Calories 269; Fat 7.9g (sat 3.6g, mono 3.2g, poly 1g); Protein 25g; Carb 21.6g; Fiber 1.8g; Chol 49mg; Iron 0.7mg; Sodium 606mg; Calc 113mg

TURKEY MEAT LOAF SLIDERS

PointsPlus value per serving: 9

HANDS-ON TIME: 12 min. ▪ **TOTAL TIME:** 19 min.

The breadcrumbs in the patty mixture help keep the lean ground turkey breast from drying out under the high heat of the broiler.

1 pound ground turkey breast
1 large egg
½ cup Italian-seasoned breadcrumbs
½ cup ketchup, divided
2 tablespoons grated fresh onion
Cooking spray
1 teaspoon dark brown sugar
1 (15-ounce) package mini buns (12 buns)
4 green leaf lettuce leaves, torn into thirds

1. Preheat broiler.
2. Combine turkey, egg, breadcrumbs, ¼ cup ketchup, and onion in a large bowl. Divide mixture into 12 equal portions, shaping each into a ⅓-inch-thick patty; flatten each patty slightly. Coat patties with cooking spray.
3. Combine remaining ¼ cup ketchup and brown sugar in a small bowl.
4. Place patties on a broiler pan coated with cooking spray; broil 4 minutes. Turn patties; top evenly with ketchup mixture, and broil 3 minutes or until a thermometer registers 165°.
5. Place 1 patty on bottom half of each bun; top each with 1 lettuce piece. Place top halves of buns on lettuce. YIELD: 6 SERVINGS (SERVING SIZE: 2 SANDWICHES).

PER SERVING: Calories 356; Fat 6.5g (sat 0.8g, mono 0.7g, poly 2.7g); Protein 28.1g; Carb 49.4g; Fiber 2.5g; Chol 61mg; Iron 2.6mg; Sodium 779mg; Calc 102mg

CRANBERRY-MUSTARD TURKEY PANINI

PointsPlus value per serving: 9

HANDS-ON TIME: 12 min. ▪ **TOTAL TIME:** 12 min.

⅓ cup whole-berry cranberry sauce
1 tablespoon country-style Dijon mustard
8 (1⅛-ounce) slices pumpernickel bread
8 ounces thinly sliced roasted no-salt-added deli
    turkey breast
4 (0.7-ounce) slices Gouda cheese
1 cup mixed salad greens
Cooking spray

1. Preheat panini press.
2. Combine cranberry sauce and mustard in a small bowl. Spread evenly over 4 bread slices; top each with 2 ounces turkey, 1 cheese slice, and ¼ cup greens. Cover with remaining bread slices. Coat both sides of sandwiches with cooking spray.
3. Place sandwiches on panini press. Grill 2 minutes or until cheese melts. Cut sandwiches in half before serving. YIELD: 4 SERVINGS (SERVING SIZE: 1 SANDWICH).

PER SERVING: Calories 348; Fat 8.1g (sat 4.6g, mono 2.3g, poly 1g); Protein 28.1g; Carb 40.4g; Fiber 4.7g; Chol 70mg; Iron 3.2mg; Sodium 750mg; Calc 186mg

NO PANINI PRESS?

You don't have to have a panini press to make excellent grilled sandwiches. Instead, use two skillets: one to heat and one to place on top of the sandwiches, and press them down as they cook. For the bottom skillet, we like to use a grill pan to create the same grill marks, but the recipe works just as well if you use a regular nonstick skillet. Cook the sandwiches 2 minutes on each side or until golden brown.

Kung Pao Pork,
page 93

Smoked Chicken–Pesto Pizza,
page 102

Tex-Mex Meat Loaf,
page 90

Chicken with Mushroom
and Herb Sauce, *page* 98

Grilled Fajita Steak Salad, *page 112*

Greek Braised Chicken Thighs, *page 105*

Dolmas Salad, *page 119*

Breaded Chicken Cutlets with
Sun-Dried Tomato Aioli, *page 101*

Grilled Shrimp and Orzo Salad with
Sun-Dried Tomato Vinaigrette, *page 111*

Catfish Po'Boys, *page 123*

Bison Burgers with Goat
Cheese Mayo, *page 124*

Grilled Eggplant Sandwiches, *page 123*

Mojito Fruit Salad, *page 108*

Black and Blue Wraps, *page 124*

Grilled Asparagus with Blue Cheese–Walnut Topping, *page 146*

Blackened Okra, *page 150*

Summer Vegetable Sauté, *page 151*

Chicken Enchilada Chowder,
page 162

Lamb and Black Bean
Chili, *page 162*

Herbed Potato Salad, *page 171*

sides

Blackened Okra, page 150

GRILLED ASPARAGUS WITH BLUE CHEESE–WALNUT TOPPING

PointsPlus value per serving: 1   *pictured on page 140*

HANDS-ON TIME: 17 min. ■ **TOTAL TIME:** 17 min.

Look for asparagus with medium to large spears for grilling since thinner spears could potentially fall through grill grates.

   1 pound asparagus spears (about 26 spears)
   1 red bell pepper, quartered lengthwise and seeded
   Cooking spray
   ¼ teaspoon kosher salt
   ⅛ teaspoon freshly ground black pepper
   2 tablespoons crumbled blue cheese
   1 tablespoon finely chopped walnuts, toasted

1. Preheat grill to medium-high heat.
2. Snap off tough ends of asparagus. Place asparagus and bell pepper on a large baking sheet; coat vegetables with cooking spray. Sprinkle with salt and pepper.
3. Place bell pepper on grill rack coated with cooking spray. Grill 4 minutes. Add asparagus to grill rack; grill 6 minutes or just until vegetables begin to char, turning vegetables over after 3 minutes. Remove vegetables from grill. Cut bell pepper lengthwise into ¼-inch-wide strips.
4. Place asparagus and bell pepper on a serving platter. Sprinkle vegetables with blue cheese and walnuts. YIELD: 4 SERVINGS (SERVING SIZE: ¼ OF VEGETABLE MIXTURE).

PER SERVING: Calories 50; Fat 2.8g (sat 0.9g, mono 0.5g, poly 1.0g); Protein 2.8g; Carb 4.5g; Fiber 2.0g; Chol 3.2mg; Iron 1.5mg; Sodium 181mg; Calc 41mg

GINGERED BEETS

PointsPlus value per serving: 2

HANDS-ON TIME: 10 min. ■ **TOTAL TIME:** 1 hr., 40 min.

These beets are equally good the next day, eaten cold atop a bed of fresh greens.

   Cooking spray
   2¾ pounds small red and yellow beets, trimmed
      and peeled
   1 tablespoon olive oil
   ½ teaspoon freshly ground black pepper
   4 shallots, peeled and halved
   2 garlic cloves, peeled
   2 teaspoons grated fresh orange rind
   1½ teaspoons grated peeled fresh ginger

1. Preheat oven to 450°.
2. Line a roasting pan with foil. Coat foil with cooking spray. Cut each beet into 4 wedges. Combine beets and next 4 ingredients in bottom of prepared roasting pan, tossing gently.
3. Bake at 450° for 45 minutes or until beets are lightly brown and tender, stirring occasionally.
4. Place beets in a medium bowl. Add orange rind and ginger; toss well. YIELD: 8 SERVINGS (SERVING SIZE: ½ CUP).

PER SERVING: Calories 73; Fat 2.0g (sat 0.3g, mono 1.3g, poly 0.3g); Protein 2.2g; Carb 13.1g; Fiber 2.2g; Chol 0mg; Iron 1.0mg; Sodium 81mg; Calc 24mg

BUYING AND STORING BEETS

Beets range in color from yellow to purple. When buying, look for small to medium beets with firm, smooth skin and no soft spots. Those with the stems and leaves attached are best. The leafy green tops leach nutrients from the root, so immediately trim them to about an inch. Store the beets in airtight containers in the refrigerator for up to two weeks.

BEET AND APPLE SLAW

PointsPlus value per serving: 2

HANDS-ON TIME: 16 min. ■ **TOTAL TIME:** 16 min.

Raw beets are sweet and crunchy and loaded with antioxidants. Use a food processor to quickly shred the beets.

   2 tablespoons brown sugar
   2 tablespoons cider vinegar
   1 tablespoon fresh orange juice
   1 tablespoon olive oil
   1 teaspoon grated peeled fresh ginger
   ½ teaspoon kosher salt
   1½ cups shredded peeled Granny Smith apple
   4 large beets, trimmed, peeled, and shredded

1. Combine first 6 ingredients in a large bowl, stirring with a whisk until sugar dissolves. Add apple and beets, toss. Serve immediately, or chill until ready to serve. YIELD: 8 SERVINGS (SERVING SIZE: ABOUT ½ CUP).

PER SERVING: Calories 58; Fat 1.8g (sat 0.3g, mono 1.3g, poly 0.2g); Protein 0.7g; Carb 10.7g; Fiber 1.4g; Chol 0mg; Iron 0.4mg; Sodium 153mg; Calc 11mg

Many dishes benefit from the bold, fragrant flavor of fresh ginger. Use a vegetable peeler to remove the thin skin. If you don't have one, you can use the edge of a spoon. Cut the ginger into large pieces. Rub the pieces across a fine grater, such as a Microplane®.

ORANGE BROCCOLI AMANDINE

PointsPlus value per serving: 2

HANDS-ON TIME: 5 min. ■ **TOTAL TIME:** 11 min.

"Amandine" is a culinary term meaning a garnish of almonds. Traditionally, it's green beans that get this treatment, but we've shaken things up a bit by dressing up broccoli.

1 bunch broccoli, cut into spears
2 teaspoons butter
1 teaspoon olive oil
3 tablespoons sliced almonds
1 teaspoon grated fresh orange rind
⅓ cup fresh orange juice
¼ teaspoon salt
¼ teaspoon freshly ground black pepper

1. Arrange broccoli spears in a vegetable steamer. Steam, covered, 5 minutes or until crisp-tender.
2. Heat butter and oil in a large nonstick skillet over medium-high heat until butter melts; add almonds. Sauté 2 minutes or until lightly browned. Stir in orange rind, juice, salt, and pepper.
3. Add broccoli to pan; toss to coat with almond mixture. Serve immediately. YIELD: 6 SERVINGS (SERVING SIZE: ⅙ OF BROCCOLI).

PER SERVING: Calories 76; Fat 3.9g (sat 1.1g, mono 1.8g, poly 0.7g); Protein 3.1g; Carb 9.3g; Fiber 3.7g; Chol 3.4mg; Iron 0.8mg; Sodium 148mg; Calc 50mg

LEMON-PARMESAN BROCCOLINI

PointsPlus value per serving: 3

HANDS-ON TIME: 12 min. ■ **TOTAL TIME:** 12 min.

1¼ pounds broccolini (3 bunches)
1½ tablespoons olive oil
2 garlic cloves, minced
1 ounce grated fresh Parmesan cheese (about ¼ cup)
2 teaspoons grated fresh lemon rind
¼ teaspoon freshly ground black pepper
⅛ teaspoon salt

1. Place broccolini into a large saucepan of boiling water; cook 3 minutes or until crisp-tender. Drain and plunge broccolini into ice water; drain. Pat dry with paper towels.
2. Heat a large nonstick skillet over medium-high heat. Add oil to pan; swirl to coat. Add garlic; sauté 30 seconds. Add broccolini; cook 5 minutes or until it begins to brown, stirring occasionally. Add cheese and remaining ingredients; toss to coat. YIELD: 5 SERVINGS (SERVING SIZE: ⅕ OF BROCCOLINI).

PER SERVING: Calories 108; Fat 5.8g (sat 1.7g, mono 3.4g, poly 0.5g); Protein 6.4g; Carb 8.6g; Fiber 1.5g; Chol 5.7mg; Iron 1.0mg; Sodium 189mg; Calc 152mg

Broccolini is a cross between regular broccoli and Chinese broccoli, and its entire stalk is tender enough for eating. If your local supermarket doesn't carry it, substitute regular broccoli.

SPICY SAUTÉED BRUSSELS SPROUTS

PointsPlus value per serving: 1

HANDS-ON TIME: 13 min. ■ **TOTAL TIME:** 26 min.

Cooking spray
1 teaspoon olive oil
⅛ teaspoon crushed red pepper
2 cups trimmed halved Brussels sprouts
⅛ teaspoon salt
2 garlic cloves, minced
¾ cup water

1. Heat a large nonstick skillet over medium-high heat. Coat pan with cooking spray. Add oil to pan; swirl to coat. Add red pepper; cook 30 seconds or until fragrant. Add Brussels sprouts; cook 2 minutes or until edges begin to brown (do not stir). Add salt and garlic; toss well to coat. Cook 4 minutes longer or until Brussels sprouts are slightly tender.
2. Add ¾ cup water to pan; cook 13 to 15 minutes or until Brussels sprouts are tender. YIELD: 4 SERVINGS (SERVING SIZE: ABOUT ½ CUP).

PER SERVING: Calories 32; Fat 1.3g (sat 0.2g, mono 0.8g, poly 0.2g); Protein 1.6g; Carb 4.5g; Fiber 1.7g; Chol 0mg; Iron 0.7mg; Sodium 85mg; Calc 21mg

BLUE CHEESE–NAPA CABBAGE SLAW

PointsPlus value per serving: 2

HANDS-ON TIME: 7 min. ■ **TOTAL TIME:** 7 min.

The buttermilk–blue cheese dressing is a creamy, tangy twist on typical sweet-and-sour cabbage slaw.

¼ cup nonfat buttermilk
2 tablespoons canola mayonnaise
1 tablespoon cider vinegar
1½ teaspoons sugar
½ teaspoon freshly ground black pepper
2 ounces blue cheese, crumbled
6 cups shredded napa (Chinese) cabbage

1. Combine first 5 ingredients in a large bowl, stirring with a whisk. Stir in blue cheese. Add cabbage; toss to coat. Serve immediately. YIELD: 8 SERVINGS (SERVING SIZE: ABOUT ⅔ CUP).

PER SERVING: Calories 68; Fat 4.8g (sat 1.6g, mono 2.0g, poly 0.8g); Protein 2.6g; Carb 3.7g; Fiber 0.8g; Chol 6.6mg; Iron 0mg; Sodium 139mg; Calc 92mg

SPICED ROASTED CARROTS

PointsPlus value per serving: 3

HANDS-ON TIME: 8 min. ■ **TOTAL TIME:** 33 min.

Garam masala is a pungent spice blend that usually includes peppercorns, cloves, cinnamon, cumin, and cardamom. It doesn't take much of this intense powder to have a big impact on flavor.

1½ pounds carrots, cut into 2-inch pieces
1 tablespoon olive oil
½ teaspoon garam masala
¼ teaspoon kosher salt
½ cup golden raisins
2 tablespoons chopped fresh cilantro

1. Preheat oven to 450°.
2. Combine first 4 ingredients in a large bowl, tossing to coat. Spread carrot mixture in a single layer on a large rimmed baking sheet. Bake at 450° for 25 minutes, stirring once.
3. Add raisins and cilantro; toss well. YIELD: 6 SERVINGS (SERVING SIZE: ½ CUP).

PER SERVING: Calories 104; Fat 2.7g (sat 0.4g, mono 1.7g, poly 0.5g); Protein 1.5g; Carb 20.7g; Fiber 3.8g; Chol 0mg; Iron 0.7mg; Sodium 160mg; Calc 46mg

ROASTED CARROTS AND PARSNIPS WITH DILL

PointsPlus value per serving: 2

HANDS-ON TIME: 8 min. ■ **TOTAL TIME:** 28 min.

1 pound carrots, cut into ⅓-inch pieces
1 pound parsnips, cut into ½-inch pieces
Cooking spray
2 teaspoons olive oil
½ teaspoon freshly ground black pepper
¼ teaspoon salt
1 tablespoon chopped fresh dill
1 teaspoon grated fresh lemon rind

1. Preheat oven to 450°.
2. Arrange carrots and parsnips on a large baking sheet coated with cooking spray. Drizzle with oil and sprinkle with pepper and salt, tossing to coat.
3. Bake at 450° for 20 minutes or just until tender. Sprinkle with dill and lemon rind, tossing gently. YIELD: 7 SERVINGS (SERVING SIZE: ½ CUP).

PER SERVING: Calories 88; Fat 1.8g (sat 0.3g, mono 1.0g, poly 0.3g); Protein 1.4g; Carb 18.0g; Fiber 5.1g; Chol 0mg; Iron 0.6mg; Sodium 136mg; Calc 46mg

ROASTED CAULIFLOWER WITH CILANTRO

PointsPlus value per serving: 2

HANDS-ON TIME: 5 min. ■ TOTAL TIME: 23 min.

2 (10-ounce) packages cauliflower florets
1 tablespoon olive oil
2 tablespoons chopped fresh cilantro
½ teaspoon salt
¼ teaspoon crushed red pepper
Cooking spray

1. Preheat oven to 450°.
2. Cut large cauliflower florets into uniform pieces. Place cauliflower in a large bowl. Drizzle with olive oil. Sprinkle with cilantro, salt, and red pepper. Toss to coat. Transfer cauliflower to a broiler pan coated with cooking spray.
3. Bake at 450° for 18 minutes or until cauliflower is crisp–tender and lightly browned. YIELD: 4 SERVINGS (SERV-ING SIZE: ¾ CUP).

PER SERVING: Calories 68; Fat 4.0g (sat 0.6g, mono 2.5g, poly 0.4g); Protein 2.7g; Carb 7.1g; Fiber 2.9g; Chol 0mg; Iron 0.6mg; Sodium 338mg; Calc 31mg

GRILLED CORN WITH BASIL-MINT BUTTER

PointsPlus value per serving: 3

HANDS-ON TIME: 8 min. ■ TOTAL TIME: 13 min.

4 ears shucked corn
Cooking spray
2 tablespoons yogurt-based spread
2 teaspoons chopped fresh basil
2 teaspoons chopped fresh mint
½ teaspoon grated fresh lemon rind
⅛ teaspoon freshly ground black pepper

1. Preheat grill to medium–high heat.
2. Coat corn evenly with cooking spray. Place corn on grill rack coated with cooking spray. Grill 10 minutes or until tender, turning occasionally.
3. While corn grills, combine spread and remaining ingredients in a small bowl. Spread about 1½ teaspoons mixture over each ear of corn. YIELD: 4 SERVINGS (SERVING SIZE: 1 EAR OF CORN).

PER SERVING: Calories 102; Fat 3.8g (sat 0.7g, mono 0.8g, poly 1.8g); Protein 2.9g; Carb 17.3g; Fiber 2.5g; Chol 0mg; Iron 0.5mg; Sodium 59mg; Calc 4mg

GRILLED SUCCOTASH

PointsPlus value per serving: 2

HANDS-ON TIME: 23 min. ■ **TOTAL TIME:** 23 min.

This speedy side does double duty as an easy appetizer served alongside baked tortilla chips for scooping.

- 2 ears shucked corn
- 1 medium-sized red bell pepper, halved and seeded
- 1 small red onion, cut into 4 slices
- Cooking spray
- 1 cup frozen fordhook lima beans, thawed
- 1 tablespoon water
- 2 teaspoons olive oil
- ½ teaspoon ground cumin
- ½ teaspoon freshly ground black pepper
- ¼ teaspoon salt
- 2 tablespoons chopped fresh parsley

1. Preheat grill to high heat.
2. Coat corn, bell pepper, and onion with cooking spray. Place corn on grill rack; grill 10 minutes. Add bell pepper and onion; grill 5 minutes or until vegetables are tender and charred, turning occasionally. While vegetables cook, boil beans for 8 minutes; drain.
3. Place pepper in a paper bag; fold to close tightly. Let stand 5 minutes. Peel and discard skin. Chop pepper and onion. Cut kernels from corn. Combine corn, bell pepper, onion, and cooked beans in a large bowl.
4. Combine water and next 4 ingredients, stirring with a whisk. Add to vegetable mixture; toss to coat. Sprinkle with parsley. YIELD: 7 SERVINGS (SERVING SIZE ½ CUP).

PER SERVING: Calories 70; Fat 1.9g (sat 0.3g, mono 1g, poly 0.3g); Protein 2.7g; Carb 11.6g; Fiber 2.7g; Chol 0mg; Iron 0.8mg; Sodium 97mg; Calc 14mg

ROASTED FENNEL

PointsPlus value per serving: 2

HANDS-ON TIME: 4 min. ■ **TOTAL TIME:** 22 min.

This side dish is ready when you are. Serve immediately, or chill a bit before serving, which will give the vinegar a more pronounced flavor.

- 1 (1¼-pound) fennel bulb with stalks
- 2 tablespoons sherry vinegar
- 1 tablespoon olive oil
- ¼ teaspoon kosher salt
- ¼ teaspoon freshly ground black pepper

1. Preheat oven to 425°.
2. Trim tough outer leaves from fennel; mince feathery fronds to measure 2 tablespoons. Set chopped fronds aside. Remove and discard stalks. Cut fennel bulb in half lengthwise; discard core. Cut each half crosswise into ¼-inch slices.
3. Combine vinegar and remaining ingredients, stirring with a whisk. Add fennel; toss well. Spread fennel mixture on a baking sheet. Bake at 425° for 18 minutes or until lightly browned and tender. Sprinkle with chopped fennel fronds before serving. YIELD: 5 SERVINGS (SERVING SIZE: ½ CUP).

PER SERVING: Calories 61; Fat 2.9g (sat 0.4g, mono 2g, poly 0.3g); Protein 1.4g; Carb 8.3g; Fiber 3.5g; Chol 0mg; Iron 0.9mg; Sodium 155mg; Calc 56mg

BLACKENED OKRA

PointsPlus value per serving: 1   *pictured on page 141*

HANDS-ON TIME: 6 min. ■ **TOTAL TIME:** 15 min.

- 1 pound fresh okra pods
- ⅜ teaspoon salt
- ¼ teaspoon ground red pepper
- ⅛ teaspoon freshly ground black pepper
- ⅛ teaspoon dried thyme
- ⅛ teaspoon dried oregano
- ⅛ teaspoon paprika
- ⅛ teaspoon onion powder
- ⅛ teaspoon garlic powder
- 1 teaspoon canola oil

1. Trim ends from okra pods; cut in half lengthwise. Combine salt and next 7 ingredients in a small bowl.
2. Heat a large nonstick skillet over medium-high heat. Add oil to pan; swirl to coat. Add okra; cook 2 minutes without stirring. Stir; cook 5 minutes, stirring every 1 minute or until slightly charred. Sprinkle seasoning mixture over okra; cook an additional 30 seconds, turning with spatula. YIELD: 6 SERVINGS (SERVING SIZE: ½ CUP).

PER SERVING: Calories 31; Fat 0.9g (sat 0.1g, mono 0.5g, poly 0.3g); Protein 1.6g; Carb 5.5g; Fiber 2.5g; Chol 0mg; Iron 0.7mg; Sodium 154mg; Calc 63mg

HARICOTS VERTS WITH SHALLOTS AND PINE NUTS

PointsPlus value per serving: 2

HANDS-ON TIME: 8 min. ■ **TOTAL TIME:** 8 min.

Haricots verts are small, tender French green beans that usually don't need trimming. They often come in microwave-ready packages for quick and easy steaming

- **1 (8-ounce) package steam-in-bag haricots verts**
- **2 tablespoons pine nuts**
- **2 teaspoons butter**
- **⅓ cup thinly sliced shallots (1 large)**
- **¼ teaspoon salt**
- **¼ teaspoon freshly ground black pepper**

1. Cook haricots verts according to package directions.
2. While beans cook, heat a medium nonstick skillet over medium heat. Add pine nuts; cook 2 minutes or until toasted, shaking pan frequently. Remove pine nuts from pan.
3. Add butter to pan. Cook over medium heat until butter melts. Add shallots; sauté 3 minutes or until tender. Add haricots verts; sauté 2 minutes or until thoroughly heated. Sprinkle beans with salt, pepper, and pine nuts. YIELD: 4 SERVINGS (SERVING SIZE: ¼ OF BEANS).

PER SERVING: Calories 69; Fat 4.8g (sat 1.4g, mono 1.3g, poly 1.5g); Protein 1.6g; Carb 6.3g; Fiber 2.2g; Chol 5.1mg; Iron 0.7mg; Sodium 163mg; Calc 34mg

HOW TO EASILY SLICE SHALLOTS

These alliums look like extra-large garlic cloves and have a mild onion flavor. To prepare them, slice off both the root end and tip of the shallot, and discard. Peel off the papery skin. It's OK (and easier) to peel off a thin layer of the edible flesh. Halve the shallots lengthwise, and lay the halves flat on a cutting board. Cut each half into thin slices.

SESAME SUGAR SNAP PEAS

PointsPlus value per serving: 2

HANDS-ON TIME: 11 min. ■ **TOTAL TIME:** 14 min.

- **2 tablespoons rice vinegar**
- **2 teaspoons brown sugar**
- **2 teaspoons lower-sodium soy sauce**
- **2 teaspoons dark sesame oil**
- **¼ teaspoon freshly ground black pepper**
- **Cooking spray**
- **3 (8-ounce) packages sugar snap peas, trimmed**
- **2 teaspoons toasted sesame seeds**

1. Combine first 5 ingredients in a large bowl.
2. Heat a large nonstick skillet over medium-high heat. Coat pan with cooking spray. Add peas to pan; sauté 3 minutes or until crisp-tender.
3. Add peas to vinegar mixture, tossing to coat. Sprinkle with sesame seeds. YIELD: 6 SERVINGS (SERVING SIZE: 1 CUP).

PER SERVING: Calories 85; Fat 2.1g (sat 0.2g, mono 0.8g, poly 0.9g); Protein 3.2g; Carb 14.8g; Fiber 2.9g; Chol 0mg; Iron 2.5mg; Sodium 44mg; Calc 59mg

SUMMER VEGETABLE SAUTÉ

PointsPlus value per serving: 1   *pictured on page 141*

HANDS-ON TIME: 15 min. ■ **TOTAL TIME:** 15 min.

- **1 tablespoon olive oil**
- **1 cup vertically sliced sweet onion**
- **2 small yellow squash, halved lengthwise and thinly sliced (2¼ cups)**
- **1 medium zucchini, halved lengthwise and thinly sliced (2¼ cups)**
- **1 cup grape tomatoes, halved**
- **2 tablespoons thinly sliced fresh basil**
- **¼ teaspoon salt**
- **¼ teaspoon freshly ground black pepper**

1. Heat a large nonstick skillet over medium-high heat. Add oil to pan; swirl to coat. Add onion; sauté 4 minutes or until crisp-tender. Add squash and zucchini; cook 7 minutes or until tender and golden, stirring occasionally. Add tomatoes; cook 1 minute. Stir in basil, salt, and pepper. Serve immediately. YIELD: 6 SERVINGS (SERVING SIZE: ABOUT ½ CUP).

PER SERVING: Calories 50; Fat 2.4g (sat 0.4g, mono 1.7g, poly 0.3g); Protein 1.6g; Carb 6.6g; Fiber 1.8g; Chol 0mg; Iron 0.4mg; Sodium 106mg; Calc 25mg

PARMESAN-GARLIC CREAMED SPINACH

PointsPlus value per serving: 3

· **HANDS-ON TIME:** 15 min. ■ **TOTAL TIME:** 15 min.

Don't be worried about wilting spinach in a dry skillet—the spinach releases moisture almost immediately, preventing it from sticking to the pan.

2 (9-ounce) packages fresh spinach
½ cup fat-free milk
2 teaspoons all-purpose flour
¼ teaspoon freshly ground black pepper
⅛ teaspoon salt
Cooking spray
2 garlic cloves, minced
3 ounces ⅓-less-fat cream cheese, cut into small pieces
1 ounce grated fresh Parmesan cheese (about ¼ cup)

1. Heat a large nonstick skillet over medium–high heat. Add half of spinach; sauté 2 minutes or until spinach wilts. Remove spinach from pan, and place in a colander. Repeat procedure with remaining spinach. Drain well, pressing spinach with the back of a spoon until barely moist.
2. Combine milk and next 3 ingredients in a small bowl, stirring with a whisk until smooth. Heat a medium saucepan over medium heat. Coat pan with cooking spray. Add garlic to pan; sauté 30 seconds. Add milk mixture, stirring with a whisk. Bring to a boil; cook 1 minute or until thick, stirring constantly with a whisk. Stir in cheeses. Cook 1 minute, stirring constantly with a whisk. Stir in spinach; cook 1 minute or until thoroughly heated. **YIELD: 5 SERVINGS (SERVING SIZE: ABOUT ½ CUP).**

PER SERVING: Calories 106; Fat 5.9g (sat 3.5g, mono 0.5g, poly 0.2g); Protein 7.3g; Carb 7.6g; Fiber 2.3g; Chol 17.6mg; Iron 2.9mg; Sodium 304mg; Calc 209mg

SPINACH AND CHEESE POTATO GRATIN

PointsPlus value per serving: 4

HANDS-ON TIME: 25 min. ■ **TOTAL TIME:** 1 hr., 40 min.

Use a mandoline to get uniform, thinly sliced potatoes.

1 teaspoon olive oil
2 garlic cloves, minced
1 (9-ounce) package fresh spinach
4 cups thinly sliced peeled Yukon gold potatoes
    (1½ pounds)
Cooking spray
4 ounces Gruyère cheese, shredded and divided
3 tablespoons all-purpose flour
¾ teaspoon salt
½ teaspoon freshly ground black pepper
2 cups 1% low-fat milk

1. Preheat oven to 375°.
2. Heat a large nonstick skillet over medium–high heat. Add oil to pan; swirl to coat. Add garlic; sauté 30 seconds. Add spinach; sauté 1 to 2 minutes or until spinach wilts. Place spinach mixture in a colander, pressing with back of a spoon until barely moist.
3. Arrange half of potatoes in an 11 x 7–inch baking dish coated with cooking spray. Spread spinach mixture over potatoes; sprinkle with half of cheese. Top with remaining potatoes.
4. Place flour, salt, and pepper in a medium bowl. Gradually add milk, stirring with a whisk until blended. Pour milk mixture over potatoes; sprinkle with remaining cheese.
5. Bake, uncovered, at 375° for 1 hour or until cheese begins to brown. Let stand 15 minutes. **YIELD: 9 SERVINGS (SERVING SIZE: ⅑ OF CASSEROLE).**

PER SERVING: Calories 173; Fat 5.3g (sat 2.8g, mono 1.8g, poly 0.3g); Protein 8.1g; Carb 24.3g; Fiber 2.6g; Chol 16.6mg; Iron 1.4mg; Sodium 312mg; Calc 218mg

BUTTERMILK MASHED POTATOES

PointsPlus value per serving: 3

HANDS-ON TIME: 6 min. ▪ **TOTAL TIME:** 17 min.

The addition of fat-free milk helps smooth out the tang from the buttermilk in this classic comfort food.

> 2 (8-ounce) pre-wrapped microwavable
>   baking potatoes
> ½ cup fat-free milk
> 4 teaspoons butter
> ⅓ cup nonfat buttermilk
> ¼ teaspoon salt
> ¼ teaspoon freshly ground black pepper

1. Microwave potatoes according to package directions for multiple potatoes; cool slightly. Cut each potato in half lengthwise; scoop out pulp and place in a medium bowl.
2. Combine milk and butter in a 1-cup glass measuring cup; microwave at HIGH 1 minute or until butter melts. Add milk mixture to potatoes; mash with a potato masher. Stir in buttermilk, salt, and pepper. YIELD: 5 SERVINGS (SERVING SIZE: ½ CUP).

PER SERVING: Calories 107; Fat 3.2g (sat 2.0g, mono 0.8g, poly 0.1g); Protein 3.2g; Carb 17.2g; Fiber 1.1g; Chol 8.8mg; Iron 0.7mg; Sodium 170mg; Calc 63mg

MARSHMALLOW-TOPPED BAKED SWEET POTATOES

PointsPlus value per serving: 3

HANDS-ON TIME: 9 min. ▪ **TOTAL TIME:** 18 min.

Bake these casserole-inspired individual sweet potatoes to help keep those holiday portions under control.

> 2 (6- to 7-ounce) sweet potatoes
> 1 tablespoon brown sugar
> 1 tablespoon butter, softened
> 2 low-fat cinnamon graham crackers, coarsely crushed
>   (½ cup)
> ½ cup miniature marshmallows

1. Place potatoes in a medium microwave-safe bowl (do not pierce potatoes with a fork). Cover with plastic wrap; vent. Microwave at HIGH 8 minutes or until done.
2. Combine brown sugar and butter in a small bowl. Cut each potato lengthwise; fluff with a fork. Top potatoes evenly with butter mixture; sprinkle evenly with graham crackers and marshmallows.

3. Preheat broiler.
4. Place potatoes on a small baking sheet. Broil 30 seconds or until marshmallows are browned. Serve immediately. YIELD: 4 SERVINGS (SERVING SIZE: 1 POTATO HALF).

PER SERVING: Calories 135; Fat 3.0g (sat 1.8g, mono 0.8g, poly 0.1g); Protein 1.6g; Carb 25.9g; Fiber 2.9g; Chol 7.6mg; Iron 0.6mg; Sodium 85mg; Calc 24mg

ROASTED GARLIC AND HERB POLENTA

PointsPlus value per serving: 3

HANDS-ON TIME: 6 min. ▪ **TOTAL TIME:** 58 min.

Roasting garlic makes the cloves so soft that they can be spread, and it sweetens the pungent bite usually associated with fresh garlic.

> 1 whole garlic head
> 2 cups fat-free milk
> 2 cups water
> ¼ teaspoon salt
> 1 cup instant polenta
> 2 ounces ⅓-less-fat cream cheese, softened and
>   cut into pieces (about ¼ cup)
> 2 tablespoons chopped fresh parsley
> ¼ teaspoon freshly ground black pepper

1. Preheat oven to 400°.
2. Remove white papery skin from garlic heads (do not peel or separate the cloves). Wrap head in foil. Bake at 400° for 40 minutes; cool 10 minutes. Separate cloves; squeeze to extract garlic pulp. Discard skins.
3. Combine milk, 2 cups water, and salt in medium saucepan; bring to a boil over medium heat. Gradually stir in polenta. Cover; reduce heat to low, and cook 2 minutes. Remove from heat.
4. Stir in prepared garlic, cream cheese, parsley, and pepper, stirring until cream cheese melts. YIELD: 7 SERVINGS (SERVING SIZE: ABOUT ½ CUP).

PER SERVING: Calories 126; Fat 1.8g (sat 1.2g, mono 0.3g, poly 0.1g); Protein 4.8g; Carb 17.5g; Fiber 2.3g; Chol 7.2mg; Iron 0.2mg; Sodium 153mg; Calc 158mg

BARLEY RISOTTO WITH ROSEMARY SAUTÉED MUSHROOMS

PointsPlus value per serving: 3

HANDS-ON TIME: 17 min.   ■   **TOTAL TIME:** 52 min.

Olive oil-flavored cooking spray
1 cup finely chopped onion
1 cup uncooked pearl barley
3½ cups fat-free, lower-sodium chicken broth
1 ounce grated fresh Parmesan cheese (about ¼ cup)
¼ teaspoon freshly ground black pepper
2 teaspoons olive oil
1 garlic clove, minced
1 (8-ounce) package sliced cremini mushrooms
2 teaspoons chopped fresh rosemary

1. Preheat oven to 400°.
2. Heat a 4-quart ovenproof saucepan over medium heat. Coat pan with cooking spray. Add onion to pan; sauté 4 minutes or until tender. Add barley; sauté 1 minute. Add broth; bring to a boil over medium-high heat, stirring occasionally. Cover, and transfer pan to oven.
3. Bake at 400° for 40 minutes or until barley is tender and most of liquid is absorbed. Stir in cheese and pepper.
4. While barley mixture bakes, heat a large nonstick skillet over medium-high heat. Add oil to pan; swirl to coat. Add garlic; sauté 30 seconds. Add mushrooms; sauté 5 minutes or until browned. Stir in rosemary. Add mushrooms to barley mixture; stir gently to combine. YIELD: 9 SERVINGS (SERVING SIZE: ½ CUP).

PER SERVING: Calories 117; Fat 2.2g (sat 0.7g, mono 1.0g, poly 0.3g); Protein 4.8g; Carb 20.2g; Fiber 4.0g; Chol 2.3mg; Iron 0.7mg; Sodium 236mg; Calc 61mg

ARMENIAN RICE PILAF

PointsPlus value per serving: 5

HANDS-ON TIME: 20 min.   ■   **TOTAL TIME:** 1 hr., 1 min.

No peeking! The secret to perfect pilaf is to never lift the lid to stir or peek while the rice is cooking.

2 tablespoons butter
½ cup uncooked fine egg noodles
2 tablespoons minced shallots
1 cup uncooked long-grain white rice
2 cups fat-free, lower-sodium chicken broth
¼ teaspoon salt
¼ teaspoon freshly ground black pepper
2 tablespoons pine nuts, toasted
2 tablespoons thinly sliced fresh mint leaves

1. Melt butter in a large saucepan over low heat. Add noodles; sauté 1 minute or just until noodles begin to brown. Add shallots; sauté 1 minute. Add rice, stirring to coat. Stir in broth, salt, and pepper; bring to a boil. Cover, reduce heat, and simmer 20 minutes or until liquid is absorbed. Remove from heat; let stand, covered, 10 minutes. Add pine nuts and mint; fluff with a fork. YIELD: 6 SERVINGS (SERVING SIZE: ⅔ CUP).

PER SERVING: Calories 188; Fat 6.2g (sat 2.7g, mono 1.6g, poly 1.2g); Protein 3.7g; Carb 29.1g; Fiber 0.7g; Chol 15.6mg; Iron 1.7mg; Sodium 279mg; Calc 15mg

TOASTING PINE NUTS

Toasting intensifies flavor, but nuts are delicate and can quickly go from toasty to charred in seconds. For successful toasting, eschew the stovetop since it's almost impossible not to burn them. Instead, spread the nuts in a single layer on a baking sheet, and bake at 350° for as little as two minutes (longer for denser nuts). Stir the nuts frequently so they toast evenly. They're done when they've turned golden brown and smell fragrant.

MEDITERRANEAN ORZO

PointsPlus value per serving: 4

HANDS-ON TIME: 9 min.   ■   **TOTAL TIME:** 15 min.

Pair this flavorful side with Greek-seasoned chicken or lamb, or simple pan-seared salmon.

1 tablespoon olive oil, divided
⅓ cup diced red onion
1 small garlic clove, minced
2 cups hot cooked orzo (1 cup uncooked pasta)
1 cup chopped fresh baby spinach
1 cup diced plum tomato
1½ ounces crumbled feta cheese (about ½ cup)
2 tablespoons chopped pitted kalamata olives
¼ teaspoon salt
¼ teaspoon freshly ground black pepper

1. Heat a small nonstick skillet over medium-high heat. Add 1 teaspoon oil to pan; swirl to coat. Add onion and garlic; sauté 2 minutes or until tender. Remove from heat.
2. Combine onion mixture, remaining 2 teaspoons oil, orzo, and remaining ingredients in a large bowl; toss gently until spinach wilts. Serve immediately. YIELD: 6 SERVINGS (SERVING SIZE: ⅔ CUP).

PER SERVING: Calories 164; Fat 4.8g (sat 1.2g, mono 2.6g, poly 0.6g); Protein 5.4g; Carb 24.4g; Fiber 2.0g; Chol 3.8mg; Iron 0.3mg; Sodium 223mg; Calc 36mg

soups & stews

Chicken Enchilada Chowder, *page 162*

MANGO GAZPACHO

PointsPlus value per serving: 4

HANDS-ON TIME: 22 min. ■ **TOTAL TIME:** 4 hr., 22 min.

Fragrant, incredibly sweet Champagne mangoes are not as fibrous as their traditional counterpart. They will produce a smoother, more velvety soup. If you can't find them, substitute traditional mangoes instead.

1 garlic clove, halved
3 Champagne mangoes, peeled, coarsely
    chopped, and divided
⅔ cup fresh orange juice
2 tablespoons fresh lime juice
1 tablespoon seasoned rice vinegar
⅔ cup chopped English cucumber
1 jalapeño pepper, quartered and seeded
¼ cup thinly sliced green onions
2 tablespoons chopped fresh cilantro

1. Drop garlic through food chute with food processor on; process until minced. Add ⅓ of chopped mango, orange juice, lime juice, and vinegar; process 2 minutes or until mango is puréed. Add remaining chopped mango, cucumber, and jalapeño pepper; pulse 8 times or until finely chopped, scraping down sides of bowl. Pour into a bowl; stir in green onions and cilantro. Cover and chill at least 4 hours. YIELD: 4 SERVINGS (SERVING SIZE: ¾ CUP).

PER SERVING: Calories 136; Fat 0.9g (sat 0.0g, mono 0.3g, poly 0.2g); Protein 0.6g; Carb 32.6g; Fiber 2.1g; Chol 0.0mg; Iron 0.3mg; Sodium 78mg; Calc 15mg

BUYING CUCUMBER

Cucumbers add a cool, refreshing quality to soups, salads, and entrées. When shopping for cucumbers, look for those that are blemish-free with a dark green exterior. Softening first occurs at the ends, so feel the vegetable to make sure it's fresh and firm.

CHILLED PEA AND MINT SOUP

PointsPlus value per serving: 2

HANDS-ON TIME: 9 min. ■ **TOTAL TIME:** 3 hr., 47 min.

Petite green peas and fresh mint make this the perfect chilled soup for a spring lunch.

2 teaspoons olive oil
1½ cups chopped onion
2 garlic cloves, minced
2 cups organic vegetable broth
¼ cup fresh mint leaves
1 (16-ounce) bag frozen petite green peas,
    partially thawed
¼ cup light sour cream

1. Heat a large saucepan over medium–high heat. Add oil to pan; swirl to coat. Add onion to pan; sauté 3 minutes or until golden brown. Add garlic; sauté 1 minute. Add broth; bring to a simmer. Remove pan from heat. Add mint; cover and steep 30 minutes.
2. Add peas to broth mixture; cover and chill at least 3 hours. Place half of pea mixture in a blender; process until smooth. Repeat procedure with remaining half of pea mixture. Ladle soup into bowls; top evenly with sour cream. YIELD: 8 SERVINGS (SERVING SIZE: ½ CUP SOUP AND 1½ TEASPOONS SOUR CREAM).

PER SERVING: Calories 80; Fat 1.9g (sat 0.6g, mono 0.9g, poly 0.3g); Protein 3.6g; Carb 12.6g; Fiber 3.1g; Chol 2.5mg; Iron 1.0mg; Sodium 213mg; Calc 32.7mg

YUKON GOLD VICHYSSOISE

PointsPlus value per serving: 3

HANDS-ON TIME: 12 min. ■ **TOTAL TIME:** 2 hr., 47 min.

With their buttery texture, Yukon gold potatoes give this soup a velvety smoothness without much added cream. Vichyssoise is traditionally a cold potato-leek soup, but it would be equally delicious served warm. For a vegetarian soup, use organic vegetable broth.

1 tablespoon olive oil
2 cups thinly sliced leek (about 1 large)
4 cups fat-free, lower-sodium chicken broth
3 cups cubed peeled Yukon gold potato
¼ cup reduced-fat sour cream
¼ teaspoon freshly ground black pepper
Chopped fresh chives (optional)

1. Heat a Dutch oven over medium heat. Add oil to pan; swirl to coat. Add leek to pan; sauté 5 minutes or until tender. Add broth and potato to pan. Bring to a boil; reduce heat, and simmer 20 minutes or until potato is tender. Cool 10 minutes.
2. Place half of potato mixture in a blender. Remove center piece of blender lid (to allow steam to escape); secure blender lid on blender. Place a clean towel over opening in blender lid (to avoid splatters). Blend until smooth. Pour into a large bowl. Repeat procedure with remaining potato mixture. Stir in sour cream and black pepper. Cover and chill 2 hours or until cold. Garnish with chives, if desired. **YIELD: 6 SERVINGS (SERVING SIZE: 1 CUP).**

PER SERVING: Calories 124; Fat 3.7g (sat 1.1g, mono 2.0g, poly 0.4g); Protein 2.9g; Carb 20.5g; Fiber 2.0g; Chol 5.2mg; Iron 0.9mg; Sodium 316mg; Calc 41mg

BLENDING SOUPS

When pureeing hot soup in a blender, be sure to remove the center piece of the lid to allow the hot steam to escape. Otherwise, you may end up with soup all over your kitchen. The reason: Hot soup confined to a small, enclosed space like a blender can create enough pressure to literally blow off the lid. Place a towel over the opening to avoid splatters and to protect your hand from the heat.

CREAMY ROASTED CAULIFLOWER SOUP

PointsPlus value per serving: 3

HANDS-ON TIME: 7 min. ■ **TOTAL TIME:** 52 min.

Roasting the cauliflower and onions lends a subtle sweetness to this rich, satisfying soup. Cut large cauliflower florets in half to ensure even roasting.

2 (10-ounce) packages cauliflower florets, large pieces halved
1 medium onion, cut into ½-inch-thick wedges
1½ tablespoons olive oil
Cooking spray
2 garlic cloves, minced
2 cups organic vegetable broth
2 cups 2% reduced-fat milk
2 teaspoons chopped fresh thyme
⅜ teaspoon salt
¼ teaspoon freshly ground black pepper
2 teaspoons fresh lemon juice

1. Preheat oven to 450°.
2. Place cauliflower and onion on a large rimmed baking sheet. Drizzle with oil; toss to coat. Bake at 450° for 30 minutes or just until vegetables are tender and browned.
3. Heat a large Dutch oven over medium-high heat. Coat pan with cooking spray. Add garlic to pan; sauté 30 seconds. Add roasted vegetables, broth, and next 4 ingredients. Bring to a boil; cover, reduce heat, and simmer 10 minutes or until vegetables are very tender.
4. Place half of soup mixture in a blender. Remove center piece of blender lid (to allow steam to escape); secure blender lid on blender. Place a clean towel over opening in blender lid (to avoid splatters). Blend until smooth. Repeat procedure with remaining soup mixture. Stir in lemon juice. **YIELD: 5 SERVINGS (SERVING SIZE: 1 CUP).**

PER SERVING: Calories 128; Fat 6.3g (sat 1.8g, mono 3.5g, poly 0.6g); Protein 5.8g; Carb 13.8g; Fiber 3.3g; Chol 7.8mg; Iron 0.7mg; Sodium 480mg; Calc 148mg

CREAMY CHEDDAR-ONION SOUP

PointsPlus value per serving: 6

HANDS-ON TIME: 19 min. ■ **TOTAL TIME:** 19 min.

So good on a chilly night...this thick, cheesy soup will warm you to your toes.

2 lower-sodium bacon slices
½ cup chopped yellow onion
2 cups fat-free, lower-sodium chicken broth, divided
2 cups 2% reduced-fat milk
⅓ cup all-purpose flour
4 ounces reduced-fat sharp cheddar cheese, shredded
¼ teaspoon dry mustard
¼ teaspoon salt
¼ teaspoon freshly ground black pepper

1. Cook bacon in a Dutch oven over medium heat until crisp. Remove bacon from pan, reserving 2 teaspoons drippings. Crumble bacon, and set aside. Add onion to drippings in pan; sauté 4 minutes.
2. Add 1 cup broth and milk to pan. Combine flour with remaining 1 cup chicken broth in a small bowl, stirring with a whisk until well blended. Add to pan, stirring with a whisk to combine. Cook over medium heat until thick (about 5 minutes), stirring constantly. Remove from heat; stir in cheese, dry mustard, salt, and pepper, stirring until cheese melts. Ladle soup evenly into bowls; sprinkle evenly with reserved bacon. YIELD: 4 SERVINGS (SERVING SIZE: 1 CUP SOUP AND ½ TABLESPOON BACON).

PER SERVING: Calories 239; Fat 12.3g (sat 7.1g, mono 4.1g, poly 0.8g); Protein 14.0g; Carb 16.7g; Fiber 0.7g; Chol 34.6mg; Iron 0.6mg; Sodium 712mg; Calc 352mg

POTATO SOUP WITH CORNED BEEF AND CABBAGE

PointsPlus value per serving: 8

HANDS-ON TIME: 20 min. ■ **TOTAL TIME:** 28 min.

We loved this soup so much that we gave it one of our highest ratings. To achieve your desired consistency when reheating any leftovers (if there are any), just stir in some chicken broth or fat-free milk.

5 (8-ounce) pre-wrapped microwavable baking potatoes
3 ounces all-purpose flour (about ⅔ cup)
6 cups 2% reduced-fat milk
1¼ teaspoons salt, divided
½ teaspoon freshly ground black pepper
1 cup reduced-fat sour cream
½ cup sliced green onions
2 ounces shredded Gruyère or Swiss cheese (about ½ cup)
1 teaspoon canola oil
2 cups thinly sliced savoy cabbage
¼ teaspoon caraway seeds
4 ounces thinly sliced lean deli corned beef, cut into strips

1. Microwave potatoes according to package directions for multiple potatoes; cool slightly. Peel potatoes; coarsely mash.
2. Weigh or lightly spoon flour into dry measuring cups; level with a knife. Place flour in a large Dutch oven. Gradually add milk; cook over medium heat until thick and bubbly (about 12 minutes), stirring constantly with a whisk.
3. Stir in mashed potatoes, 1 teaspoon salt, and pepper. Reduce heat to low; cook over low heat 5 minutes or until thoroughly heated, stirring occasionally. Stir in sour cream and green onions. Remove from heat; add cheese, stirring until cheese melts.
4. Heat a large nonstick skillet over medium–high heat. Add oil to pan; swirl to coat. Add cabbage, caraway seeds, corned beef, and remaining ¼ teaspoon salt; sauté 2 minutes or just until cabbage begins to wilt. Ladle soup into bowls; spoon cabbage mixture evenly into center of each serving. YIELD: 9 SERVINGS (SERVING SIZE: 1¼ CUPS SOUP AND ABOUT ¼ CUP CABBAGE MIXTURE).

PER SERVING: Calories 322; Fat 9.6g (sat 5.6g, mono 2.8g, poly 0.6g); Protein 14.0g; Carb 45.5g; Fiber 2.9g; Chol 39.6mg; Iron 1.4mg; Sodium 582mg; Calc 303mg

GINGERED BUTTERNUT SQUASH SOUP WITH RYE CROUTONS

PointsPlus value per serving: 3

HANDS-ON TIME: 15 min. ■ **TOTAL TIME:** 35 min.

Use frozen puréed squash for a quick weeknight supper. Look for a brand that doesn't contain added salt.

½ cup (½-inch) cubes rye bread
1 tablespoon olive oil
2 tablespoons grated peeled fresh ginger
3 garlic cloves, minced
1 cup water
1 cup fat-free, lower-sodium chicken broth
¼ teaspoon salt
2 (12-ounce) packages frozen puréed butternut
    squash, thawed
2 teaspoons chopped fresh thyme
3 tablespoons light sour cream

1. Preheat oven to 400°.
2. Spread bread cubes in a single layer on an ungreased baking sheet. Bake at 400° for 7 minutes or until crisp.
3. While bread cubes bake, heat a large saucepan over medium-high heat. Add oil to pan; swirl to coat. Add ginger and garlic; sauté 30 seconds. Add 1 cup water and next 3 ingredients. Bring to a boil; cover, reduce heat, and simmer 20 minutes. Stir in thyme. Ladle soup into bowls. Top each serving evenly with sour cream and croutons. Serve immediately. YIELD: 6 SERV-INGS (SERVING SIZE: ¾ CUP SOUP, 1½ TEASPOONS SOUR CREAM, AND 2 TEASPOONS CROUTONS).

PER SERVING: Calories 112; Fat 3.2g (sat 0.9g, mono 1.8g, poly 0.4g); Protein 3.2g; Carb 20g; Fiber 1.9g; Chol 0mg; Iron 1.2mg; Sodium 215mg; Calc 42mg

WHITE BEAN–SPINACH SOUP

PointsPlus value per serving: 3

HANDS-ON TIME: 9 min. ■ **TOTAL TIME:** 38 min.

You can omit the bacon and use vegetable broth instead of the chicken broth to transform this soup into a hearty vegetarian option for lunch or dinner.

2 center-cut bacon slices
1½ cups chopped onion
½ cup chopped celery
½ cup chopped carrot
2 garlic cloves, chopped
2 cups fat-free, lower-sodium chicken broth
2 cups water
¼ teaspoon freshly ground black pepper
2 (15.8-ounce) cans great Northern or cannellini
    beans, rinsed and drained
3 cups chopped fresh spinach
¼ teaspoon crushed red pepper

1. Cook bacon in a Dutch oven over medium heat until crisp. Remove bacon from pan, reserving 1 teaspoon drippings. Crumble bacon, and set aside.
2. Add onion, celery, carrot, and garlic to drippings in pan; sauté 5 minutes or until soft. Add broth, 2 cups water, black pepper, and beans; bring to a boil. Reduce heat; simmer 15 minutes.
3. Place 2 cups bean mixture in a blender. Remove center piece of blender lid (to allow steam to escape); secure blender lid on blender. Place a clean towel over opening in blender lid (to avoid splatters). Blend until smooth. Return puree to pan; stir in spinach. Cook 1 minute or until spinach wilts. Stir in red pepper. Ladle soup into bowls; sprinkle evenly with crumbled bacon. YIELD: 6 SERVINGS (SERVING SIZE: 1 CUP SOUP AND 1 TEASPOON BACON).

PER SERVING: Calories 124; Fat 1.5g (sat 0.7g, mono 0.6g, poly 0.2g); Protein 7.9g; Carb 20.5g; Fiber 5.9g; Chol 3.2mg; Iron 1.9mg; Sodium 372mg; Calc 77mg

BEEFY MINESTRONE

PointsPlus value per serving: 4

HANDS-ON TIME: 29 min. ■ **TOTAL TIME:** 1 hr., 1 min.

Although ditalini pasta is classic in minestrone, any small, shaped pasta, such as seashells or elbow macaroni will work. Broth and water combine to keep the sodium levels in check.

- 8 ounces lean ground beef
- 1 tablespoon olive oil
- 1 cup chopped onion
- ⅔ cup diced peeled carrot
- ⅔ cup diced celery
- 3 garlic cloves, minced
- 1 tablespoon tomato paste
- 2 cups water
- 1 teaspoon dried Italian seasoning
- ½ teaspoon freshly ground black pepper
- 1 (28-ounce) can petite diced tomatoes, undrained
- 1 (15.5-ounce) can cannellini beans, rinsed and drained
- 1 (14.5-ounce) can lower-sodium beef broth
- ¼ teaspoon salt
- 1 bay leaf
- ½ cup uncooked ditalini (very short tube-shaped pasta)
- 2 cups chopped fresh baby spinach
- 3 tablespoons grated fresh Parmesan cheese

1. Heat a Dutch oven over medium–high heat. Add beef to pan; cook 8 minutes or until browned, stirring to crumble; drain. Wipe pan with a paper towel.
2. Reduce heat to medium. Add oil to pan; swirl to coat. Add onion, carrot, and celery; sauté 10 minutes. Add garlic; sauté 1 minute. Return beef to pan; stir in tomato paste. Add 2 cups water, Italian seasoning, and next 6 ingredients; bring to a boil, stirring occasionally. Cover, reduce heat, and simmer 25 minutes, stirring occasionally.
3. Add pasta to pan; cook, uncovered, 7 minutes or until pasta is done, stirring occasionally. Remove from heat; stir in spinach. Ladle soup into bowls; sprinkle evenly with cheese. YIELD: 8 SERVINGS (SERVING SIZE: 1 CUP SOUP AND 1 TEASPOON CHEESE).

PER SERVING: Calories 172; Fat 5.1g (sat 1.7g, mono 2.5g, poly 0.4g); Protein 11.6g; Carb 20.3g; Fiber 3.9g; Chol 16.8mg; Iron 2.4mg; Sodium 452mg; Calc 76.9mg

BROWNING GROUND BEEF

Don't add ground meat fresh out of the refrigerator to a hot pan. The still-cold meat will cool the pan, causing the meat to release its juices, which keep it flavorful and moist. Instead, let your meat come to room temperature before you add it to the pan.

CHICKEN AND WILD RICE SOUP

PointsPlus value per serving: 6

HANDS-ON TIME: 16 min. ■ **TOTAL TIME:** 19 min.

The flavor of your favorite creamy version of this soup without the fat and calories makes this cool-weather soup a winner.

- 1 (2.75-ounce) package quick-cooking wild rice
- ½ teaspoon salt, divided
- 1 tablespoon olive oil
- ½ cup chopped carrot
- 1 (8-ounce) container prechopped celery, pepper, and onion mix
- 1 (8-ounce) package presliced mushrooms
- 2 cups chopped cooked chicken breast
- ½ teaspoon dried Italian seasoning
- ¼ teaspoon freshly ground black pepper
- 3 cups fat-free, lower-sodium chicken broth

1. Cook rice according package directions, adding ¼ teaspoon salt and omitting fat. Set aside.
2. Heat a Dutch oven over medium–high heat. Add oil to pan; swirl to coat. Add carrot and celery, pepper, and onion mix to pan; sauté 3 minutes. Add mushrooms; sauté 3 minutes. Add chicken, Italian seasoning, black pepper, and remaining ¼ teaspoon salt; sauté 1 minute. Stir in broth and prepared rice; cook 3 minutes or until thoroughly heated. YIELD: 4 SERVINGS (SERVING SIZE: 1⅔ CUPS).

PER SERVING: Calories 293; Fat 6.1g (sat 1.2g, mono 3.3g, poly 0.9g); Protein 28.0g; Carb 22.9g; Fiber 2.7g; Chol 59.5mg; Iron 1.6mg; Sodium 715mg; Calc 45mg

SUMMER VEGETABLE CHICKEN SOUP

PointsPlus value per serving: 4

HANDS-ON TIME: 12 min. ■ **TOTAL TIME:** 42 min.

Freeze this soup to preserve the flavor of fresh-from-the-farm summer vegetables, and enjoy it later in the year.

1 tablespoon olive oil
1 cup chopped onion
2 garlic cloves, minced
3 cups fat-free, lower-sodium chicken broth
1½ cups (1-inch) cut green beans
1 cup frozen baby lima beans
2 yellow squash, halved lengthwise and thinly
    sliced (1½ cups)
1 large zucchini, halved lengthwise and thinly
    sliced (1½ cups)
2 cups shredded skinless, boneless rotisserie
    chicken breast
⅜ teaspoon salt
¼ teaspoon freshly ground black pepper
1 (14.5-ounce) can diced tomatoes, undrained

1. Heat a 5-quart Dutch oven over medium-high heat. Add oil to pan; swirl to coat. Add onion; sauté 5 minutes or until tender. Add garlic; sauté 30 seconds. Stir in broth, green beans, and lima beans. Bring to a boil; cover, reduce heat, and simmer 10 minutes.
2. Add yellow squash and zucchini. Cover and simmer 10 minutes or until vegetables are tender. Stir in chicken and remaining ingredients; cook, uncovered, 2 minutes or until thoroughly heated. YIELD: 8 SERVINGS (SERVING SIZE: 1 CUP).

PER SERVING: Calories 192; Fat 3.3g (sat .7g, mono 1.7g, poly .6g); Protein 17.9g; Carb 23g; Fiber 7.1g; Chol 30mg; Iron 2.5mg; Sodium 426mg; Calc 56mg

ROTISSERIE CHICKEN

When you purchase rotisserie chicken from your grocery store, look for a bird that's just been cooked. Most stores follow a schedule and the packages are labeled with the time the chickens came off the spit. Stick with the original, unflavored versions, which are more versatile.

SMOKED CHICKEN–CORN CHOWDER

PointsPlus value per serving: 7

HANDS-ON TIME: 13 min. ■ **TOTAL TIME:** 36 min.

This is one hearty bowlful of flavor that chooses to bypass the traditional cream base often associated with chowders. The smoked chicken really adds a distinctive character.

1 tablespoon olive oil
1 cup chopped onion
2 garlic cloves, minced
2 cups fat-free, lower-sodium chicken broth
2 cups chopped peeled baking potato
2 cups frozen whole-kernel corn
½ cup water
½ teaspoon freshly ground black pepper
2 (14.5-ounce) cans diced tomatoes with basil, garlic,
    and oregano, undrained
2 cups shredded smoked chicken
3 tablespoons chopped fresh flat-leaf parsley

1. Heat a Dutch oven over medium-high heat. Add oil to pan; swirl to coat. Add onion; sauté 3 minutes. Add garlic; sauté 1 minute. Add broth and next 5 ingredients; bring to a boil. Cover, reduce heat, and simmer 20 minutes or until potato is tender. Stir in chicken; cook 3 minutes or until thoroughly heated. Ladle soup evenly into bowls. Sprinkle evenly with parsley. YIELD: 6 SERVINGS (SERVING SIZE: 1⅔ CUPS).

PER SERVING: Calories 266; Fat 4.9g (sat 1.0g, mono 2.6g, poly 0.9g); Protein 21.0g; Carb 35.7g; Fiber 3.9g; Chol 39.7mg; Iron 2.8mg; Sodium 553mg; Calc 49.0mg

CHICKEN ENCHILADA CHOWDER

PointsPlus value per serving: *7*   *pictured on page 142*

HANDS-ON TIME: 12 min. ■ **TOTAL TIME:** 46 min.

Offer a variety of toppings so each person can customize their own bowl of chowder. We recommend chopped fresh cilantro, diced avocado, light sour cream, and crushed baked tortilla chips.

Cooking spray
1 cup chopped onion
1 cup frozen whole-kernel corn
1 cup fat-free milk
1 (15-ounce) can black beans, rinsed and drained
1 (14.5-ounce) can no-salt-added diced tomatoes, drained
1 (10.75-ounce) can condensed reduced-fat, reduced-sodium cream of chicken soup, undiluted
1 (10-ounce) can mild red enchilada sauce
3 cups shredded cooked chicken breast (about 11½ ounces)
6 tablespoons crumbled cotija cheese

1. Heat a large Dutch oven over medium heat. Coat pan with cooking spray. Add onion to pan; sauté 3 minutes or until tender. Stir in corn and next 5 ingredients. Bring to a boil; reduce heat, and simmer, uncovered, 20 minutes, stirring occasionally. Stir in chicken; simmer 10 minutes, stirring occasionally. Ladle chowder into bowls; sprinkle with cheese. YIELD: 6 SERVINGS (SERVING SIZE: 1 CUP CHOWDER AND 1 TABLESPOON CHEESE).

PER SERVING: Calories 286; Fat 7g (sat 2.8g, mono 1.9g, poly 1.1g); Protein 29.3g; Carb 25.4g; Fiber 4.9g; Chol 71.1mg; Iron 1.6mg; Sodium 706mg; Calc 147mg

COTIJA

This white cheese has a sharp, salty flavor that softens but doesn't melt. You can find it in large supermarkets or Hispanic markets. If you can't find it, Parmesan or feta are good substitutes.

LAMB AND BLACK BEAN CHILI

PointsPlus value per serving: *8*   *pictured on page 143*

HANDS-ON TIME: 14 min. ■ **TOTAL TIME:** 41 min.

Ask your butcher to grind a lean portion of lamb for this hearty chili.

1½ pounds lean ground lamb
Cooking spray
1 cup chopped onion
2 garlic cloves, minced
1 cup dry red wine
2 teaspoons chili powder
½ teaspoon salt
1½ teaspoons dried oregano
1½ teaspoons bottled roasted ground cumin
1 teaspoon unsweetened cocoa
1 teaspoon light brown sugar
¼ teaspoon crushed red pepper
3 (15-ounce) cans black beans, rinsed and drained
2 (14.5-ounce) cans diced tomatoes, undrained

1. Heat a Dutch oven over medium–high heat. Add lamb to pan; cook 6 minutes or until browned, stirring to crumble. Drain well.
2. Return pan to heat. Coat pan with cooking spray. Add onion and garlic to pan; sauté 4 minutes or until tender. Return lamb to pan; add wine and remaining ingredients. Bring to a boil; reduce heat, cover, and simmer 20 minutes. YIELD: 8 SERVINGS (SERVING SIZE: ABOUT 1¼ CUPS).

PER SERVING: Calories 324; Fat 14g (sat 5.5g, mono 5.7g, poly 1.1g); Protein 24g; Carb 25g; Fiber 7.3g; Chol 66mg; Iron 3.7mg; Sodium 687mg; Calc 78mg

seasonal menus

Herbed Potato Salad, *page 171*

Fall Menu

Serves 4

Total **PointsPlus** value per serving: 16

Herb-Crusted Pork Tenderloin, page 164

Parmesan-Thyme Butternut Squash, page 165

Sautéed Spinach with Pine Nuts, page 165

Cinnamon, Apple, and Raisin Crisp, page 165

GAME PLAN:

1. One day in advance:
- Peel and cut butternut squash into cubes for **Parmesan-Thyme Butternut Squash.**

2. About 1 hour before the meal:
- Assemble **Cinnamon, Apple, and Raisin Crisp.** Set aside.
- Place squash and shallots for **Parmesan-Thyme Butternut Squash** in oven to bake.

3. While vegetables bake:
- Prepare **Herb-Crusted Pork Tenderloin.** Place tenderloin in oven with vegetables.

4. While tenderloin stands:
- Reduce oven temperature to 375°, and place assembled **Cinnamon, Apple, and Raisin Crisp** in oven.
- Prepare **Sautéed Spinach with Pine Nuts.**
- Toss together remaining ingredients for **Parmesan-Thyme Butternut Squash.**

HERB-CRUSTED PORK TENDERLOIN

PointsPlus value per serving: 4

HANDS-ON TIME: 10 min. ■ **TOTAL TIME:** 40 min.

Use any combination of herbs in this recipe.

1½ tablespoons chopped fresh rosemary
1 tablespoon olive oil
1 tablespoon chopped fresh thyme
1 tablespoon chopped fresh parsley
¼ teaspoon salt
¼ teaspoon freshly ground black pepper
1 (1-pound) pork tenderloin, trimmed
Cooking spray

1. Preheat oven to 450°.
2. Combine first 6 ingredients in small bowl; rub herb mixture over pork. Place pork on rack of a broiler pan coated with cooking spray.
3. Bake at 450° for 10 minutes. Reduce oven temperature to 400°; bake an additional 10 minutes or until a thermometer registers 145° (medium-rare). Let stand 10 minutes. Cut tenderloin crosswise into 12 slices.

YIELD: 4 SERVINGS (SERVING SIZE: 3 SLICES).

PER SERVING: Calories 158; Fat 6.1g (sat 1.3g, mono 3.4g, poly 0.8g); Protein 23.9g; Carb 0.5g; Fiber 0.3g; Chol 74mg; Iron 1.4mg; Sodium 208mg; Calc 12mg

PARMESAN-THYME BUTTERNUT SQUASH

PointsPlus value per serving: 3

HANDS-ON TIME: 10 min. ■ **TOTAL TIME:** 45 min.

Look for pre-cubed butternut squash at your local supermarket to avoid peeling and cubing the squash yourself.

   1 (1-pound) butternut squash, peeled and cut into ½-inch
       cubes
   1 shallot, peeled and cut into eighths
   Cooking spray
   1 ounce grated fresh Parmesan cheese (about ¼ cup)
   1 tablespoon butter
   2 teaspoons chopped fresh thyme
   ¼ teaspoon salt
   ¼ teaspoon freshly ground black pepper

1. Preheat oven to 450°.
2. Arrange squash and shallots in a single layer on a baking sheet coated with cooking spray. Bake at 450° for 35 minutes or until squash is tender and browned, stirring once.
3. Place vegetable mixture in a bowl. Add cheese and remaining ingredients; toss well. **YIELD: 4 SERVINGS (SERVING SIZE: ⅔ CUP).**

PER SERVING: Calories 115; Fat 5.2g (sat 3.1g, mono 1.4g, poly 0.2g); Protein 4.2g; Carb 14.9g; Fiber 2.4g; Chol 14mg; Iron 1mg; Sodium 286mg; Calc 136mg

SAUTÉED SPINACH WITH PINE NUTS

PointsPlus value per serving: 3

HANDS-ON TIME: 12 min. ■ **TOTAL TIME:** 12 min.

Packed with iron, calcium, vitamins C and K, and many more valuable nutrients, spinach could probably be called one of the world's most nutrient-dense foods. All we know is it just tastes best when prepared simply, as we've done here.

   3 tablespoons pine nuts
   2 teaspoons olive oil
   2 garlic cloves, minced
   2 (9-ounce) packages fresh spinach
   2 teaspoons balsamic vinegar
   ¼ teaspoon salt
   ¼ teaspoon freshly ground black pepper

1. Place pine nuts in a large skillet; cook over medium heat 3 minutes or until lightly browned, shaking pan frequently. Remove nuts from pan; set aside.

2. Add oil and garlic to pan; sauté 30 seconds. Add 1 package of spinach; sauté 2 minutes or until spinach wilts. Transfer to a bowl.
3. Add remaining 1 package of spinach to pan; sauté 2 minutes or until spinach wilts. Transfer to bowl. Stir in vinegar, salt, and pepper; top with nuts. Serve immediately. **YIELD: 4 SERVINGS (SERVING SIZE: ABOUT ⅔ CUP).**

PER SERVING: Calories 97; Fat 7.1g (sat 0.7g, mono 2.8g, poly 2.6g); Protein 4.6g; Carb 6.5g; Fiber 3.1g; Chol 0mg; Iron 3.9mg; Sodium 249mg; Calc 131mg

CINNAMON, APPLE, AND RAISIN CRISP

PointsPlus value per serving: 6

HANDS-ON TIME: 12 min. ■ **TOTAL TIME:** 1 hr., 7 min.

Feel free to substitute whole-wheat flour for the all-purpose in the topping; it adds fiber and bumps up the wholesome flavor.

   1.5 ounces all-purpose flour (about ⅓ cup)
   ½ cup packed light brown sugar
   ⅓ cup old-fashioned rolled oats
   ¾ teaspoon ground cinnamon, divided
   ¼ cup chilled butter, cut into small pieces
   3 tablespoons chopped walnuts
   8½ cups thinly sliced peeled Braeburn apple (about 2
       pounds)
   ½ cup raisins
   2 tablespoons maple syrup
   Cooking spray

1. Preheat oven to 375°.
2. Weigh or lightly spoon flour into a dry measuring cup; level with a knife. Combine flour, brown sugar, oats, and ¼ teaspoon cinnamon in a medium bowl; cut in butter with a pastry blender or 2 knives until mixture resembles coarse meal. Stir in walnuts.
3. Combine apple, raisins, maple syrup, and remaining ½ teaspoon cinnamon in a large bowl; toss well. Spoon apple mixture into an 8-inch square glass or ceramic baking dish coated with cooking spray. Sprinkle with crumb mixture.
4. Bake at 375° for 55 minutes or until apple slices are tender and topping is golden brown. Serve warm. **YIELD: 9 SERVINGS (SERVING SIZE: ½ CUP).**

PER SERVING: Calories 221; Fat 7.2g (sat 3.5g, mono 1.6g, poly 1.5g); Protein 1.8g; Carb 40.4g; Fiber 2.3g; Chol 14mg; Iron 0.8mg; Sodium 50mg; Calc 31mg

Winter Menu

Serves 8

Total **PointsPlus** value per serving: 18

Almond-Crusted Turkey Cutlets, page 166

Roasted Brussels Sprouts, page 167

Cranberry-Orange Wild Rice, page 167

Pumpkin Cake, page 167

GAME PLAN:

1. About 1 hour before the meal:
- Prepare and bake **Pumpkin Cake.**

2. While cake cools:
- Increase oven temperature to 450°. Prepare and cook **Roasted Brussels Sprouts.**

3. While sprouts cook:
- Prepare rice for **Cranberry-Orange Wild Rice.**

4. While rice cooks:
- Prepare and cook **Almond-Crusted Turkey Cutlets.**
- Combine remaining ingredients for **Cranberry-Orange Wild Rice.**

ALMOND-CRUSTED TURKEY CUTLETS

PointsPlus value per serving: 8

HANDS-ON TIME: 32 min. ■ **TOTAL TIME:** 32 min.

Lean turkey cutlets get all dressed up in a nutty Dijon and thyme coating.

- 16 (2-ounce) turkey cutlets
- ½ teaspoon salt
- ½ teaspoon freshly ground black pepper
- 2 large eggs
- 2 teaspoons Dijon mustard
- 1⅓ cups sliced almonds
- 1 cup dry breadcrumbs
- 2 teaspoons chopped fresh thyme
- 3 tablespoons olive oil, divided
- Cooking spray

1. Sprinkle cutlets evenly with salt and pepper. Combine eggs and mustard in a shallow dish. Combine almonds, breadcrumbs, and thyme in another shallow dish.

2. Dip cutlets in egg mixture; dredge in almond mixture, pressing firmly to adhere. Shake off excess almond mixture.

3. Heat a large nonstick skillet over medium heat. Add 1 tablespoon oil to pan; swirl to coat. Add 5 cutlets to pan; coat cutlets with cooking spray. Cook 3 to 4 minutes on each side or until done. Repeat procedure two times with remaining oil, remaining cutlets, and cooking spray. YIELD: 8 SERVINGS (SERVING SIZE: 2 CUTLETS).

PER SERVING: Calories 326; Fat 15.1g (sat 2g, mono 9.2g, poly 2.9g); Protein 34.7g; Carb 13.5g; Fiber 2.5g; Chol 98mg; Iron 3mg; Sodium 394mg; Calc 73mg

ROASTED BRUSSELS SPROUTS

PointsPlus value per serving: 1

HANDS-ON TIME: 10 min. ■ **TOTAL TIME:** 25 min.

We bet you'll change your mind about Brussels sprouts once you've tried them roasted with garlic and onion. These sprouts are cooked until crisp-tender, so they still have some crunch. Roast them a few minutes longer if you prefer your sprouts more tender.

- ½ cup sliced onion
- 1 tablespoon olive oil
- ¼ teaspoon salt
- ¼ teaspoon freshly ground black pepper
- 2 garlic cloves, minced
- 1 pound Brussels sprouts, trimmed and halved lengthwise

1. Preheat oven to 450°.
2. Combine all ingredients in a large bowl, tossing well to coat. Arrange in a single layer on a foil-lined jelly-roll pan.
3. Bake at 450° for 15 to 18 minutes or until sprouts are browned and crisp-tender, stirring once. YIELD: 8 SERV-INGS (SERVING SIZE: ½ CUP).

PER SERVING: Calories 44; Fat 1.9g (sat 0.3g, mono 1.3g, poly 0.3g); Protein 2.1g; Carb 6g; Fiber 2.3g; Chol 0mg; Iron 0.8mg; Sodium 88mg; Calc 27mg

CRANBERRY-ORANGE WILD RICE

PointsPlus value per serving: 4

HANDS-ON TIME: 13 min. ■ **TOTAL TIME:** 13 min.

Utilizing a quick-cooking version of wild rice means this side dish is ready in less than 15 minutes as compared to nearly an hour.

- 2 (2.75-ounce) packages quick-cooking wild rice
- 1 cup sweetened dried cranberries
- ½ cup sliced green onions
- 4 teaspoons olive oil
- 1 teaspoon grated fresh orange rind
- ½ teaspoon salt
- ½ teaspoon freshly ground black pepper

1. Cook rice according to package directions, omitting salt and fat.
2. Combine rice and remaining ingredients. Serve immediately. YIELD: 8 SERVINGS (SERVING SIZE: ABOUT ½ CUP).

PER SERVING: Calories 183; Fat 2.3g (sat 0.3g, mono 1.6g, poly 0.2g); Protein 3.9g; Carb 29.4g; Fiber 2.4g; Chol 0mg; Iron 0.7mg; Sodium 150mg; Calc 19mg

PUMPKIN CAKE

PointsPlus value per serving: 5

HANDS-ON TIME: 7 min. ■ **TOTAL TIME:** 1 hr., 7 min.

We not only gave this cake high marks for its autumn flavors, but we also liked that you can whip it up in a flash.

- 3 large egg whites
- 1 (16.25-ounce) box white cake mix
- 1 (15-ounce) can pumpkin
- ½ teaspoon pumpkin pie spice
- ¼ cup canola oil
- Cooking spray
- 1 cup frozen fat-free whipped topping, thawed (optional)

1. Preheat oven to 350°.
2. Place first 5 ingredients in a large bowl. Beat with a mixer at low speed 30 seconds; scrape sides of bowl. Beat at medium-high speed 2 minutes. Pour batter into a 13 x 9–inch metal baking pan coated with cooking spray.
3. Bake at 350° for 30 minutes or until a wooden pick inserted in center comes out clean. Cool completely on a wire rack. Cut into 16 pieces. Top each serving with 1 tablespoon whipped topping, if desired. YIELD: 16 SERV-INGS (SERVING SIZE: 1 PIECE).

PER SERVING: Calories 166; Fat 6.8g (sat 0.7g, mono 3.5g, poly 2.2g); Protein 2.4g; Carb 24.6g; Fiber 1.4g; Chol 0mg; Iron 0.6mg; Sodium 203mg; Calc 61mg

Spring Menu

Serves 8

Total **PointsPlus** value per serving: 16

Frozen Honeydew Limeade, page 168

Crustless Ham, Leek, and Asparagus Quiche, page 168

Mixed Greens with Poppy Seed Vinaigrette, page, 169

Raspberry-Lemon Cream Bars, page 169

GAME PLAN:

1. **About 4 hours before the meal:**
   - Cube honeydew, and place in freezer.

2. **About 1½ hours before the meal:**
   - Prepare and bake **Raspberry-Lemon Cream Bars.**

3. **While bars bake:**
   - Prepare **Crustless Ham, Leek, and Asparagus Quiche.**

4. **While quiche cools:**
   - Prepare **Mixed Greens with Poppy Seed Vinaigrette** and **Frozen Honeydew Limeade.**

FROZEN HONEYDEW LIMEADE

PointsPlus value per serving: 4

HANDS-ON TIME: 10 min. ■ **TOTAL TIME:** 3 hr., 10 min.

4 cups (1-inch) cubed honeydew melon
2 cups fresh lime juice (about 12 limes)
2 cups lime sparkling water, chilled
1 cup sugar
½ cup mint leaves
4 cups sugar-free ginger ale, chilled
Lime slices (optional)

1. Freeze cubed honeydew at least 3 hours.
2. Place 2 cups frozen honeydew, 1 cup lime juice, 1 cup sparkling water, ½ cup sugar, and ¼ cup mint in a blender; process until smooth. Repeat procedure with remaining honeydew, lime juice, sparkling water, sugar, and mint.
3. Pour ½ cup ginger ale in bottom of each of 8 chilled glasses. Pour 1 cup honeydew mixture in each glass; stir gently. Garnish with lime slices, if desired. YIELD: 8 SERVINGS (SERVING SIZE: 1½ CUPS).

PER SERVING: Calories 146; Fat 0.2g (sat 0.1g, mono 0g, poly 0.1g); Protein 0.9g; Carb 38.5g; Fiber 1.3g; Chol 0mg; Iron 0.9mg; Sodium 60mg; Calc 25mg

CRUSTLESS HAM, LEEK, AND ASPARAGUS QUICHE

PointsPlus value per serving: 4

HANDS-ON TIME: 10 min. ■ **TOTAL TIME:** 1 hr., 2 min.

2 teaspoons olive oil
1 cup thinly sliced leek (about 1 large)
1½ cups (1-inch) sliced asparagus (about ½ pound)
6 ounces lower-sodium ham, cut into ½-inch pieces (about 1 cup)
Cooking spray
⅔ cup 2% reduced-fat milk
½ teaspoon salt
¼ teaspoon freshly ground black pepper
4 large eggs
2 large egg whites
4 ounces shredded reduced-fat Swiss cheese (about 1 cup)

1. Preheat oven to 325°.
2. Heat a large nonstick skillet over medium-high heat. Add oil to pan; swirl to coat. Add leek; sauté 1 minute. Add asparagus and ham; sauté 4 minutes or until asparagus is tender and ham is golden. Spoon mixture into a 9-inch pie plate coated with cooking spray. Cool slightly.
3. Combine milk and next 4 ingredients, stirring with a whisk. Sprinkle asparagus mixture with cheese. Pour egg mixture over cheese.
4. Bake at 325° for 30 minutes or until quiche is set. Let stand 15 minutes before serving. YIELD: 8 SERVINGS (SERVING SIZE: 1 SLICE).

PER SERVING: Calories 136; Fat 7.3g (sat 2.6g, mono 2.1g, poly 0.6g); Protein 14g; Carb 5.2g; Fiber 0.7g; Chol 124mg; Iron 1.4mg; Sodium 402mg; Calc 185mg

MIXED GREENS WITH POPPY SEED VINAIGRETTE

PointsPlus value per serving: 2

HANDS-ON TIME: 5 min. ■ TOTAL TIME: 5 min.

Any fresh spring fruit would be a nice addition to this salad. Superfine sugar is granulated sugar that's very finely ground and dissolves instantly. To make your own, place granulated sugar in a food processor; process 1 to 2 minutes or until very finely ground. Don't process too long or you'll end up with powdered sugar.

1 tablespoon superfine sugar
2 tablespoons red wine vinegar
2 tablespoons olive oil
2 teaspoons poppy seeds
1½ tablespoons minced shallots (about 1 small)
¼ teaspoon salt
1 (5-ounce) package gourmet salad greens
⅓ cup chopped hazelnuts, toasted

1. Combine first 6 ingredients in a large bowl, stirring with a whisk until sugar dissolves. Add greens; toss gently to coat. Divide salad among plates. Sprinkle evenly with hazelnuts. YIELD: 8 SERVINGS (SERVING SIZE: ¾ CUP SALAD AND 2 TEASPOONS HAZELNUTS).

PER SERVING: Calories 75; Fat 6.7g (sat 0.7g, mono 4.7g, poly 0.9g); Protein 1.1g; Carb 3.7g; Fiber 1g; Chol 0mg; Iron 0.5mg; Sodium 80mg; Calc 17mg

RASPBERRY-LEMON CREAM BARS

PointsPlus value per serving: 6

HANDS-ON TIME: 9 min. ■ TOTAL TIME: 1 hr., 26 min.

This recipe makes a few extra bars that will last for several days stored in the refrigerator. Freeze for a few minutes for easiest slicing.

Cooking spray
1 (11-ounce) package refrigerated sugar cookie dough
¼ cup low-sugar raspberry preserves
1 (10-ounce) jar lemon curd
1 teaspoon grated fresh lemon rind
1½ cups frozen reduced-calorie whipped topping, thawed
Fresh raspberries (optional)

1. Preheat oven to 350°.
2. Line an 8-inch square metal baking pan with foil, allowing foil to extend over edge of pan. Coat foil with cooking spray. Press cookie dough evenly in bottom of prepared pan.
3. Bake at 350° for 15 minutes or until edges are golden. Cool completely in pan on a wire rack.
4. Spread preserves evenly over cooled crust. Combine lemon curd and lemon rind in a medium bowl. Gently fold in whipped topping. Spread lemon mixture over preserves in pan. Freeze 30 minutes or until firm. Cut into 12 bars. Garnish with raspberries, if desired. Store covered in refrigerator. YIELD: 12 SERVINGS (SERVING SIZE: 1 BAR).

PER SERVING: Calories 222; Fat 7.6g (sat 2.9g, mono 3.1g, poly 0.7g); Protein 0.9g; Carb 38.9g; Fiber 2.4g; Chol 27mg; Iron 0.3mg; Sodium 89mg; Calc 0mg

Summer Menu

Serves 4

Total **PointsPlus** value per serving: 15

Grilled Halibut with Grilled Corn Salad, page 170

Tomato-Arugula Salad, page 171

Herbed Potato Salad, page 171

Watermelon Sorbet, page 171

GAME PLAN:

1. One day ahead:
- Prepare **Herbed Potato Salad.**

2. About 3 hours before the meal:
- Prepare **Watermelon Sorbet.**

3. About 1 hour before the meal:
- Prepare **Grilled Halibut with Grilled Corn Salad.**

4. Right before the meal:
- Prepare **Tomato-Arugula Salad.**

GRILLED HALIBUT WITH GRILLED CORN SALAD

PointsPlus value per serving: 7

HANDS-ON TIME: 34 min. ■ **TOTAL TIME:** 44 min.

Serve the corn salad warm or at room temperature as a colorful side for the citrusy halibut.

1 medium-sized red bell pepper
1 (1½-pound) center-cut halibut fillet, skinned
1 tablespoon grated fresh lemon rind
1 tablespoon fresh lemon juice
¼ cup finely chopped fresh basil, divided
¼ teaspoon salt, divided
¼ teaspoon freshly ground black pepper, divided
4 (½-inch-thick) slices onion
3 large ears shucked corn
Cooking spray
2 tablespoons red wine vinegar
4 teaspoons olive oil

1. Preheat grill to medium-high heat.
2. Cut bell pepper in half lengthwise; discard seeds and membranes. Cut each half into 2 pieces.
3. Cut fish crosswise into 4 equal pieces; sprinkle one side of fish pieces evenly with lemon rind, lemon juice, 2 tablespoons basil, ⅛ teaspoon salt, and ⅛ teaspoon black pepper.
4. Coat fish, bell pepper, onion, and corn with cooking spray. Place fish and vegetables on grill rack coated with cooking spray; cook fish, onion, and bell pepper 2 to 3 minutes on each side or until fish flakes easily when tested with a fork and vegetables are lightly charred. Grill corn 4 to 5 minutes, turning to cook evenly.
5. Let corn cool 5 minutes. Chop bell pepper and onion; cut kernels from ears of corn. Combine vegetables, vinegar, oil, remaining 2 tablespoons basil, remaining ⅛ teaspoon salt, and remaining ⅛ teaspoon black pepper in a bowl; toss gently. Serve fish with vegetable mixture. YIELD: 4 SERVINGS (SERVING SIZE: 1 FISH PIECE AND ¾ CUP VEGETABLE MIXTURE).

PER SERVING: Calories 275; Fat 8.2g (sat 1.4g, mono 4.7g, poly 1.3g); Protein 34.4g; Carb 16.4g; Fiber 2.4g; Chol 83mg; Iron 0.9mg; Sodium 276mg; Calc 26mg

TOMATO-ARUGULA SALAD

PointsPlus value per serving: 2

HANDS-ON TIME: 10 min. ■ **TOTAL TIME:** 10 min.

The peppery bite of arugula and the tanginess of the dressing complement the flavor of the tomatoes.

> 2 tablespoons olive oil
> 2 tablespoons white wine vinegar
> 1½ teaspoons Dijon mustard
> ¼ teaspoon freshly ground black pepper
> 5 cups arugula
> 2 cups cherry tomatoes, halved
> ½ cup thinly sliced red onion
> ½ cup thinly sliced celery

1. Combine first 4 ingredients in a large bowl, stirring with a whisk. Add arugula, tomato, onion, and celery, tossing well. Serve immediately. YIELD: 4 SERVINGS (SERVING SIZE: 1½ CUPS).

PER SERVING: Calories 91; Fat 7.1g (sat 1.0g, mono 5.0g, poly 0.9g); Protein 1.7g; Carb 6.2g; Fiber 1.8g; Chol 0mg; Iron 0.8mg; Sodium 68mg; Calc 66mg

HERBED POTATO SALAD

PointsPlus value per serving: 4   *pictured on page 144*

HANDS-ON TIME: 20 min. ■ **TOTAL TIME:** 1 hr., 30 min.

Make this potato salad up to one day ahead. We liked the combination of parsley, dill, and tarragon, but feel free to use any combination of herbs that you like.

> 1 pound unpeeled Yukon gold potatoes, cut into
>   ¾-inch pieces
> ⅓ cup light mayonnaise
> ¼ cup finely chopped red onion
> 2½ tablespoons chopped fresh herbs (such as parsley,
>   dill, and tarragon)
> 2 tablespoons white wine vinegar
> ¼ teaspoon freshly ground black pepper
> ⅛ teaspoon salt

1. Place potato in a saucepan; cover with water. Bring to a boil. Reduce heat; simmer 10 minutes or until tender. Drain. Cool slightly.
2. Combine mayonnaise and next 5 ingredients in a large bowl. Add potato, tossing gently to coat. Cover and chill at least 1 hour. YIELD: 4 SERVINGS (SERVING SIZE: ABOUT ¾ CUP).

PER SERVING: Calories 162; Fat 6.7g (sat 1g, mono 1.5g, poly 4g); Protein 2.7g; Carb 23.4g; Fiber 1.8g; Chol 7mg; Iron 1.2mg; Sodium 240mg; Calc 22mg

WATERMELON SORBET

PointsPlus value per serving: 2

HANDS-ON TIME: 6 min. ■ **TOTAL TIME:** 2 hr., 36 min.

Nothing says summer quite like watermelon, and this frosty dessert showcases the warm-weather staple. The riper the watermelon, the sweeter the sorbet will be. You can also prepare the sorbet in an 8-inch square glass or ceramic baking dish. Cover and freeze until firm, stirring occasionally.

> 5 cups cubed seeded watermelon
> 2 tablespoons sugar
> 3 tablespoons refrigerated limeade

1. Place watermelon and sugar in a blender or food processor; process until smooth. Stir in limeade. Pour mixture into the freezer can of a 1-quart ice-cream freezer; freeze according to manufacturer's instructions. Spoon sorbet into a freezer-safe container; cover and freeze 2 hours or until firm. Let stand 10 minutes at room temperature before serving. YIELD: 6 SERVINGS (SERVING SIZE: ½ CUP).

PER SERVING: Calories 58; Fat 0.2g (sat 0g, mono 0.1g, poly 0.1g); Protein 0.8g; Carb 14.6g; Fiber 0.5g; Chol 0mg; Iron 0.3mg; Sodium 1mg; Calc 9mg

Summer Vegetarian Menu

Serves 4

Total **PointsPlus** value per serving: 15

Paella with Soy Chorizo, page 172

Yellow Gazpacho, page 173

Artichoke Salad, page 173

Lemon Panna Cotta, page 173

GAME PLAN:

1. One day ahead:
- Prepare **Lemon Panna Cotta** and **Yellow Gazpacho.**

2. About 2 hours before the meal:
- Prepare **Artichoke Salad,** omitting arugula.

3. About 45 minutes before the meal:
- Prepare **Paella with Soy Chorizo.**

4. Right before the meal:
- Stir arugula into **Artichoke Salad.**

PAELLA WITH SOY CHORIZO

PointsPlus value per serving: 6

HANDS-ON TIME: 6 min. ■ **TOTAL TIME:** 29 min.

Blooming the saffron in water helps to release its characteristic yellow hue.

¾ cup water
Pinch of saffron threads, crushed
Cooking spray
6 ounces organic soy chorizo
½ cup chopped onion
½ cup refrigerated prechopped green, yellow,
    and red bell pepper mix
2 garlic cloves, minced
2 cups cooked whole-grain brown rice
1 cup frozen shelled edamame (green soybeans),
    thawed
¼ teaspoon freshly ground black pepper
2 plum tomatoes, chopped
2 tablespoons chopped fresh cilantro

1. Place ¾ cup water and saffron in a small bowl; let stand 15 minutes.
2. Heat a large nonstick skillet over medium-high heat. Coat pan with cooking spray. Add chorizo and next 3 ingredients to pan; cook 5 minutes or until onion is tender and chorizo is lightly browned, stirring to crumble chorizo.
3. Stir in saffron mixture, rice, and next 3 ingredients. Cook 3 minutes or until thoroughly heated, stirring frequently. Sprinkle with cilantro. YIELD: 4 SERVINGS (SERVING SIZE: ABOUT 1 CUP).

PER SERVING: Calories 257; Fat 6.2g (sat 0.2g, mono 2.7g, poly 2.6g); Protein 15.7g; Carb 31.2g; Fiber 4.9g; Chol 0mg; Iron 3mg; Sodium 406mg; Calc 110mg

YELLOW GAZPACHO

PointsPlus value per serving: 1

HANDS-ON TIME: 10 min. ▪ **TOTAL TIME:** 10 min.

The flavors continue to develop the longer this soup chills.

    1 garlic clove
    2 large yellow tomatoes, peeled, seeded, and
        halved (about 1 pound)
    ½ cup chopped Vidalia or other sweet onion
    ½ cup chopped seeded peeled cucumber
    2 tablespoons sherry vinegar
    ¼ teaspoon salt
    ¼ teaspoon freshly ground black pepper
    1 jalapeño pepper, seeded and coarsely chopped
    4 teaspoons chopped fresh chives (optional)

1. Drop garlic through food chute with food processor on; process until minced. Cut tomato halves into large chunks; add to food processor. Add onion and next 5 ingredients. Process 1 minute or until smooth. Pour pureed soup into a large bowl.
2. Cover and chill until ready to serve. Ladle soup into bowls. Sprinkle with chives, if desired. YIELD: 4 SERVINGS (SERVING SIZE: ABOUT ½ CUP).

PER SERVING: Calories 32; Fat 0.4g (sat 0.1g, mono 0.1g, poly 0.1g); Protein 1.5g; Carb 6.2g; Fiber 1.4g; Chol 0mg; Iron 0.7mg; Sodium 175mg; Calc 21.7mg

ARTICHOKE SALAD

PointsPlus value per serving: 5

HANDS-ON TIME: 8 min. ▪ **TOTAL TIME:** 8 min.

If you're preparing this ahead, hold out the arugula and stir it in just before serving.

    2 large navel oranges, divided
    2 tablespoons white balsamic vinegar
    ¼ teaspoon salt
    ¼ teaspoon freshly ground pepper
    3 tablespoons extra-virgin olive oil
    1 (9-ounce) package frozen artichoke hearts, thawed
    ½ cup thinly sliced red onion
    1 cup arugula

1. Grate rind and squeeze juice from 1 orange to measure 1 teaspoon and ⅓ cup, respectively; place in small bowl. Add vinegar, salt, and pepper. Gradually add oil, stirring with a whisk.
2. Peel remaining orange, removing white pith. Cut orange crosswise into 8 slices; place in a medium bowl. Add artichoke hearts and onion. Pour dressing over artichoke mixture; toss gently to coat. Add arugula; toss gently, and serve immediately. YIELD: 4 SERVINGS (SERVING SIZE: 1 CUP).

PER SERVING: Calories 175; Fat 12.1g (sat 1.5g, mono 7.5g, poly 1.5g); Protein 3.5g; Carb 15.9g; Fiber 8g; Chol 0mg; Iron 0.8mg; Sodium 233mg; Calc 78mg

LEMON PANNA COTTA

PointsPlus value per serving: 3

HANDS-ON TIME: 9 min. ▪ **TOTAL TIME:** 24 hr., 19 min.

Panna cotta is an eggless custard characterized by a very silky texture. We replace the traditional heavy cream with a combination of 2% milk and fat-free half-and-half to give this lightened version the same texture as higher-fat recipes.

    1½ cups 2% reduced-fat milk
    1 tablespoon grated fresh lemon rind
    ½ teaspoon vanilla extract
    1 envelope unflavored gelatin
    ½ cup sugar
    1½ cups fat-free half-and-half
    Cooking spray
    Fresh blueberries (optional)

1. Combine first 3 ingredients in a medium saucepan. Sprinkle gelatin over milk mixture; let stand 10 minutes. Cook over medium-low heat 3 minutes, stirring until gelatin dissolves. Increase heat to medium; stir in sugar. Cook, stirring constantly, 1 minute or until sugar dissolves. Remove from heat; stir in half-and-half.
2. Pour mixture evenly into 6 (6-ounce) ramekins or custard cups coated with cooking spray. Cover and chill overnight.
3. Loosen edges of custards with a knife or rubber spatula. Invert custards onto plates. Serve with blueberries, if desired. YIELD: 6 SERVINGS (SERVING SIZE: 1 PANNA COTTA).

PER SERVING: Calories 142; Fat 1.4g (sat 0.8g, mono 0.3g, poly 0.1g); Protein 3g; Carb 25.9g; Fiber 0.1g; Chol 5mg; Iron 0mg; Sodium 87mg; Calc 114mg

	MONDAY	TUESDAY	WEDNESDAY	THURSDAY
BREAKFAST	poached egg, 1 large turkey bacon, 3 slices light orange juice, 1 cup	Honey-Almond Oatmeal (Stir 1 tablespoon each of honey and slivered almonds into 1 cup hot cooked oatmeal. - *PointsPlus* value per serving: 6) fat-free milk, 1 cup	wheat bran flakes cereal, 1 cup fat-free milk, 1 cup strawberries, 1 cup	Ham-and-Swiss Quiche Cups, 3 servings, page 19 light orange juice, 1 cup raspberries, 1 cup
LUNCH	Rosemary Chicken Salad Wrap (Combine ½ cup chopped cooked chicken breast, 2 tablespoons low-fat mayonnaise, 1 teaspoon chopped fresh rosemary, and a dash each of salt and pepper. Place lettuce leaves and roasted red peppers down center of 1 [7-inch] whole-wheat tortilla; top with chicken mixture and wrap tightly. - *PointsPlus* value per serving: 7) blueberry fat-free Greek yogurt, 1 (6-ounce) carton	tacos, 2 fast-food with lettuce and tomato apple slices, 1 medium fat-free milk, 1 cup	Mediterranean Tuna Pasta Salad, 1 serving, page 111 pear, 1 medium fat-free milk, 1 cup	chili with beans, 1 cup salad greens, 2 cups light Italian dressing, 2 tablespoons fat-free milk, 1 cup
DINNER	Tilapia Piccata, 1 serving, page 70 mashed potatoes, ½ cup steamed green beans, 1 cup fat-free milk, 1 cup	Vegetable Bolognese, 1 serving, page 83 mixed salad greens, 2 cups light balsamic vinaigrette, 2 tablespoons	Chile-Lime Flank Steak, 1 serving, page 89 baked sweet potato, 1 large Parmesan-Garlic Creamed Spinach, 1 serving, page 152	roasted turkey breast, 4 ounces Buttermilk Mashed Potatoes, 1 serving, page 153 Spicy Sautéed Brussels Sprouts, 1 serving, page 148
SNACK	mozzarella string cheese, 1 pear, 1 medium	strawberry fat-free Greek yogurt, 1 (6-ounce) carton grapes, 1 cup	cucumber slices and carrot sticks, 1 cup hummus, ¼ cup	Brown Sugar Fudge Brownies, 1 serving, page 44 Fat-free milk, 1 cup
PointsPlus VALUE	Total *PointsPlus* value for the day: 28	Total *PointsPlus* value for the day: 30	Total *PointsPlus* value for the day: 28	Total *PointsPlus* value for the day: 29

One day's menu provides at least two servings of dairy and at least five servings of fruits and/or vegetables.

FRIDAY	SATURDAY	SUNDAY	
wheat bran flakes cereal, 1 cup **fat-free milk,** 1 cup **banana,** 1 small **light orange juice,** 1 cup	**oatmeal,** 1 cup **turkey bacon,** 3 slices **orange,** 1 medium	**scrambled eggs,** 1 egg and 1 egg white **high-fiber whole-wheat toast,** 1 slice **light orange juice,** 1 cup	BREAKFAST
grilled chicken tenders, 4 ounces **Tomato-Basil Salad** (Top 3 slices of red ripe tomatoes with 2 tablespoons each crumbled feta cheese and chopped fresh basil; drizzle with 2 tablespoons light balsamic vinaigrette dressing. - **PointsPlus** value per serving: 2) **whole-wheat French bread,** 1 ounce	**Smoked Pork Quesadillas,** 1 serving, page 94 **baby carrots,** 10 **fat-free milk,** 1 cup	**spinach and mushroom pizza,** 1 light frozen entrée **blueberries,** 1 cup **fat-free milk,** 1 cup	LUNCH
Shrimp and Jalapeño Cheese Grits, 1 serving, page 75 **steamed asparagus,** 12 spears **fat-free milk,** 1 cup	**Smoked Chicken–Corn Chowder,** 1 serving, page 161 **cornbread,** 1 square **Spinach Salad with Strawberries and Walnuts** (Top 1½ cups baby spinach leaves with ¼ cup sliced strawberries, 2 tablespoons light balsamic vinaigrette dressing, and 1 tablespoon chopped walnuts. - **PointsPlus** value per serving: 2)	**hamburger patty,** made with 4 ounces lean ground beef **light wheat hamburger bun,** 1 tomato slice and lettuce leaf, 1 each **watermelon cubes,** 1 cup	DINNER
Marinated Cheese, 2 servings, page 23 **whole-wheat pita chips,** 1 ounce	**apple,** 1 medium **blueberry fat-free Greek yogurt,** 1 (6-ounce) carton	**Chocolate-Raspberry Soufflés,** 1 serving, page 39 **fat-free milk,** 1 cup	SNACK
Total PointsPlus value for the day: 32	**Total PointsPlus** value for the day: 31	**Total PointsPlus** value for the day: 30	PointsPlus VALUE

7-Day Menu Planner

WEEK 1

	MONDAY	TUESDAY	WEDNESDAY	THURSDAY
BREAKFAST	**Honey Whole-Wheat Biscuits,** 1 serving, page 28 **honey,** 1 tablespoon **fat-free milk,** 1 cup **blueberries,** 1 cup	**hard-cooked egg,** 1 **high-fiber whole-wheat toast,** 1 slice **banana,** 1 small	**low-fat multi-grain frozen waffles,** 2 frozen **low-calorie maple syrup,** 2 tablespoons **fat-free milk,** 1 cup **strawberries,** 1 cup	**strawberry fat-free Greek yogurt,** 1 (6-ounce) carton **low-fat granola,** ½ cup **blueberries,** 1 cup
LUNCH	**White Bean–Spinach Soup,** 1 serving, page 159 **whole-wheat pita chips,** 1 ounce **cantaloupe cubes,** 1 cup	**Couscous Salad with Chicken** (Combine ¾ cup cooked and cooled whole-wheat herbed couscous; ¼ cup each chopped cucumber, chopped tomato, and chopped green bell pepper; and 3 ounces shredded skinless rotisserie chicken breast. Add 2 tablespoons each crumbled feta cheese and light olive oil vinaigrette dressing; toss gently to combine. - ***PointsPlus*** value per serving: 9)	**Spinach and Mushroom Enchiladas,** 1 serving, page 84 **pineapple chunks,** 1 cup **fat-free milk,** 1 cup	**turkey submarine sandwich,** 1 low-fat (6-inch) on wheat bread without mayo and with cheese, lettuce, and tomato **apple,** 1 medium
DINNER	**Creamy Chicken and Rice Casserole,** 1 serving, page 97 **sautéed squash and zucchini,** 1 cup **fat-free milk,** 1 cup	**watermelon cubes,** 1 cup **Classic Lasagna,** 1 serving, page 91 **mixed salad greens,** 2 cups **reduced-fat Italian dressing,** 2 tablespoons **fat-free milk,** 1 cup	**steamed shrimp,** 6 ounces **Roasted Garlic and Herb Polenta,** 1 serving, page 153 **steamed asparagus,** 12 spears	**Kung Pao Pork,** 1 serving, page 93 **steamed brown rice,** ½ cup **Roasted Broccoli** (Toss 1½ cups broccoli with 2 teaspoons olive oil and dash each of salt and garlic powder. Bake at 475° for 14 minutes. - ***PointsPlus*** value per serving: 2)
SNACK	**light microwave popcorn,** 3 cups **mozzarella string cheese,** 1	**Honey-Granola Yogurt** (Gently stir ¼ cup low-fat granola into 1 [6-ounce] carton vanilla fat-free Greek yogurt; drizzle with 1 tablespoon honey. ***PointsPlus*** value per serving: 7)	**Creamy Avocado-Edamame Dip,** 1 serving, page 18 **baked tortilla chips,** 12 chips	**Butterscotch Drop Cookies,** 1 serving, page 42 **fat-free milk,** 1 cup
PointsPlus VALUE	Total ***PointsPlus*** value for the day: 28	Total ***PointsPlus*** value for the day: 31	Total ***PointsPlus*** value for the day: 30	Total ***PointsPlus*** value for the day: 31

One day's menu provides at least two servings of dairy and at least five servings of fruits and/or vegetables.

	FRIDAY	SATURDAY	SUNDAY	
BREAKFAST	**Salsa-Cheese Scramble** (Whisk together 1 egg, 2 egg whites, 1 tablespoon chopped green onion, and a dash of salt and pepper. Scramble egg mixture until done; remove from pan, and sprinkle with 2 tablespoons each reduced fat cheddar cheese and salsa. - *PointsPlus* value per serving: 5) **pineapple cubes,** 1 cup	**Blueberry-Lime Coffee Cake,** 1 serving, page 33 **fat-free milk,** 1 cup **strawberries,** 1 cup	**Banana-Maple Waffles** (Toast 2 low-fat multi-grain frozen waffles; top with 1 small banana, sliced, and 3 tablespoons warm low-calorie maple syrup. - *PointsPlus* value per serving: 6) **fat-free milk,** 1 cup	
LUNCH	**Peanut Butter-Banana-Honey Muffin** (Spread 2 tablespoons peanut butter over the cut sides of a toasted whole-wheat English muffin. Top with a sliced small banana; drizzle with 1 tablespoon honey. Eat open-faced. - *PointsPlus* value per serving: 10) **fat-free milk,** 1 cup	**Grilled Lamb Salad,** 1 serving, page 113 **warm pita bread,** ½ **grapes,** 1 cup	**grilled chicken sandwich,** 1 fast-food without mayonnaise and with lettuce and tomato **fruit salad,** 1 cup	
DINNER	**Chicken and Wild Rice Soup,** 1 serving, page 160 **Squash-Corn Muffins,** 1 serving, page 30 **baby spinach leaves,** 2 cups **light balsamic vinaigrette dressing,** 2 tablespoons	**Roasted Spaghetti Squash with Marinara,** 1 serving, page 84 **steamed green beans,** 1 cup **fat-free milk,** 1 cup	**Seared Tuna Steaks with Wasabi Aioli,** 1 serving, page 71 **whole-wheat pasta,** ½ cup **steamed carrots,** 1 cup	
SNACK	**strawberry fat-free Greek yogurt,** 1 (6-ounce) carton **cantaloupe cubes,** 1 cup	**hummus,** ¼ cup **baby carrots,** 1 cup	**pear,** 1 **gingersnaps,** 2 cookies **fat-free milk,** 1 cup	
PointsPlus VALUE	**Total** *PointsPlus* value for the day: 30	**Total** *PointsPlus* value for the day: 30	**Total** *PointsPlus* value for the day: 32	

7-Day Menu Planner

WEEK 2

	MONDAY	TUESDAY	WEDNESDAY	THURSDAY
BREAKFAST	**high-fiber whole-wheat toast,** 1 slice **peanut butter,** 2 tablespoons **banana,** 1 small	**whole-wheat English muffin,** 1 **fat-free cottage cheese,** 1 cup **strawberries,** 1 cup	**Strawberry-Almond Muffins,** 1 serving, page 31 **fat-free milk,** 1 cup **cantaloupe cubes,** 1 cup	**oatmeal,** 1 cup **raisins,** 1 tablespoon **fat-free milk,** 1 cup **honeydew melon cubes,** 1 cup
LUNCH	**Smoked Chicken–Pesto Pizza,** 1 serving, page 102 **plums,** 2 small **fat-free milk,** 1 cup	**Roast Beef–Veggie Wrap** (Spread 2 tablespoons light garlic-and-herb cream cheese over an 8-inch whole-wheat tortilla. Top with 2 ounces lean deli roast beef, ½ cup torn lettuce leaves, and 2 tablespoons each chopped roasted red peppers and shredded carrot. Gently roll up tortilla. - **PointsPlus** value per serving: 8) **pear,** 1 medium	**Turkey Club Sandwich** (Spread 2 teaspoons each fat-free mayonnaise and Dijon mustard over 2 slices high-fiber wheat bread. Place 2 ounces sliced deli turkey, 1 [0.75-ounce] slice reduced-fat Swiss cheese, 2 lettuce leaves, 2 tomato slices, and 2 slices cooked turkey bacon, halved, on 1 bread slice; top with remaining bread slice. - **PointsPlus** value per serving: 8) **grapes,** 1 cup **baby carrots,** 1 cup	**canned minestrone soup,** 1 cup **orange,** 1 medium **Cheese Muffin** (Place 1 [0.75-ounce] slice reduced-fat cheddar cheese on the cut side of a whole-wheat English muffin half; toast until melted. - **PointsPlus** value per serving: 3) **fat-free milk,** 1 cup
DINNER	**Tex-Mex Meat Loaf,** 1 serving, page 90 **mashed potatoes,** ½ cup **green beans,** 1 cup	**rotisserie chicken breast,** 3 ounces with skin removed **Mediterranean Orzo,** 1 serving, page 154 **Lemon-Parmesan Broccolini,** 1 serving, page 147	**Broccoli-Feta Calzones,** 1 serving, page 86 **peach,** 1 medium **fat-free milk,** 1 cup	**Beer-Braised Honey-Lime Brisket,** 1 serving, page 92 **corn,** 1 medium ear **Blue Cheese–Napa Cabbage Slaw,** 1 serving, page 148
SNACK	**pomegranate fat-free Greek yogurt,** 1 (6-ounce) carton **grapes,** 1 cup	**reduced-fat chocolate sandwich cookies,** 3 **fat-free milk,** 1 cup **apple,** 1 medium	**Frozen Strawberry Mojito,** 1 serving, page 25 **baked tortilla chips,** 12	**mozzarella string cheese,** 1 **cantaloupe cubes,** 1 cup **pretzels,** 16 small
PointsPlus VALUE	Total **PointsPlus** value for the day: 29	Total **PointsPlus** value for the day: 30	Total **PointsPlus** value for the day: 31	Total **PointsPlus** value for the day: 31

One day's menu provides at least two servings of dairy and at least five servings of fruits and/or vegetables.

	FRIDAY	SATURDAY	SUNDAY
BREAKFAST	**Egg-and-Cheese Sandwich** (Split and toast 1 whole-wheat English muffin. Place 1 scrambled egg on bottom half of muffin; top with 1 [0.75-ounce] slice reduced-fat cheddar cheese and top half of muffin. - *PointsPlus* value per serving: 7) **Light orange juice,** 1 cup	**Banana Bread Pancakes,** 1 serving, page 32 **fat-free milk,** 1 cup	**Maple Walnut Oatmeal** (Stir 2 tablespoons low-calorie maple syrup and 1 tablespoon chopped toasted walnuts into 1 cup hot cooked oatmeal. - *PointsPlus* value per serving: 6) **fat-free milk,** 1 cup **blueberries,** 1 cup
LUNCH	**hamburger,** 1 small fast-food **Lettuce leaf and tomato slice,** 1 each **fat-free milk,** 1 cup **watermelon cubes,** 1 cup	**Spinach-Parmesan Frittata** (Sauté ¼ cup onion in 1 teaspoon olive oil in a small non-stick skillet over medium-high heat; add 1½ cups spinach leaves, stirring until wilted. Combine 1 egg, 3 egg whites, and a dash each salt and pepper, stirring with a whisk. Pour egg mixture into pan; top with 2 table-spoons grated Parmesan cheese. Cook until set. - *PointsPlus* value per serving: 5) **strawberries,** 1 cup	**chicken teriyaki,** 1 light frozen entrée **cucumber and carrot sticks,** 1 cup **apple,** 1 medium
DINNER	**Almond-Crusted Salmon,** 1 serving, page 69 **Garlicky Sautéed Asparagus** (Heat 2 teaspoons butter and ½ teaspoon minced garlic in a small nonstick skillet over medium-high heat. Add 12 trimmed asparagus spears, and cook 6 to 8 minutes or until crisp-tender, stirring occasionally. - *PointsPlus* value per serving: 2)	**Peanutty Chicken Lettuce Cups,** 1 serving, page 99 **pineapple cubes,** 1 cup **fat-free milk,** 1 cup	**lean pork loin,** 4 ounces trimmed and cooked **Roasted Sweet Potato Salad,** 1 serving, page 117 **Sesame Sugar Snap Peas,** 1 serving, page 151
SNACK	**fat-free cottage cheese,** 1 cup **fruit salad,** 1 cup	**Pimiento Cheese Pinwheels,** 4 servings, page 21 **apple,** 1 medium	**orange,** 1 medium **peach fat-free Greek yogurt,** 1 (6-ounce) carton
PointsPlus VALUE	**Total** *PointsPlus* **value for the day: 28**	**Total** *PointsPlus* **value for the day: 26**	**Total** *PointsPlus* **value for the day: 28**

7-Day Menu Planner

WEEK 3

	MONDAY	TUESDAY	WEDNESDAY	THURSDAY
BREAKFAST	instant grits, 1 packet butter, 1 teaspoon fat-free milk, 1 cup raspberries, 1 cup	Veggie Omelet with Goat Cheese, 1 serving, page 78 light orange juice, 1 cup	wheat bran flakes cereal with raisins, 1 cup fat-free milk, 1 cup banana, 1 small	instant grits, 1 packet butter, 1 teaspoon fat-free milk, 1 cup honeydew melon cubes, 1 cup
LUNCH	Cobb Salad Lettuce Cups, 1 serving, page 113 grapes, 1 cup peach fat-free Greek yogurt, 1 (6-ounce) carton	ham and cheddar whole-grain hot sandwich, 1 frozen light pocket apple, 1 medium carrot sticks, 10	BLT with Avocado (Lightly toast 2 slices high-fiber whole-wheat bread. Spread 2 teaspoons light mayonnaise evenly over 1 slice; top with 3 slices turkey bacon, 1 green lettuce leaf, and 2 slices each red ripe tomato and avocado. Top with remaining toasted bread slice. - *PointsPlus* value per serving: 7) fat-free milk, 1 cup peach, 1 medium	Pasta Salad with Tuna (Combine ¾ cup cooked whole-wheat penne pasta; 2 ounces light tuna in water; ¼ cup chopped tomato; 2 tablespoons each light olive oil vinaigrette, chopped fresh basil, and grated Parmesan; and a dash each salt and pepper. Toss well to combine. Serve over a bed of lettuce. - *PointsPlus* value per serving: 8) raspberries, 1 cup
DINNER	Mediterranean-Style Grouper, 1 serving, page 66 Spinach and Cheese Potato Gratin, 1 serving, page 152 steamed broccoli, 1 cup	Beef Fajita Soft Tacos, 1 serving, page 88 raspberries, 1 cup fat-free milk, 1 cup	Rosemary Roasted Turkey Tenderloin, 1 serving, page 106 whole-wheat couscous, ½ cup Carrots with Honey Butter (Steam 1 cup carrot slices; toss carrots with 2 teaspoons butter, 1 teaspoon honey and a dash of salt. - *PointsPlus* value per serving: 3)	Rosted Asparagus and Tomato Pizza, 1 serving, page 86 salad greens, 2 cups light balsamic vinaigrette dressing, 2 tablespoons
SNACK	apple, 1 medium peanut butter, 1 tablespoon fat-free milk, 1 cup	blueberry fat-free Greek yogurt, 1 (6-ounce) carton pineapple chunks, 1 cup	mixed raw vegetables (broccoli florets, baby carrots, cucumber slices), 1 cup roasted red pepper hummus, ¼ cup	vanilla fat-free Greek yogurt, 1 (6-ounce) carton gingersnaps, 3 cookies
PointsPlus VALUE	Total *PointsPlus* value for the day: 31	Total *PointsPlus* value for the day: 29	Total *PointsPlus* value for the day: 30	Total *PointsPlus* value for the day: 28

One day's menu provides at least two servings of dairy and at least five servings of fruits and/or vegetables.

	FRIDAY	SATURDAY	SUNDAY	
BREAKFAST	wheat bran flakes cereal with raisins, 1 cup fat-free milk, 1 cup grapefruit, 1 half	Bacon-Cheese Grits (Stir 2 tablespoons reduced-fat sharp cheddar cheese, 2 slices crumbled turkey bacon, and a dash of salt into 1 packet hot cooked instant grits. - *PointsPlus* value per serving: 4) light orange juice, 1 cup	Silver Dollar Pancakes with Cherry-Orange Syrup, 1 serving, page 32 fat-free milk, 1 cup blueberries, 1 cup	
LUNCH	Cheesy Black Bean Burrito (Combine ⅓ cup each brown rice and canned, drained black beans, and ¼ cup picante sauce. Spoon down center of 1 [8-inch] whole-wheat tortilla; top with ¼ cup reduced-fat Mexican blend cheese. Microwave for 30 seconds or until cheese is melted. - *PointsPlus* value per serving: 10) baby carrots, 1 cup fat-free milk, 1 cup	canned tomato-basil soup, 1 cup whole-wheat French bread, 1 ounce mozzarella string cheese, 1 strawberry fat-free Greek yogurt, 1 (6-ounce) carton	pepperoni French bread pizza, 1 light frozen entrée cucumber slices, 1 cup grapes, 1 cup	
DINNER	flank steak, lean and trimmed, 4 ounces cooked Grilled Romaine with Tomato Dressing, 1 serving, page 110 raspberries, 1 cup	Shrimp Primavera Alfredo, 1 serving, page 74 steamed green beans, 1 cup pear, 1 medium	Greek Braised Chicken Thighs, 1 serving, page 105 steamed wild rice, ½ cup steamed asparagus, 12 spears	
SNACK	Blueberry-Banana Smoothie (Combine 1 small banana, 1 [6-ounce] carton blueberry fat-free Greek yogurt, ½ cup blueberries, and ¼ cup light orange juice in a blender; process until smooth. - *PointsPlus* value per serving: 4)	Cinnamon Apple Tart, 1 serving, page 39 fat-free milk, 1 cup	fat-free cottage cheese, 1 cup strawberries, 1 cup	
PointsPlus VALUE	Total *PointsPlus* value for the day: 29	Total *PointsPlus* value for the day: 29	Total *PointsPlus* value for the day: 31	

WEEK 4

181

SEASONAL PRODUCE GUIDE

When you use fresh fruits, vegetables, and herbs, you don't have to do much to make them taste great. Although many fruits, vegetables, and herbs are available year-round, you'll get better flavor and prices when you buy what's in season. The Seasonal Produce Guide below helps you choose the best produce so you can create sensational meals all year long.

Spring

Fruits
Bananas
Blood oranges
Coconuts
Grapefruit
Kiwifruit
Lemons
Limes
Mangoes
Navel oranges
Papayas
Passionfruit
Pineapples
Strawberries
Tangerines
Valencia oranges

Vegetables
Artichokes
Arugula
Asparagus
Avocados
Baby leeks
Beets
Belgian endive
Broccoli
Cauliflower
Dandelion
   greens
Fava beans
Green onions
Green peas
Kale
Lettuce
Mushrooms
Radishes
Red potatoes
Rhubarb
Snap beans
Snow peas
Spinach
Sugar snap peas
Sweet onions
Swiss chard

Herbs
Chives
Dill
Garlic chives
Lemongrass
Mint
Parsley
Thyme

Summer

Fruits
Blackberries
Blueberries
Boysenberries
Cantaloupes
Casaba melons
Cherries
Crenshaw melons
Grapes
Guava
Honeydew melons
Mangoes
Nectarines
Papayas
Peaches
Plums
Raspberries
Strawberries
Watermelons

Vegetables
Avocados
Beets
Bell peppers
Cabbage
Carrots
Celery
Chili peppers
Collards
Corn
Cucumbers
Eggplant
Green beans
Jicama
Lima beans
Okra
Pattypan squash
Peas
Radicchio
Radishes
Summer squash
Tomatoes

Herbs
Basil
Bay leaves
Borage
Chives
Cilantro
Dill
Lavender
Lemon balm
Marjoram
Mint
Oregano
Rosemary
Sage
Summer savory
Tarragon
Thyme

Autumn

Fruits
Apples
Cranberries
Figs
Grapes
Pears
Persimmons
Pomegranates
Quinces

Vegetables
Belgian endive
Bell peppers
Broccoli
Brussels
   sprouts
Cabbage
Cauliflower
Eggplant
Escarole
Fennel
Frisée
Leeks
Mushrooms
Parsnips
Pumpkins
Red potatoes
Rutabagas
Shallots
Sweet potatoes
Winter squash
Yukon gold
   potatoes

Herbs
Basil
Bay leaves
Parsley
Rosemary
Sage
Tarragon
Thyme

Winter

Fruits
Apples
Blood oranges
Cranberries
Grapefruit
Kiwifruit
Kumquats
Lemons
Limes
Mandarin oranges
Navel oranges
Pears
Persimmons
Pomegranates
Pomelos
Tangelos
Tangerines
Quinces

Vegetables
Baby turnips
Beets
Belgian endive
Brussels sprouts
Celery root
Chili peppers
Dried beans
Escarole
Fennel
Frisée
Jerusalem
   artichokes
Kale
Leeks
Mushrooms
Parsnips
Potatoes
Rutabagas
Sweet potatoes
Turnips
Watercress
Winter squash

Herbs
Bay leaves
Chives
Parsley
Rosemary
Sage
Thyme

GENERAL RECIPE INDEX

PointsPlus® Value Index

10 SIMPLE SIDE DISHES

Vegetable	Servings	Preparation	Cooking Instructions
Asparagus	3 to 4 per pound	Snap off tough ends. Remove scales, if desired.	To steam: Cook, covered, on a rack above boiling water 2 to 3 minutes. To boil: Cook, covered, in a small amount of boiling water 2 to 3 minutes or until crisp-tender.
Broccoli	3 to 4 per pound	Remove outer leaves and tough ends of lower stalks. Wash; cut into spears.	To steam: Cook, covered, on a rack above boiling water 5 to 7 minutes or until crisp-tender.
Carrots	4 per pound	Scrape; remove ends, and rinse. Leave tiny carrots whole; slice large carrots.	To steam: Cook, covered, on a rack above boiling water 8 to 10 minutes or until crisp-tender. To boil: Cook, covered, in a small amount of boiling water 8 to 10 minutes or until crisp-tender.
Cauliflower	4 per medium head	Remove outer leaves and stalk. Wash. Break into florets.	To steam: Cook, covered, on a rack above boiling water 5 to 7 minutes or until crisp-tender.
Corn	4 per 4 large ears	Remove husks and silks. Leave corn on the cob, or cut off kernels.	To boil: Cook, covered, in boiling water to cover 8 to 10 minutes (on cob) or in a small amount of boiling water 4 to 6 minutes (kernels).
Green beans	4 per pound	Wash; trim ends, and remove strings. Cut into 1½-inch pieces.	To steam: Cook, covered, on a rack above boiling water 5 to 7 minutes. To boil: Cook, covered, in a small amount of boiling water 5 to 7 minutes or until crisp-tender.
Potatoes	3 to 4 per pound	Scrub; peel, if desired. Leave whole, slice, or cut into chunks.	To boil: Cook, covered, in boiling water to cover 30 to 40 minutes (whole) or 15 to 20 minutes (slices or chunks). To bake: Bake at 400° for 1 hour or until done.
Snow peas	4 per pound	Wash; trim ends, and remove tough strings.	To steam: Cook, covered, on a rack above boiling water 2 to 3 minutes. Or sauté in cooking spray or 1 teaspoon oil over medium-high heat 3 to 4 minutes or until crisp-tender.
Squash, summer	3 to 4 per pound	Wash; trim ends, and slice or chop.	To steam: Cook, covered, on a rack above boiling water 6 to 8 minutes. To boil: Cook, covered, in a small amount of boiling water 6 to 8 minutes or until crisp-tender.
Squash, winter *(including acorn, butternut, and buttercup)*	2 per pound	Rinse; cut in half, and remove all seeds. Leave in halves to bake, or peel and cube to boil.	To boil: Cook cubes, covered, in boiling water 20 to 25 minutes. To bake: Place halves, cut sides down, in a shallow baking dish; add ½ inch water. Bake, uncovered, at 375° for 30 minutes. Turn and season, or fill; bake an additional 20 to 30 minutes or until tender.